1.15

Christine Spahn Smith

International Encyclopedia of Unified Science

International Encyclopedia
of
Unified Science

Volume I, Nos. 1-5

Edited by

Otto Neurath   Rudolf Carnap

Charles Morris

The University of Chicago Press   Chicago, Illinois

This edition combines in two cloth-bound volumes the ten numbers of Volume I of the International Encyclopedia of Unified Science.

FOURTH PRINTING

CONTENTS

CONTENTS

Encyclopedia and Unified Science

Otto Neurath, Niels Bohr, John Dewey,
Bertrand Russell, Rudolf Carnap,
Charles W. Morris

Encyclopedia and Unified Science

Contents:

Unified Science as Encyclopedic Integration

Otto Neurath

I. Unity of Science Movement

Unified science became historically the subject of this *Encyclopedia* as a result of the efforts of the unity of science movement, which includes scientists and persons interested in science who are conscious of the importance of a universal scientific attitude.

The new version of the idea of unified science is created by the confluence of divergent intellectual currents. Empirical work of scientists was often antagonistic to the logical constructions of a priori rationalism bred by philosophico-religious systems; therefore, "empiricalization" and "logicalization" were considered mostly to be in opposition—the two have now become synthesized for the first time in history. Certain empiricists began to appreciate logical analysis and construction as universal scientific aids; other thinkers, especially interested in the historical importance of scientific imagination—many call it rationalistic fancy—stress their opposition to all kinds of a priori reasoning and demand empirical tests for all their theories. The term 'logical empiricism' expresses very well this new type of synthesis; it may be used synonymously with the term 'empirical rationalism.' To further all kinds of scientific synthesis is one of the most important purposes of the unity of science movement, which is bringing together scientists in different fields and in different countries, as well as persons who have some interest in science or hope that science will help to ameliorate personal and social life. The terms 'unified science' and 'unity of science,' used before this movement came into being, are becoming more and more widespread in usage. This movement has found in the International Congresses for the Unity of Science its organized contemporary expression. These congresses, held yearly, show a new field for co-operation.[1] Physicists are familiar with co-operation in the field of physics, biologists in the field of biology; the same type of scientific co-operation is shown by these congresses, because the members of these congresses and all scientists in the movement co-operate in the field of unified science—physicists with biologists, biologists with sociologists, and other specialists with logicians and mathematicians. One important work within the wider unity of science movement will be this *Encyclopedia*.

The *International Encyclopedia of Unified Science* aims to show how various scientific activities such as observation, experimentation, and reasoning can be synthesized, and how all these together help to evolve unified science. These efforts to synthesize and systematize wherever possible are not directed at creating *the* system of science; this *Encyclopedia* continues the work of the famous French *Encyclopédie* in this and other respects.

About one hundred and ninety years ago D'Alembert wrote a *Discours préliminaire* for the French *Encyclopédie*, a gigantic work achieved by the co-operation of a great many specialists. Although a lover of the systematizing scientific mind, D'Alembert objected to the making of a universal system, just as Condillac opposed such attempts in his *Traité des systèmes*, in which he criticized the great rationalistic systems of his day. D'Alembert's idea of the procedure of empirical science was mostly based on Francis Bacon, and the idea of science in general on Newton; no comprehensive idea of "logicalization" stimulated the Encyclopedists. One must carefully look at their work as an important example of organized co-operation. Perhaps the same kind of scientific tolerance will appear in this *Encyclopedia* which appeared in the French *Encyclopédie* when D'Alembert, in his Introduction, opposed Rousseau's aggressions against science and yet expressed his pleasure that Rousseau had become a collaborator in the work. As a modern scientific man, D'Alembert stressed the degree to which all scientific activities depend upon social institutions. Today this idea is so familiar that this *Encyclopedia* will give it special attention. Succeeding generations may better be able to assess how far this present *Encyclopedia* expresses living activities, old traditions, and a rising future.

II. Mosaic of Empirical Science

Continual scientific activity throughout the centuries gives rise step by step to a distinctive intellectual environment. The history of this evolution of empirical science and scientific empiricism can be regarded as the history of a "mosaic," the pattern of which has been formed by combining new observations and new logical constructions of diverse character and origin. The generations of the "mosaicists" are not only inlaying the stones but also changing certain stones for others and varying the whole pattern. Scientific thinkers who were combating one another in social and intellectual conflicts must nevertheless often be regarded as the contributors of little stones to the same part of the whole pattern.

The history of philosophy, on the contrary, can be written as a history of philosophical systems formed by certain persons who concentrated upon and focused attention upon particular groups of ideas. Such a focalization can be more easily correlated to certain social situations than can the mosaic of empirical science to its historical environment. One can speak about a "republic of scientists" which makes a scientific pattern but not about a "republic of philosophers."

Science as a whole can be regarded as a combination of an enormous number of elements, collected little by little. One example may show this: The principle of Huyghens says that each point on an expanding sphere of light can be regarded as a center of a new expanding sphere of light. While the followers of the emission theory could use the idea of a certain periodicity, the followers of Huyghens at first lacked it; Euler used the idea of the periodicity of undulation but objected to the principle of Huyghens. It happened subsequently that Huyghens' principle, together with periodicity and other factors, formed the theory of light of the nineteenth century. In the same way, in the modern theory of economics one finds a connecting of elements of diverse origin. Smith and Ricardo did show certain correlations of the market system but did not concentrate their interest in certain decreases of wealth as did Sismondi; in that part of modern theory which deals with business cycles one finds more elements of Marxism than of Smithian ideas. Only a complicated comparative scheme could show the amalgamation of various elements, the common and different features of various theories. In a similar way one might analyze this *Encyclopedia* and show the elements which form the idea of a unified science.

Modern empiricism has grown up in the scientific tradition, in the activities of daily life, and in philosophico-religious speculations. The more or less common thought of the Middle Ages, which was mainly based on a literature written in Latin, Arabic, Hebrew, or Greek, was also influenced by other peoples outside the Mediterranean. Indian and Chinese influences were not very strong, but increased in later times. The social ideas of Quesnay, Montesquieu, Voltaire, and other thinkers were directly influenced by Chinese ideas. One also finds such an influence in philosophers, for instance, in Leibniz. Scholasticism, roughly speaking, was the native soil of all European thinking. No great attention was devoted to empirical studies within the structure of scholasticism, but one sees scientific research and reasoning arising within this structure. Men who wrote about physical problems also gave metaphysical explanations or combined empirically tested statements with purely traditional statements. Certain elements of optics in the works of Roger Bacon (about 1250) or in the works of other Scholastics, such as Dietrich of Freiberg, are of the same type as the corresponding explanations of Snellius or Descartes (about 1600); nevertheless, Roger Bacon discussed the question of the distance between the western coast of Spain and the eastern coast of Asia without arguing empirically or making particular proposals for research. Macrobius had previously analyzed Cicero's *Somnium Scipionis* and his explanations dealing with the five zones of the globe, with the antipodes and the continent "Australis";

Roger Bacon did not discuss these matters systematically and maintained only that the distance was relatively short, using quotations from Aristotle, from an apocryphal book of the Bible, and from a well-known saint, thus preparing for the discovery of America by Columbus. The fourteenth-century Oresme, a mathematician, physicist, and economist of importance, discussed a great many questions in a modern manner, but he holds a far from universal scientific attitude, as appears when his work as a whole is analyzed.

The increasing number of technical inventions and geographical discoveries, together with the increasing secularization of politics, produced a new attitude and the necessity to analyze and combine a great deal of empirical data. Machiavelli, for instance, discussed problems of social organization in an attitude far from the Scholastic tradition. A long series of historians and economists, physicists and biologists, did the same in the following centuries and worked out a modern idea of the world. Alexander von Humboldt has shown in his *Kosmos* how such empirical studies can be correlated without the help of philosophico-religious construction. Empiristic interest spread in the public not only in the field of technical activities but also in daily life: during the eighteenth century, for instance, microscopy was a hobby as photography is now. That physiognomic and phrenologic studies became popular can be regarded as a sign of a growing—though only uncritical—empirical interest.

The evolution of a comprehensive empiricism in opposition to the traditional systems has started with work in decentralized camps. Scholasticism was based on a well-organized movement, but not so the young empirical science. In the *Encyclopedia of Unified Science* this historical situation and its consequences will be demonstrated by showing the formation of the mosaic of scientific activities.

III. From Metaphysical Comprehensiveness to Empiristic Synthesis

All-embracing vision and thought is an old desire of humanity. Gnosticism was not only characterized by realistic ideas pertaining to astrology and magic but was also full of ideas dealing with angel-like "emanations" and personified concepts and qualities. Elements of these "cosmic poems"—if one may use this term—combined with elements of Platonism, Aristotelianism, and other philosophical and religious tendencies, formed the background of the medieval desire for a comprehensive viewpoint—a desire which can also be found in medieval mysticism and not only in Scholastic intellectual systems. A bewildering multiplicity of logical processes were performed by the deductions from and combinations of dogmatic texts of the Catholic church, statements from the Bible, the Church Fathers, Aristotle, and others. One finds mainly theological explanations (moral theology and other theological disciplines included) and medieval cosmology (references to heaven, purgatory, hell, and other places for the soul) in the Scholastic systems. Both *Summae* of Thomas Aquinas are representative of these structures. The logical instrument of the Scholastics was sharpened for nonempiristic purposes. Their interest in logical combination, in discussion, and in argument can be illustrated by the subjects of the trivium and the quadrivium: grammar, logic, rhetoric; arithmetic, music, geometry, and astronomy.

This interest in combining concepts and statements without empirical testing prepared a certain attitude which appeared in the following ages as metaphysical construction. The neglect of testing facts and using observation statements in connection with all systematized ideas is especially found in the different idealistic systems. One may use Hegel's *Encyclopedia* as an example of this type. His comprehensive work can be regarded as substituting a priori philosophico-religious statements for traditional theological statements, and as joining these philosophico-religious statements to metaphysically transformed empirical statements. Hegel's vigor and all-embracing enthusiasm stimulated such empirical thinkers as Feuerbach, Marx, and Engels; they received more thoughts that breathe and words that burn from Hegel than from the books in which Helvetius, Holbach, and others wrote about the world in an empirical sense. Neither Hegel nor Schelling encouraged a scientific attitude and produced logical analyses or particular theses which could be used directly in the sciences, as did, for instance, certain ideas of Descartes and Leibniz. Schelling's *Naturphilosophie* influenced chemists and other scientists; the results were such that Liebig and others had to fight Schellingism in their own scientific camp.

The large and panoramic systems of idealistic philosophy are, as it were, late branches of a deformed scholasticism. Hegelianism is a typical metaphysical system of our age; Thomism is a typical Scholastic system which is still living in the Catholic church and also attracting some persons outside the Catholic church. Both these systems have not so far shown any disposition to logicalize empirical science, to form a quasi-addition to their philosophico-religious structures. Synthesis of empirical science was not directly supported by metaphysical and theological systems, though certain stimulations came from them.

Collections of interesting subjects, biographical, geographical, philological, and other data were already known in the Middle Ages, but in the seventeenth and eighteenth centuries some enormous encyclopedias of a new type were published (not so large as the Chinese, however). The French philosophical opposition organized the great French *Encyclopédie*. It was not a *"faute de mieux* encyclopedia" in place of a comprehensive system, but an alternative to systems. Since the Encyclopedists stressed the view that empirical statements were to be used not only for science (in spite of the fact that one can find not a few metaphysical and theological explanations in the work itself) but also for engineering and other technical purposes, collections of pictures were added to the text. The French *Encyclopédie* and its empirical attitude were combated by the church and government. Persons writing papers which seemed able to stimulate social perturbation had to fear persecution. Diderot (a polyhistor such as Voltaire but, unlike him, not doing experimental research) had to permit of textual variations by the publisher who feared the powerful enemies of the *Encyclopédie*. This encyclopedia had no comprehensive unity despite the expression of a certain empirical attitude; it was organized by means of a classification of sciences, references, and other devices.

More constructive ideas formed the basis of Comte's *Philosophie positive*. Comte, familiar with mathematics and physics, on the one hand, and very interested in social problems, on the other (the term 'sociology' was coined by him), tried to combine his ordering and classification of science with historical interests. Spencer's gigantic work, the system of *Synthetic Philosophy*, is also an example of this synthetic tendency which avoids metaphysical construction (this is not the place to discuss some metaphysical arguments in Comte's and Spencer's work) but endeavors to substitute an empirical scientific whole for philosophical speculations. One must stress the fact that Spencer's interest was concentrated in biology and sociology, because it is a usual prejudice that the idea of unified science and the unity of science movement is especially based on an interest in physics. Neither the Encyclopedists nor Comte and Spencer nor similar thinkers made an attempt to organize a logical synthesis of science.

IV. Scientific Attitude and Systematization of Empirical Procedure

The parallel increase of the scientific attitude and the systematic analysis of scientific procedures prepared the way for logical empiricism. During the Renaissance modern thinkers began to be interested in the procedure of empirical science and in the scientific attitude. Leonardo da Vinci, a universal genius influenced by the Scholastics, became a man with a comprehensive scientific attitude. He worked in different fields of engineering, was interested in scientific problems, and of course in all matters connected with painting. He began to feel the common root of all empirical science and stressed, for instance, the importance of "generalization" and other scientific aids. He understood what we call the empirical procedure. The universality and versatility of Leonardo da Vinci and other thinkers, scientists, and amateurs in science were stimuli of great importance for the origin of a comprehensive empiricism and a scientific attitude.

History shows us a great many scientists whose scientific attitude is not equally maintained in the various fields of thought. Such a scientist may be very critical in his own domain, for instance in physics, but of a totally different behavior when he speaks about "free will," "social privileges," or similar traditional problems. On such occasions some scientists sharply change their criticism and exactness of arguments and their style of language. Newton, for instance, was a scientist in whom theological speculations and scientific empiricism existed partly side by side, partly in actual connection—he speaks, for instance, about space as *sensorium dei*. A comprehensive scientific attitude has come into being, within scientific activity, since the Renaissance, but neither Leonardo da Vinci, nor Galileo a hundred years after him, analyzed the rules of empirical procedure or the scientific attitude. Francis Bacon was not very active in science or engineering, but he promoted certain ideas of empiricism successfully, especially the idea of "induction" as a scientific aid, in spite of the fact that he gave very poor examples in his work and did not recognize the scientific importance of Galileo and other empirical thinkers of his time.

Modern scientific empiricism attained very late in its development a comprehensive work which analyzes empirical procedure in all scientific fields: John Stuart Mill's *A System of Logic, Ratiocinative and Inductive, Being a Connected View of the Principles of Evidence and the Methods of Scientific Investigation.* Mill does not question the fact that astronomy and social science, physics and biology, are sciences of the same type. Mill, who was familiar with the problem of utilitarianism, with political economy and governmental practice as a pupil of his father, and with Bentham (who is not even now sufficiently appreciated), could effectively use Whewell's famous *History of the Inductive Sciences from the Earliest to the Present Times.* Mill's work influenced modern empiricism despite the fact that many of his particular statements were criticized. This type of comprehensiveness is also represented by the *Principles of Science* of Stanley Jevons; he was an economist like Mill and one of the promoters of modern symbolic logic. Karl Pearson's *The Grammar of Science* details the measures and procedures of modern science. Karl Pearson was very interested in biological and sociological questions, as was his teacher, Galton, but he was also familiar with physics.

But neither Mill nor other thinkers of similar type applied logical analysis consistently to the various sciences, thus attempting to make science a whole on a "logicalized" basis. They only achieved a comprehensive understanding of all the arguments which a scientist needs if he makes generalizations and tests scientific hypotheses. This *Encyclopedia* will show modern attempts to reform generalization, classification, testing, and other scientific activities, and to develop them by means of modern logic.

V. Logical Analysis of Scientific Statements

One science after the other separated from the mother-philosophy; scientists became more capable of solving difficult scientific problems than were philosophers occupied by a great many unscientific speculations and the particular problems of their own systems. One example may demonstrate this situation. During the eighteenth century people of different interests discussed the problem of "inertia." Some were influenced by Descartes, who used the term 'motion' when a body which is in the neighborhood of a second body is later found in the neighborhood of a third body. 'Space' and 'groups of bodies' were for these people more or less the same terms and 'empty absolute space' seemed to be a meaningless term. Others used the idea on which actual physical calculation was based in these times. The question arose whether to describe "inertia" in terms of relative correlations between bodies (a certain body together with the fixed stars), in terms of absolute space, or by means of other conceptions. Euler (about 1750) discussed the kinds of argumentation and was inclined to oppose the opinion that inertia could depend upon the totality of the fixed stars—

an opinion which is similar to modern ideas and which has been developed step by step by Mach and others. Kant, discussing this group of problems and analyzing Euler's paper, did not feel that this idea about correlation between inertia and the fixed stars was important enough to be criticized and did not even mention this, for him, strange construction, being more interested in his own a priori philosophy and in supporting Newton's ideas. The "essayistic" criticism by Hume and similar thinkers loosened the firmness and coherence of compact traditional opinions, but Kant, who stimulated some scientists, formed new barriers of peculiar rigidness by focusing and regulating criticism and skepticism. The essayist-philosopher Nietzsche showed how much of an antiscientific attitude can be found in Kant's system, which reduces the power of science and thus opens the doors to metaphysical and philosophico-religious speculations.

The evolution of non-Euclidean geometry, for instance, which prepared modern theories of measuring time and space, was hardly supported by modern philosophers—another example of the inadequacy of philosophers. One can rather assume that the ideas of Gauss, Bolyai, Lobachevski, and others were impeded by Kantianism: they had to start by opposing all kinds of apriorism. Not a few philosophers opposed the theory of relativity. The new intellectual environment was prepared more by specialists in physics and mathematics, or by certain imaginative amateurs in the field of science, and by poets, than by systematic philosophers. How many people may have been educated in the field of scientific imagination by Jonathan Swift!

A long series of imaginative analyses started with the animated statue imagined by Condillac, who had been influenced in his thought by Locke, Lamettrie, and others. Imagined statues which received one sense after another are relatives of Caspar Hauser and all the many children who have been found in the woods or other isolated places. These imagined and real beings are the subject matter of an old and rich literature which helped to prepare a logico-empirical attitude by means of imaginative analysis. Helmholtz and others, opposing Kant's ideology, imagined (partly for pedagogical purposes) two-dimensional beings on a sphere discussing geometrical problems. About the middle of the nineteenth century Fechner and others fancied dreamlands of different kinds: three-dimensional beings of different ages were produced by cutting off slices from a four-dimensional sausage. Some scientists fear such imaginative analogies as unreliable guides and demand the use of more systematic analysis. Actually, the history of all these imaginations has to be regarded as a part of the history of the empiristic mosaic. One must add to these significant imaginings that of two-dimensional beings who, traversing a hill, observe a retardation region, an indifference region, and an acceleration region of a geometrically homogeneous world. One could imagine a country ("Aeonia") in which beings could be repaired as are machines. There could be beings with connected nerves, or powerful beings consisting of a brain, one muscle, and one sense organ, but using complicated mechanical devices. Poincaré's problem of similar worlds (our world, reduced or enlarged in size) was also analyzed imaginatively about the middle of the nineteenth century by Eberty (*Die Gestirne und die Weltgeschichte*, newly edited by Gregorius Itelson with an introduction by Albert Einstein), who fancied also a trip throughout the universe quicker than light, in concordance with certain thoughts of Humboldt and Babbage. Renouvier (*Uchronie, l'utopie dans l'histoire*) used imagination in the field of history: how history really happened and how it might have happened. Lichtenberg, together with Chodowiecki (well known by his graphic work) and Sonya Kovalevska, the mathematician, elaborated similar fantasies for single individuals.

From these imaginations one can enter into the problem of behavioristics, logico-empirical analysis, and poetry. One can ask whether a blind man can make a complete physical description by means of certain devices or how the sensorium of Siamese twins is formed in the common part of their body, and similar concrete questions; one can write stimulating imaginative novels as did H. G. Wells, or a book of logico-empirical analysis like Carnap's *Logischer Aufbau der Welt*. To what extent imaginative constructions will be useful in the future may remain an open question.

All these imaginative analyses and constructions formed a part of the "essayistic" analysis of scientific argumentation such as that made by Poincaré, Duhem, and others. Their modern logical analysis of scientific statements, hypotheses, and theories was prepared for by many thinkers: the physicist Brewster, for instance, said that it is of the greatest importance that the same value d, characterizing the periodicity of light, could be found in the undulation theory and in the emission theory. John F. W. Herschel was anticipating Poincaré and Duhem when he wrote in his *Preliminary Discourse on the Study of Natural Philosophy* that one might imagine such a development of Newton's theory that it could solve certain problems which seemed reserved for the undulation theory. This sort of analysis of scientific statements was strongly supported by historico-critical studies. Mach's leading books dealing with mechanics, optics, and theory of heat characterize this tendency. He, by his paradigmatic analysis of concepts such as space and inertia, furthered the evolution of Einstein's theory of relativity. He did not make new experiments for this particular purpose but used, of course, the physical knowledge of his time. The fact that Duhem, Enriques, Mach, and others were active in their special sciences in logical analysis of scientific statements, and in the historical analysis of science, suggests the idea that the "history of the history of science" should be very instructive. In centuries in which such an analysis of scientific statements was not evolved as a special activity, historians of science were often busy with the analysis of scientific statements as a preparation for their historical analysis. A history of the history of optics, for instance, from Joseph Priestley (*The History and the Present State of Discoveries Relating to Vision, Light, and Colors* [1772], written as a part of a universal history of physics) up to Ernst Mach (*Die Prinzipien der physikalischen Optik* [1921]) shows clearly the increase of logicalization.

Corresponding historical sequences may be found in all scientific fields. The systematic analysis of "planned economy," for instance, has to be based on various fundamental problems; one group of problems deals with describing various possibilities: Thomas More's *Utopia* and Francis Bacon's *Nova Atlantis* are of another type of social analysis than are the plans of Ballod-Atlanticus or Popper-Lynkeus—plans which are forerunners of the science of socio-economic planning. Such kinds of social imagination can be combined with historico-social analyses like those made by Montesquieu, Stein, Marx, and others. The structure of economics is logically not so developed as the structure of physics, and so the history of the history of economics is not so abundant in logico-empirical analysis as is the history of the history of optics. Whewell's description and discussion of Linnaeus' problems dealing with classification and systematization give a picture of the logico-empirical analysis of sciences in the time of Whewell. A corresponding description and discussion of biological ideas from Linnaeus' classifications up to Woodger's formalization of biology should put a scientist in a position to compare directly the logico-empirical analysis of our time with the logico-empirical analysis made by a historian of science a hundred years ago.

A comparison of the argumentation in cosmology, geology, physics, biology, behavioristics ("psychology"), history, and social sciences in different ages will be furthered by the unity of science movement. An increasing number of scientists are busy with such problems, and one can hope for great success if scientists analyzing various sciences co-operate with men concerned with the history and logic of science. The inconsistency of the historically given universal pattern appears immediately. Successive editions of the *Encyclopedia of Unified Science* would show progress in logical analysis of scientific statements. Perhaps a special technique will be evolved which is able to describe systematically all these changes in the different sciences, thus continuing the work of Ernst Mach, whose centennial will be celebrated this year.

VI. Logico-empirical Integration

The mosaic pattern of empirical science progressively shows more marked interconnections than in the times in which empirical studies were relatively isolated. Scientific analysis of the sciences led to the observation that an increase of logical intercorrelation between statements of the same science and between statements of different sciences is a historical fact; one finds rationalism (as a quality of our experience), as it were, empirically, and may use the term 'empirical rationalism' with this meaning in which Gregorius Itelson proposed it, not merely as "rationalism based on experience." Comprehensiveness arises thus as a scientific need and is no longer a desire for vision only. The evolving of all such logical connections and the integration of science is a new aim of science.

Logical empiricism or empirical rationalism can also be regarded as a regeneration of certain elements of a priori rationalism. The *Scientia generalis* of Leibniz was the background of his "panlogism"—if this term is permitted in this sense and can be regarded as a "secularization of logic." The driving power of panlogism in the framework of a priori rationalism depends partly upon the idea that one can anticipate by means of logical combinations the progress of empirical science and not simply fructify its results or give certain suggestions. Leibniz was the first and last of the great philosophers who planned seriously to work out a comprehensive calculus adequate for all scientific progress. He promoted a universal logicalization of the whole of human thinking by means of a general calculus and a general terminology. He worked as a scientist and also began to organize scientific co-operation by means of scientific academies, but he was far from attempting or executing a universal scientific empiricism—too busy writing his *Théodicée*, elaborating the *Monadology*, and moreover getting entangled in theological disputes and church diplomacy.

His career was closely connected with Scholastic influences. As a boy he played, as it were, with logical elements such as "notions" and "subnotions." Young Leibniz at twenty years of age published his *Ars combinatoria*, which is influenced by Raimundus Lullus and other Scholastic authors. He was later influenced by the rationalistic Descartes and other modern thinkers, but he made clear that one could successfully use certain ideas of such Scholastic thinkers as Thomas Aquinas. Leibniz, the grandfather of modern logistic, transformed the often vague logical ideas of Scholasticism, and took the first steps toward modern exactness in logic, preparing the way for a great many modern ideas in the field of mathematics and logic.

He planned to organize a large encyclopedia, together with an *Atlas universalis*, in close connection with his *Characteristica universalis*. The plan embraced not only scientific disciplines, including rational grammar, moral science, geo-politics, but also natural theology. This gigantic plan was intended to form a logically organized whole. One may say that the *Pansophia* of Comenius (who came in touch with Leibniz) together with his *Orbis pictus* can be regarded as the parallel to the *Encyclopedia* and the *Atlas* of Leibniz. Both these pairs of works are based on a philosophico-religious rationalism and correspond in a certain sense to the medieval pair: Scholastic system and the overwhelming visual presentation in a medieval Catholic church.

Since Leibniz, like other a priori rationalists, was seeking *the* system of science and *the* logical key for it, one can understand that such an ideal was strange to empiricists. Most of the logical studies of Leibniz were not published, and only a few persons, like Lambert, were interested in special logistic problems. Public opinion was against formal logic. Kant and his followers discredited formal logic and thus petrified the aversion of Galileo and others against logic as an instrument of the traditional scholasticism. The growing new logic of Boole, De Morgan, and Grassman was not supported by philosophical thinkers of this period. Bolzano, for instance, influenced Austrian scientists and pedagogues about the middle of the nineteenth century by certain of his ideas, but his important investigations in the logical field (one example: *Paradoxien des Unendlichen*) were not studied and esteemed for a long period.

A universal application of logical analysis and construction

to science in general was prepared not only by the systematization of empirical procedure and the systematization of logico-
empirical analysis of scientific statements, but also by the analysis of language from different points of view. A direct route
leads from Scholastic analysis of language, made especially by
nominalists, up to Condillac (*Essai sur l'origine des connais-
sances humaines*), who influenced French and English thinkers,
to Bentham, whose multifarious work still lives today, and to
other thinkers interested in language as an aid for our daily life
and for science. The connection between modern logic and empiricism did not arise instantly. The importance of logicians of
the second half of the nineteenth century, such as Venn,
Schroeder, Peano, Frege, and others, will be expressly discussed
in the *Encyclopedia*. A few of the modern logicians, such as
Peirce and, later on, Bertrand Russell, combined the interest in
logic with an interest in empiricism. Traditional idealistic philosophers did not discuss carefully or look with favor upon this
new combination of logicalization and empiricalization. The
fact that Peirce was a logician and simultaneously interested in
empiricism was in turn important for the preparation of modern
scientific empiricism in the United States. In Europe the
Vienna Circle, the Berlin group, related thinkers in England
and Scandinavia, the Centre de synthèse in France, and the
Scientia group in Italy are evidence of the interest in this evolution of logic and empiricism. Some thinkers are mainly busy
with logical calculi, such as the members of the Polish School
or the Münster group. One cannot judge at the moment what
elements of these and other circles of thinkers may become most
essential for the future of unified science. The importance of
Riemann's geometry for modern physics did not appear at once.
What part will metalogic, semantics, and other disciplines play
in the unification of the language of the empirical sciences?

The important opinion arose (the influence of Wittgenstein,
a metaphysician in many respects, has to be mentioned in this
connection) that all statements can be expressed as "scientific
statements" and that one cannot speak of special "philosophic
statements." Some persons proposed to use the term 'phi-

losophize' for an activity which makes concepts and statements clear; others proposed to use the term 'philosophy' for 'logic of science.' If one takes the thesis seriously that in the field of knowledge one only has to deal with scientific statements, the most comprehensive field of statements must be that of unified science. If one does not care to avoid the term 'philosopher,' one may use it for persons engaged in unified science. Such "philosophers" may be specialists in one discipline and amateurs in others or comprehensive scientific amateurs like Voltaire, but not speculative thinkers.

It is common to all these persons that they do not join scientific statements with a second type of specific "philosophical" formulation; this attitude gives one the feeling that one is acting within the collective scientific atmosphere and not in the sphere of individual philosophemes. Voltaire mentioned that opinions which become common do not bear the names of their creators (Du Bois-Reymond added that Voltaire's name and activity are insufficiently known because "Voltairianism" is a quality of the age after Voltaire). Nietzsche stressed esteem for "the unpretentious truths," objecting to the fascinating errors of metaphysical ages. An evolved civilization likes, according to Nietzsche, the modest results found by means of exact methods which are fruitful for the whole future; and such manliness, simplicity, and temperance will characterize not only an increasing number but also the whole of humanity in the future. Moritz Schlick explained in a similar sense that the evolution of modern critical thinking is founded on an anonymous mass of thinkers, especially scientists, and that progress does not arise from the sensational philosophical systems which form an endless row, each contradicting the others.

Scientists may now build up systematical bridges from science to science, analyzing concepts which are used in different sciences, considering all questions dealing with classification, order, etc. Axiomatization of science seems to give an opportunity to make the use of fundamental terms more precise and to prepare the combination of different sciences; preliminary axiomatization has to be founded on a long evolution of science. We cannot anticipate a "final axiomatization."

Some difficulties in science, even within a special discipline, arise from the fact that one cannot always decide whether two scientists (for instance, psychologists) speak about the same or different problems, or whether they explain the same or different opinions, by means of different scientific languages. Unification of scientific language is one of the purposes of the unity of science movement. It is a question to what extent such unification can be furthered. One can perhaps reduce all scientific terms to one kind of term by means of a special logical technique. The thesis of physicalism which will be discussed in this *Encyclopedia* (see the following article by Carnap) emphasizes that it is possible to reduce all terms to well-known terms of our language of daily life. Another question is to what extent one can reduce the statements or laws of biology, behavioristics, or sociology to physicalistic statements or laws. All studies dealing with languages and scientific terminology are regarded seriously not only in connection with what one usually calls logical questions but also in connection with questions of sociology and behavioristics; one may ask, for instance, how problems discussed by the Dutch group of thinkers interested in "significs" are connected with problems of semantics and other new disciplines. A great many scientists, working in different fields, are pushing these analyses forward.

Since more and more scientists stress the fact that in the end one must test all theories by means of the language of daily life, the correlations between the calculus of theories and the language of daily life will be systematically analyzed.

Many people think that logic (or logistic) is, as it were, an antidote to metaphysical speculations; that is wrong: one can elaborate a speculative metaphysical system *more logico demonstrata*. There is no automatically acting antidote against statements which, though formulated in an empirical language, yet need scientific criticism. Of which temper one's mind is, one can show by presenting one's work.

VII. Unified Science and Encyclopedism

Science itself is supplying its own integrating glue instead of aiming at a synthesis on the basis of a "super science" which is to legislate for the special scientific activities. The historical tendency of the unity of science movement is toward a unified science departmentalized into special sciences, and not toward a speculative juxtaposition of an autonomous philosophy and a group of scientific disciplines. If one rejects the idea of such a super science as well as the idea of a pseudo-rationalistic anticipation of *the* system of science, what is the maximum of scientific co-ordination which remains possible? The answer given by the unity of science movement is: an encyclopedia of unified science. An encyclopedia (in contradistinction to an anticipated system or a system constructed a priori) can be regarded as the model of man's knowledge. For, since one cannot compare the historically given science with "the real science," the most one can achieve in integration of scientific work seems to be an encyclopedia, constructed by scientists in co-operation. It may happen that one must use in one hypothesis, destined for a particular purpose, a supposition which contradicts another supposition used in another hypothesis, destined for another particular purpose. One may try to eliminate such contradictions, but in the historically given science, and so in a real encyclopedia, these and other difficulties always appear.

Encyclopedism may be regarded as a special attitude; one may also speak of encyclopedism as a program. Encyclopedism starts with the analysis of certain groups of scientific statements; it may happen that these can be axiomatized and that this axiomatized group of statements can be combined with others expressed in a similar form. But such a system of statements must not be regarded as a model of the scientific knowledge of a given age. An encyclopedia and not a system is the genuine model of science as a whole. An encyclopedic integration of scientific statements, with all the discrepancies and difficulties which appear, is the maximum of integration which we can achieve. It is against the principle of encyclopedism to im-

operation, that a historian knows much about human history and can foretell the main results of a newly undertaken excavation, that an economist judging from the first symptoms can warn the public of an impending slump, that a political leader can systematically predict social changes which are arising.

One can state all these scientific prognostications in terms of everyday language—the language which is common to all men in the world irrespective of the fact that the scientist himself uses expressions and symbols in preparatory work which are mostly of an international character. Unified science is therefore supported, in general, by the scientific attitude which is based on the internationality of the use of the language of everyday life and on the internationality of the use of scientific language.

It may happen that people create and prefer certain terms and formulations not for universal understanding but for stimulating certain emotions, and may decide that in certain cases an emotional activity is more important than a scientific attitude. It is not the subject of a scientific explanation to support or oppose such a decision. If one prefers a comprehensive scientific attitude, this *Encyclopedia* tries to show him the spectrum of scientific thinking. Each scientifically oriented man knows very well that the elaboration of such an encyclopedia, like other activities, is influenced by wishing and fearing, but there is a difference between men who intend to discover such influences and others who do not. That leads one to a great many unsolved problems. Incompleteness and open questions arise in all parts of this work, but encyclopedism maintains, nevertheless, that the integration of science is an inevitable part of man's scientific activities.

VIII. Structure of the Encyclopedia

One may ask: "What program is common to all the collaborators of the *Encyclopedia?*" A program formed of statements accepted by all the collaborators would be narrow and would be a source of divergences in the near future. This *Encyclopedia* will show that scientists, though working in different scientific fields and in different countries, may nevertheless co-operate as successfully within unified science as when scientists co-operate within physics or biology. The *Encyclopedia* will perhaps be a mainstay of scientific empiricism as well as of the unity of science movement in the widest sense. The maximum of co-operation—that is the program! This co-operation strives to elaborate the framework of unified science. Encyclopedism based on logical empiricism was the general historical background which underlay the proposal of an international encyclopedia of unified science.[2]

The general purpose of the *International Encyclopedia of Unified Science* is to bring together material pertaining to the scientific enterprise as a whole. The work will not be a series of alphabetically arranged articles; rather will it be a series of monographs with a highly analytical index, which will make it possible to find the bit of information sought if the *Encyclopedia* is to be used as a reference work. Each monograph, sometimes written by more than one collaborator, is devoted to a particular group of problems. The collaborators and organizers of this work are concerned with the analysis and interrelation of central scientific ideas, with all problems dealing with the analysis of sciences, and with the sense in which science forms a unified encyclopedical whole. The new *Encyclopedia* so aims to integrate the scientific disciplines, so to unify them, so to dovetail them together, that advances in one will bring about advances in the others.

The *Encyclopedia* is to be constructed like an onion. The heart of this onion is formed by twenty pamphlets which constitute two introductory volumes. These volumes, entitled *Foundations of the Unity of Science*, are complete in themselves but also serve as the introduction to what will follow.

The first "layer" of the onion which will inclose this "heart," consisting of the first two volumes, is planned as a series of volumes which will deal with the problems of systematization in special sciences and in unified science—including logic, mathematics, theory of signs, linguistics, history and sociology of science, classification of sciences, and educational implications of the scientific attitude. In these volumes scientists with different opinions will be given an opportunity to explain their individual ideas in their own formulation, since it is a special aim of this work to stress the gaps in our present knowledge and the difficulties and discrepancies which are found at present in various fields of science. "Heart" and "first layer" together will be a completely self-contained unit. The following "layers" may deal with more specialized problems; the interests of the reader and the collaborators in the particular problems will lead the members of the Committee of Organization and the Advisory Committee to consider various possible lines of development. It is hoped that an *Atlas* can be worked out as an *Isotype Thesaurus* showing important facts by means of unified visual aids.[3] The plan of this *Encyclopedia* could not be based on a generally accepted classification of the sciences—indeed, the collaborators may perhaps find a new way to assemble systematically all the special sciences. The organizers and collaborators know very well that certain frontiers of sciences are unsatisfactory and that certain terms are not sufficiently defined. The *Encyclopedia* will eliminate these defects where possible.

This Introduction has aimed to show the historical position of the *Encyclopedia;* it is amplified by special articles. Rough outlines are augmented by the articles of Charles W. Morris and Rudolf Carnap, the one explaining how scientific empiricism is an even more comprehensive movement than logical empiricism, the other stressing the importance of the logical analysis of sciences. The other articles in this introductory monograph amplify some aspects of the problems connected with unified science. Niels Bohr and Bertrand Russell are concerned with the importance for the sciences of certain phases of the unity of science movement, while John Dewey stresses the wider social implications involved in the unification of the forces of science.

Without pursuing utopian ideals, an effort will be made to have the scientific language of the *Encyclopedia* as homogeneous as it is possible to make it at the present. The *Encyclopedia* will express the situation of a living being and not of a phantom; those who read the *Encyclopedia* should feel that scientists are speaking about science as a being of flesh and blood. The collaborators will certainly learn from their encyclopedical work. Suggestions from different sources will stimulate this activity, so that this *Encyclopedia* will become a platform for the discussion of all aspects of the scientific enterprise. In this way the *International Encyclopedia of Unified Science* hopes to avoid becoming a mausoleum or a herbarium, and to remain a living intellectual force growing out of a living need of men, and so in turn serving humanity.

NOTES

1. Plans were laid at the congress at Charles University in Prague (1934) for a series of annual congresses devoted to the unity of science. The proceedings of this preliminary congress were published in the 1935 *Erkenntnis* (Leipzig: F. Meiner) and in separate volume form as *Einheit der Wissenschaft* (F. Meiner). The First International Congress for the Unity of Science was held at the Sorbonne, Paris, in 1935, and the proceedings were published under the title *Actes du congrès international de philosophie scientifique* (Paris: Hermann & Cie, 1936). The proceedings of the second congress, held at Copenhagen in 1936 and devoted to the problem of causality, appeared in the 1937 *Erkenntnis* and also as an independent volume (*Das Kausalproblem* [Leipzig: F. Meiner; Copenhagen: Levin & Munksgaard]). The third congress (Paris, 1937) took the form of a conference devoted to the project of the *International Encyclopedia of Unified Science*. Annual congresses are being planned, and preparations are now being made for the fourth congress, to be held at Girton College, Cambridge, England, July 14–19, 1938, and for the fifth congress, to be held at Harvard University, September 5–10, 1939. The general theme of this congress will be the "Logic of Science," and the publication of the *Foundations of the Unity of Science* is so arranged as to provide a background for the congress.

The International Congresses for the Unity of Science are being administered by an International Committee composed of the following members:

N. Bohr (Copenhagen)
M. Boll (Paris)
H. Bonnet (Paris)
P. W. Bridgman (Cambridge, Mass.)
E. Brunswik (Vienna, Berkeley)
R. Carnap (Chicago)
E. Cartan (Paris)
J. Clay (Amsterdam)
M. R. Cohen (Chicago)
J. Dewey (New York City)
F. Enriques (Rome)
P. Frank (Prague)
M. Fréchet (Paris)

F. Gonseth (Zurich)
J. Hadamard (Paris)
P. Janet (Paris)
H. S. Jennings (Baltimore)
J. Joergensen (Copenhagen)
E. Kaila (Helsingfors)
T. Kotarbinski (Warsaw)
A. Lalande (Paris)
P. Langevin (Paris)
K. S. Lashley (Cambridge, Mass.)
C. I. Lewis (Cambridge, Mass.)
J. Lukasiewicz (Warsaw)

G. Mannoury (Amsterdam)
R. von Mises (Istanbul)
C. W. Morris (Chicago)
O. Neurath (The Hague)
C. K. Ogden (London)
J. Perrin (Paris)
H. Reichenbach (Istanbul)
A. Rey (Paris)
C. Rist (Paris)
L. Rougier (Besançon, Cairo)
B. Russell (Petersfield)
L. S. Stebbing (London)
J. H. Woodger (London)

2. See Otto Neurath, "An International Encyclopedia of Unified Science"—a paper read at the First International Congress for the Unity of Science (Paris, 1935), published in *Actes du congrès international de philosophie scientifique* (Paris: Hermann & Cie, 1936), Part II. This idea was supported and accompanied by important explanations by the members of the Encyclopedia Committee of Organization (Rudolf Carnap, Philipp Frank, Joergen Joergensen, Charles W. Morris, Otto Neurath, Louis Rougier), who spoke about the problems, the importance, and the logical basis of this project (see papers read by Charles W. Morris, Rudolf Carnap, and Philipp Frank at the same congress). The First International Congress for the Unity of Science approved the plan and expressed willingness to help in its fulfilment. See also Otto Neurath, "L'Encyclopédie comme 'modèle,'" *Revue de synthèse*, October, 1936.

3. See Otto Neurath, *International Picture Language: The First Rules of ISOTYPE* (London: Kegan Paul, 1936).

Analysis and Synthesis in Science

Niels Bohr

Notwithstanding the admittedly practical necessity for most scientists to concentrate their efforts in special fields of research, science is, according to its aim of enlarging human understanding, essentially a unity. Although periods of fruitful exploration of new domains of experience may often naturally be accompanied by a temporary renunciation of the comprehension of our situation, history of science teaches us again and again how the extension of our knowledge may lead to the recognition of relations between formerly unconnected groups of phenomena, the harmonious synthesis of which demands a renewed revision of the presuppositions for the unambiguous application of even our most elementary concepts. This circumstance reminds us not only of the unity of all sciences aiming at a description of the external world but, above all, of the inseparability of epistemological and psychological analysis. It is just in the emphasis on this last point, which recent development in the most different fields of science has brought to the foreground, that the program of the present great undertaking distinguishes itself from that of previous encyclopedic enterprises, in which stress was essentially laid on the completeness of the account of the actual state of knowledge rather than on the elucidation of scientific methodology. It is therefore to be hoped that the forthcoming *Encyclopedia* will have a deep influence on the whole attitude of our generation which, in spite of the ever increasing specialization in science as well as in technology, has a growing feeling of the mutual dependency of all human activities. Above all, it may help us to realize that even in science any arbitrary restriction implies the danger of prejudices and that our only way of avoiding the extremes of materialism and mysticism is the never ending endeavor to balance analysis and synthesis.

Unity of Science as a Social Problem

John Dewey

I. The Scientific Attitude

Anyone who attempts to promote the unity of science must ask himself at least two basic questions: "What is meant by that whose unity is to be promoted, namely, science?" and "What sort of unity is feasible or desirable?" The following pages represent the conclusions the present writer has reached in reflecting upon these two themes.

With respect to the question as to the meaning of science, a distinction needs to be made between science as attitude and method and science as a body of subject matter. I do not mean that the two can be separated, for a method is a way of dealing with subject matter and science as a body of knowledge is a product of a method. Each exists only in connection with the other. An attitude becomes psychopathic when it is not directed to objects beyond itself. What is meant is, first, that attitude and method come before the material which is found in books, journals, and the proceedings of scientific organizations; and, second, that the attitude is manifested primarily toward the objects and events of the ordinary world and only secondarily toward that which is already scientific subject matter.

Stated in other words, the scientific method is not confined to those who are called scientists. The body of knowledge and ideas which is the product of the work of the latter is the fruit of a method which is followed by the wider body of persons who deal intelligently and openly with the objects and energies of the common environment. In its specialized sense, science is an elaboration, often a highly technical one, of everyday operations. In spite of the technicality of its language and procedures, its genuine meaning can be understood only if its connection with attitudes and procedures which are capable of being used by all persons who act intelligently is borne in mind.

On the level of common sense there are attitudes which are like those of science in its more specialized sense, while there are attitudes which are thoroughly unscientific. There are those who work by routine, by casual cut-and-try methods, those who are enslaved to dogma and directed by prejudice, just as there are those who use their hands, eyes, and ears to gain knowledge of whatever comes their way and use whatever brains they have to extract meaning from what they observe. Few would rule engineers from out the scientific domain, and those few would rest their case upon a highly dubious distinction between something called "pure" science and something else called "applied" science.

As Dr. Karl Darrow has said in his *Renaissance of Science:*

Many of the things which modern science has to tell us are fantastic and inconceivable indeed, but they have been attested by the same sort of man with the same sort of training and using the same sort of reasoning as those who have made it possible to speak over a wire with San Francisco and over the ether of space to London, to cross the Atlantic in four days by steamer and in twenty-four hours by aeroplane, to operate a railroad with power transmitted invisibly through rails, and to photograph the bones inside the body with a light no eye can see and no fire can send forth.

When the achievements of the engineer are disparaged under the name "applied" science, it is forgotten that the inquiries and the calculations required to produce these achievements are as exacting as those which generate the science called "pure." Pure science does not apply itself automatically; application takes place through use of methods which it is arbitrary to distinguish from those employed in the laboratory or observatory. And if the engineer is mentioned, it is because, once he is admitted, we cannot exclude the farmer, the mechanic, and the chauffeur, as far as these men do what they have to do with intelligent choice of means and with intelligent adaptation of means to ends, instead of in dependence upon routine and guesswork. On the other hand, it is quite possible for the scientist to be quite unscientific in forming his beliefs outside his special subject, as he does whenever he permits such beliefs to be dictated by unexamined premises accepted traditionally or caught up out of the surrounding social atmosphere.

In short, the scientific attitude as here conceived is a quality that is manifested in any walk of life. What, then, is it? On its negative side, it is freedom from control by routine, prejudice, dogma, unexamined tradition, sheer self-interest. Positively, it is the will to inquire, to examine, to discriminate, to draw conclusions only on the basis of evidence after taking pains to gather all available evidence. It is the intention to reach beliefs, and to test those that are entertained, on the basis of observed fact, recognizing also that facts are without meaning save as they point to ideas. It is, in turn, the experimental attitude which recognizes that while ideas are necessary to deal with facts, yet they are working hypotheses to be tested by the consequences they produce.

Above all, it is the attitude which is rooted in the problems that are set and questions that are raised by the conditions of actuality. The unscientific attitude is that which shuns such problems, which runs away from them, or covers them up instead of facing them. And experience shows that this evasion is the counterpart of concern with artificial problems and alleged ready-made solutions. For all problems are artificial which do not grow, even if indirectly, out of the conditions under which life, including associated living, is carried on. Life is a process which goes on in connection with an environment which is complex, physically and culturally. There is no form of interaction with the physical environment and the human environment that does not generate problems that can be coped with only by an objective attitude and an intelligent method. The home, the school, the shop, the bedside and hospital, present such problems as truly as does the laboratory. They usually present the problems in a more direct and urgent fashion. This fact is so obvious that it would be trite to mention it were it not that it shows the potential universality of the scientific attitude.

The existence of artificial problems is also an undeniable fact in human history. The existence of such problems and the expenditure of energy upon the solution of them are the chief reasons why the potentiality of scientific method is so often unrealized and frustrated. The word 'metaphysics' has many meanings, all of which are generally supposed to be so highly technical as to be of no interest to the man in the street. But in the sense that 'metaphysical' means that which is outside of experience, over and beyond it, all human beings are metaphysical when they occupy themselves with problems which do not rise out of experience and for which solutions are sought outside experience. Men are metaphysical not only in technical philosophy but in many of their beliefs and habits of thought in religion, morals, and politics. The waste of energy that results is serious enough. But this is slight compared with that which is wrought by artificial problems and solutions in preventing, deflecting, and distorting the development of the scientific attitude which is the proper career of intelligence.

II. The Social Unity of Science

When we turn from the question of what is meant by science to the question of what is meant by its unity, we seem, at first sight, to have shifted ground and to be in another field. The unity of science is usually referred to in connection with unification of the attained results of science. In this field the problem of attaining the unity of science is that of co-ordinating the scattered and immense body of specialized findings into a systematic whole. This problem is a real one and cannot be neglected. But there is also a human, a cultural, meaning of the unity of science. There is, for instance, the question of unifying the efforts of all those who exercise in their own affairs the scientific method so that these efforts may gain the force which comes from united effort. Even when an individual is or tries to be intelligent in the conduct of his own life-affairs, his efforts are hampered, often times defeated, by obstructions due not merely to ignorance but to active opposition to the scientific attitude on the part of those influenced by prejudice, dogma, class interest, external authority, nationalistic and racial sentiment, and similar powerful agencies. Viewed in this light, the problem of the unity of science constitutes a fundamentally important social problem.

At the present time the enemies of the scientific attitude are numerous and organized—much more so than appears at superficial glance. The prestige of science is indeed great, especially in the field of its external application to industry and war. In the abstract, few would come out openly and say that they were opposed to science. But this small number is no measure of the influence of those who borrow the results of science to advance by thoroughly unscientific and antiscientific methods private, class, and national interests. Men may admire science, for example, because it gives them the radio to use, and then employ the radio to create conditions that prevent the development of the scientific attitude in the most important fields of human activity—fields which suffer terribly because of failure to use scientific method. In particular, science is not welcomed but rather opposed when it "invades" (a word often used) the field now pre-empted by religion, morals, and political and economic institutions.

To bring about unity of the scientific attitude is, then, to bring those who accept it and who act upon it into active cooperation with one another. This problem transcends in importance the more technical problem of unification of the results of the special sciences. It takes precedence over the latter issue. For it is not too much to say that science, even in its more specialized sense, now stands at a critical juncture. It must move forward in order to maintain its achievements. If it stands still, it will be confined to the field in which it has already won victories and will see the fruits of its victories appropriated by those who will use them by antiscientific methods for nonhumane ends.

Accordingly, the great need is for those who are actuated by the scientific spirit to take counsel regarding the place and function of science in the total scene of life. It follows that a movement in behalf of the unity of science need not and should not lay down in advance a platform to be accepted. It is essentially a co-operative movement, so that detailed specific common standpoints and ideas must emerge out of the very processes of co-operation. To try to formulate them in advance and insist upon their acceptance by all is both to obstruct co-operation and to be false to the scientific spirit. The only thing necessary in the form of agreement is faith in the scientific attitude and faith in the human and social importance of its maintenance and expansion.

What has been said does not minimize the difficulties that arise from the great degree of isolated specialization that now characterizes science or the importance of overcoming these difficulties. To a great extent those who now pursue the different branches of science speak different languages and are not readily understood by one another. Translation from one branch to another is not easy. In consequence, workers tend to be deprived of the useful intellectual instruments that would be available in their own special work if there were a freer give and take.

But the needed work of co-ordination cannot be done mechanically or from without. It, too, can be the fruit only of co-operation among those animated by the scientific spirit. Convergence to a common center will be effected most readily and most vitally through the reciprocal exchange which attends genuine co-operative effort. The attempt to secure unity by defining the terms of all the sciences in terms of some one science is doomed in advance to defeat. In the house which science might build there are many mansions. The first task, to change the metaphor, is to build bridges from one science to another. There are many gaps to be spanned. It seems to me, however, that the great need is the linkage of the physico-chemical sciences with psychological and social fields of science through the intermediary of biology. I should probably be expressing my own view or that of a particular and perhaps small group if I said that convergence can best be attained by considering how various sciences may be brought together in common attack upon practical social problems. But it is wholly within the scope of the present theme to say that the co-operative endeavor held in view by the present movement for the unity of science is bound gradually to disclose the causes of present gaps and to indicate where and how bridges may be built across the gulfs that still separate workers in different fields.

A very short history has been enjoyed by free scientific method in comparison with the long history enjoyed by forces which have never felt the influence of science. Ideas that descend from the prescientific epoch are still with us and are crystallized in institutions. They are not to be exorcised by reiteration of the word 'science.' Every scientific worker is still subject to their influence, certainly outside his special field and sometimes even within it. Only constant critical care, exercised in the spirit of the scientific attitude, can bring about their gradual elimination. Ultimately, this criticism must be self-criticism. But the agencies and instrumentalities of self-criticism can be had only by means of as full and free co-operation with others as it is possible to secure.

The advance of scientific method has brought with it, where the influence of the method has been felt, a great increase in toleration. We are now in a world where there is an accelerated development of intolerance. Part of the cause for this growth can be found, I think, in the fact that tolerance so far has been largely a passive thing. We need a shift from acceptance of responsibility for passive toleration to active responsibility for promoting the extension of scientific method. The first step is to recognize the responsibility for furthering mutual understanding and free communication.

III. Education and the Unity of Science

It is perhaps within the scope of my theme to say something about the connection of the movement for the unity of science with education. I have already mentioned the fact that scientific method has reached a crisis in its history, due, in final analysis, to the fact that the ultra-reactionary and the ultra-radical combine, even while acclaiming the prestige of science in certain fields, to use the techniques of science to destroy the scientific attitude. The short history of science in comparison with the history of institutions that resist its application by the mere fact of their inertia has also been mentioned. These two influences combine to render the agencies of education the crucial point in any movement to bring about a greater and more progressive unity of the scientific spirit.

After a struggle, the various sciences have found a place for themselves in the educational institutions. But to a large extent they exist merely side by side with other subjects which have hardly felt the touch of science. This, however, is far from being the most depressing feature of the educational situation as respects the place of science. For it is also true that the spirit in which the sciences are often taught, and the methods of instruction employed in teaching them, have been in large measure taken over from traditional nonscientific subjects.

I mention certain things which confirm this statement. In the first place, science has barely affected elementary education. With a very few exceptions it has not touched the early years of the elementary school. Yet this is the time when curiosity is most awake, the interest in observation the least dulled, and desire for new experiences most active. It is also the period in which the fundamental attitudes are formed which control, subconsciously if not consciously, later attitudes and methods.

In the second place, scientific subjects are taught very largely as bodies of subject matter rather than as a method of universal attack and approach. There may be laboratories and laboratory exercises and yet this statement remain true. For they may be employed primarily in order that pupils acquire a certain body of information. The resulting body of information about facts and laws has a different content from that provided in other studies. But as long as the ideal is information, the sciences taught are still under the dominion of ideas and practices that have a prescientific origin and history. Laboratory exercises and class demonstrations may be a part of a regular routine of instruction, and yet accomplish little in developing the scientific habit of mind. Indeed, except in a chosen few the mere weight of information may be a load carried in the memory, not a resource for further observation and thought.

In the third place, apart from some institutions of research and graduate departments of universities which attract relatively a small number, most money and energy go into institutions in which persons are prepared for special professional pursuits. This fact is not itself objectionable, as I have already indicated in speaking of "applied" and "pure" science. But this technical education, as it is at present conducted, is directed to narrow ends rather that to the wide and liberal end of developing interest and ability to use the scientific method in all fields of human betterment. It is quite possible, unfortunately, for a person to have the advantage of this special training and yet remain indifferent to the application of the scientific attitude in fields that lie outside his own specialized calling.

The final point is a corollary. Something called by the name of "science" gets shut off in a segregated territory of its own. There are powerful special interests which strive in any case to keep science isolated so that the common life may be immune from its influence. Those who have these special interests fear the impact of scientific method upon social issues.

They fear this impact even if they have not formulated the nature and ground of their fear. But there are influences within the status of science itself in the educational system which promote its isolation. If the schools are used for the purpose of instilling belief in certain dogmas—a use in which something called "education" becomes simply an organ of propaganda— and this use continues to grow, it will be in some measure be- cause science has not been conceived and practiced as the sole universal method of dealing intellectually with all problems. The movement to unify workers in different fields of science is itself an educative movement for those who take part in it. It is also a precondition of effort to give the scientific attitude that place in educational institutions which will create an ever increasing number of persons who habitually adopt the scientific attitude in meeting the problems that confront them.

I said that I thought that reference to education belonged within the scope of the present theme. On the one hand, the future of the scientific attitude as a socially unified force depends more upon the education of children and youth than upon any other single force. On the other hand, the teaching of science can hardly take the place which belongs to it, as an attitude of universal application, unless those who are already animated by the scientific attitude and concerned for its expansion actively co-operate. The first condition to be satisfied is that such persons bestir themselves to become aware of what the scientific attitude is and what it is about so as to become diligently militant in demonstrating its rightful claims.

The import of what has been said is that the scientific attitude and method are at bottom but the the method of free and effective intelligence. The special sciences reveal what this method is and means, and what it is capable of. It is neither feasible nor desirable that all human beings should become practitioners of a special science. But is intensely desirable and under certain conditions practicable that all human beings become scientific in their attitudes: genuinely intelligent in their ways of thinking and acting. It is practicable because all normal persons have the potential germs which make this result possible. It is desirable because this attitude forms the sole ultimate alternative to prejudice, dogma, authority, and coercive force exercised in behalf of some special interest. Those who are concerned with science in its more technical meaning are obviously those who should take the lead by co-operation with one another in bringing home to all the inherent universality of scientific method.

On the Importance of Logical Form

Bertrand Russell

The instrument of mathematical logic, which has begun to be appreciated during the present century, possesses two rather different kinds of utility—one in pure mathematics, the other in the various empirical sciences. Of the former I shall say nothing, since the ground is familiar; but on the latter there are some things to be said that bear on the importance of a modern encyclopedia.

In the empirical sciences it is not so much in relation to inference that mathematical logic is useful as in relation to analysis and the apprehension of identity and difference of form. Where identity of form is of the traditional mathematical kind, its importance has long been realized. The kinetic theory of gases has been applied to the stellar universe, which, to the non-mathematical mind, appears very different from a gas. A British mathematical professor at Tokyo was led by his location to study earthquakes, and made useful applications of his results to the vibrations of the footplates of locomotives. But, where identity of form is not of the sort that can be expressed without logical symbols, men of science have been less quick to recognize it; while the general public, through logical incompetence, has been led into grave practical errors. During the Black Death the inhabitants of Siena attributed the calamity to their presumption in planning a much enlarged cathedral, oblivious of the fact that the mortality was just as great elsewhere. Similarly, in 1931, the population of every country attributed the depression to the sins of its own government; this caused a movement to the Left where there was a Right government, and to the Right where there was a Left government. Only a few impotent intellectuals observed that the phenomenon to be explained was world-wide, not local.

The distinction between macroscopic and microscopic physics, which has become important since the rise of quantum theory, suggests possibilities as regards scientific method in other fields. Although, as a mathematical ideal, macroscopic physics may be supposed deducible from the behavior of the individual atoms, it was in fact discovered first, and its laws remain valid, for most practical purposes, in spite of the discoveries of the quantum physicists. This suggests the possibility of a social science not deduced from the laws of individual behavior but based upon laws which are only valid for large numbers. The theory of evolution, in biology, is the most striking example. Economics, in so far as it is a science, is another. Vital statistics afford another field for the observation of statistical behavior; it might be thought, for instance, that there is an inverse correlation between increase and density of the population, but Australia, though confirming this as regards rabbits, negatives it as regards human beings.

Logical method has important applications to psychology. Suppose, for example, that, in order to deal with dual and multiple personality, we desire a definition of 'person' not derived from bodily continuity. We may observe that dual personality is connected with amnesia. We may define a relation M between two experiences, consisting in the fact that one is, in whole or part, a recollection of the other, or the other of the one. If N is the ancestral relation of M, all the experiences which have to a given experience the relation N may be defined as the person to whom the given experience belongs; for the student of dual and multiple personality this is probably the most convenient definition.

I said that mathematical logic has less importance in relation to scientific inference than in relation to analysis, but this statement needs qualification. Outside mathematics, the important inferences are not deductive, i.e., they are not such as mathematical logic makes. But logic can state their character with a precision which was formerly impossible. Much has been done, for example, by Carnap, in analyzing the kind of inference upon which scientific laws are based. Since all inferences of this kind are probable, not demonstrative, the study of probability, as Reichenbach insists, is of fundamental importance in scientific method.

The importance of logical form may be illustrated by what may be called the principle of the dictionary: Given two sets of propositions such that, by a suitable dictionary, any proposition of either set can be translated into a proposition of the other set, there is no effective difference between the two sets. Suppose—to take a hypothesis that I neither affirm nor deny—that all scientific propositions can be tested in terms of physics, and can also be stated on Berkeleian principles, in terms of psychology; then the question as to which of these forms of statement is the more correct has no meaning, since both or neither must be correct. Such dictionaries, which can, as a rule, only be constructed by the help of modern logic, suffice to dispose of large numbers of metaphysical questions, and thus facilitate concentration upon genuine scientific problems.

Let us take another example of the principle of the dictionary. The general principle of relativity showed that, in expressing the laws of macroscopic physics, we can transform our co-ordinates in any way we choose, so long as topological relations in space-time are preserved as topological relations among co-ordinates. It follows that the laws of macroscopic physics are topological laws, and that the introduction of number through co-ordinates is only a practical convenience, the laws being such as can, in theory, be expressed without the use of number. The old view that measurement is of the essence of science would therefore seem to be erroneous.

The unity of science, which is sometimes lost to view through immersion in specialist problems, is essentially a unity of method, and the method is one upon which modern logic throws much new light. It may be hoped that the *Encyclopedia* will do much to bring about an awareness of this unity.

Logical Foundations of the Unity of Science

Rudolf Carnap

I. What Is Logical Analysis of Science?

The task of analyzing science may be approached from various angles. The analysis of the subject matter of the sciences is carried out by science itself. Biology, for example, analyzes organisms and processes in organisms, and in a similar way every branch of science analyzes its subject matter. Mostly, however, by 'analysis of science' or 'theory of science' is meant an investigation which differs from the branch of science to which it is applied. We may, for instance, think of an investigation of scientific *activity*. We may study the historical development of this activity. Or we may try to find out in which way scientific work depends upon the individual conditions of the men working in science, and upon the status of the society surrounding them. Or we may describe procedures and appliances used in scientific work. These investigations of scientific activity may be called history, psychology, sociology, and methodology of science. The subject matter of such studies is science as a body of actions carried out by certain persons under certain circumstances. Theory of science in this sense will be dealt with at various other places in this *Encyclopedia;* it is certainly an essential part of the foundation of science.

We come to a theory of science in another sense if we study not the actions of scientists but their results, namely, science as a body of ordered knowledge. Here, by 'results' we do not mean beliefs, images, etc., and the behavior influenced by them. That would lead us again to psychology of science. We mean by 'results' certain linguistic expressions, viz., the statements asserted by scientists. The task of the theory of science in this sense will be to analyze such statements, study their kinds and relations, and analyze terms as components of those statements and theories as ordered systems of those statements. A statement is a kind of sequence of spoken sounds, written marks, or the like, produced by human beings for specific purposes. But it is possible to abstract in an analysis of the statements of science from the persons asserting the statements and from the psychological and sociological conditions of such assertions. The analysis of the linguistic expressions of science under such an abstraction is *logic of science*.

Within the logic of science we may distinguish between two chief parts. The investigation may be restricted to the forms of the linguistic expressions involved, i.e., to the way in which they are constructed out of elementary parts (e.g., words) without referring to anything outside of language. Or the investigation goes beyond this boundary and studies linguistic expressions in their relation to objects outside of language. A study restricted in the first-mentioned way is called *formal;* the field of such formal studies is called formal logic or *logical syntax*. Such a formal or syntactical analysis of the language of science as a whole or in its various branches will lead to results of the following kinds. A certain term (e.g., a word) is defined within a certain theory on the basis of certain other terms, or it is definable in such a way. A certain term, although not definable by certain other terms, is reducible to them (in a sense to be explained later). A certain statement is a logical consequence of (or logically deducible from) certain other statements; and a deduction of it, given within a certain theory, is, or is not, logically correct. A certain statement is incompatible with certain other statements, i.e., its negation is a logical consequence of them. A certain statement is independent of certain other statements, i.e., neither a logical consequence of them nor incompatible with them. A certain theory is inconsistent, i.e., some of its statements are incompatible with the other ones. The last sections of this essay will deal with the question of the unity of science from the logical point of view, studying the logical relations between the terms of the chief branches of science and between the laws stated in these branches; thus it will give an example of a syntactical analysis of the language of science.

In the second part of the logic of science, a given language and the expressions in it are analyzed in another way. Here also, as in logical syntax, abstraction is made from the psychological and sociological side of the language. This investigation, however, is not restricted to formal analysis but takes into consideration one important relation between linguistic expressions and other objects—that of designation. An investigation of this kind is called *semantics*. Results of a semantical analysis of the language of science may, for instance, have the following forms. A certain term designates a certain particular object (e.g., the sun), or a certain property of things (e.g., iron), or a certain relation between things (e.g., fathership), or a certain physical function (e.g., temperature); two terms in different branches of science (e.g., 'homo sapiens' in biology and 'person' in economics, or, in another way, 'man' in both cases) designate (or: do not designate) the same. What is designated by a certain expression may be called its *designatum*. Two expressions designating the same are called *synonymous*. The term 'true,' as it is used in science and in everyday life, can also be defined within semantics. We see that the chief subject matter of a semantical analysis of the language of science are such properties and relations of expressions, and especially of statements, as are based on the relation of designation. (Where we say 'the designatum of an expression,' the customary phrase is 'the meaning of an expression.' It seems, however, preferable to avoid the word 'meaning' wherever possible because of its ambiguity, i.e., the multiplicity of its designata. Above all, it is important to distinguish between the semantical and the psychological use of the word 'meaning.')

It is a question of terminological convention whether to use the term 'logic' in the wider sense, including the semantical analysis of the designata of expressions, or in the narrower sense of logical syntax, restricted to formal analysis, abstracting from designation. And accordingly we may distinguish between logic of science in the narrower sense, as the syntax of the language of science, and logic of science in the wider sense, comprehending both syntax and semantics.

II. The Main Branches of Science

We use the word 'science' here in its widest sense, including all theoretical knowledge, no matter whether in the field of natural sciences or in the field of the social sciences and the so-called humanities, and no matter whether it is knowledge found by the application of special scientific procedures, or knowledge based on common sense in everyday life. In the same way the term 'language of science' is meant here to refer to the language which contains all statements (i.e., theoretical sentences as distinguished from emotional expressions, commands, lyrics, etc.) used for scientific purposes or in everyday life. What usually is called science is merely a more systematic continuation of those activities which we carry out in everyday life in order to know something.

The first distinction which we have to make is that between *formal science* and *empirical science*. Formal science consists of the analytic statements established by logic and mathematics; empirical science consists of the synthetic statements established in the different fields of factual knowledge. The relation of formal to empirical science will be dealt with at another place; here we have to do with empirical science, its language, and the problem of its unity.

Let us take 'physics' as a common name for the nonbiological field of science, comprehending both systematic and historical investigations within this field, thus including chemistry, mineralogy, astronomy, geology (which is historical), meteorology, etc. How, then, are we to draw the boundary line between physics and biology? It is obvious that the distinction between these two branches has to be based on the distinction between two kinds of things which we find in nature: organisms and nonorganisms. Let us take this latter distinction as granted; it is the task of biologists to lay down a suitable definition for the term 'organism,' in other words, to tell us the features of a thing which we take as characteristic for its being an organism. How, then, are we to define 'biology' on the basis of 'organism'? We could perhaps think of trying to do it in this way: biology is the branch of science which investigates organisms and the processes occurring in organisms, and physics is the study of nonorganisms. But these definitions would not draw the distinction as it is usually intended. A law stated in physics is intended to be valid universally, without any restriction. For example, the law stating the electrostatic force as a function of electric charges and their distance, or the law determining the pressure of a gas as a function of temperature, or the law determining the angle of refraction as a function of the coefficients of refraction of the two media involved, are intended to apply to the processes in organisms no less than to those in inorganic nature. The biologist has to know these laws of physics in studying the processes in organisms. He needs them for the explanation of these processes. But since they do not suffice, he adds some other laws, not known by the physicist, viz., the specifically biological laws. Biology presupposes physics, but not vice versa.

These reflections lead us to the following definitions. Let us call those terms which we need—in addition to logico-mathematical terms—for the description of processes in inorganic nature *physical terms*, no matter whether, in a given instance, they are applied to such processes or to processes in organisms. That sublanguage of the language of science, which contains —besides logico-mathematical terms—all and only physical terms, may be called *physical language*. The system of those statements which are formulated in the physical language and are acknowledged by a certain group at a certain time is called the physics of that group at that time. Such of these statements as have a specific universal form are called *physical laws*. The physical laws are needed for the explanation of processes in inorganic nature; but, as mentioned before, they apply to processes in organisms also.

The whole of the rest of science may be called *biology* (*in the wider sense*). It seems desirable, at least for practical purposes, e.g., for the division of labor in research work, to subdivide this wide field. But it seems questionable whether any distinctions can be found here which, although not of a fundamental nature, are at least clear to about the same degree as the distinction between physics and biology. At present, it is scarcely possible to predict which subdivisions will be made in the future. The traditional distinction between bodily (or material) and mental (or psychical) processes had its origin in the old magical and later metaphysical mind-body dualism. The distinction as a practical device for the classification of branches of science still plays an important role, even for those scientists who reject that metaphysical dualism; and it will probably continue to do so for some time in the future. But when the aftereffect of such prescientific issues upon science becomes weaker and weaker, it may be that new boundary lines for subdivisions will turn out to be more satisfactory.

One possibility of dividing biology in the wider sense into two fields is such that the first corresponds roughly to what is usually called biology, and the second comprehends among other parts those which usually are called psychology and social science. The second field deals with the behavior of individual organisms and groups of organisms within their environment, with the dispositions to such behavior, with such features of processes in organisms as are relevant to the behavior, and with certain features of the environment which are characteristic of and relevant to the behavior, e.g., objects observed and work done by organisms.

The first of the two fields of biology in the wider sense may be called biology in the narrower sense, or, for the following discussions, simply *biology*. This use of the term 'biology' seems justified by the fact that, in terms of the customary classification, this part contains most of what is usually called biology, namely, general biology, botany, and the greater part of zoölogy. The terms which are used in this field in addition to logico-mathematical and physical terms may be called biological terms in the narrower sense, or simply *biological terms*. Since many statements of biology contain physical terms besides bio-

logical ones, the *biological language* cannot be restricted to biological terms; it contains the physical language as a sublanguage
and, in addition, the biological terms. Statements and laws belonging to this language but not to physical language will be
called *biological statements* and *biological laws.*

The distinction between the two fields of biology in the wider
sense has been indicated only in a very vague way. At the
present time it is not yet clear as to how the boundary line may
best be drawn. Which processes in an organism are to be assigned to the second field? Perhaps the connection of a process
with the processes in the nervous system might be taken as
characteristic, or, to restrict it more, the connection with speaking activities, or, more generally, with activities involving signs.
Another way of characterization might come from the other
direction, from outside, namely, selecting the processes in an
organism from the point of view of their relevance to achievements in the environment (see Brunswik and Ness). There is
no name in common use for this second field. (The term 'mental sciences' suggests too narrow a field and is connected too
closely with the metaphysical dualism mentioned before.) The
term 'behavioristics' has been proposed. If it is used, it must be
made clear that the word 'behavior' has here a greater extension
than it had with the earlier behaviorists. Here it is intended
to designate not only the overt behavior which can be observed
from outside but also internal behavior (i.e., processes within
the organism); further, dispositions to behavior which may not
be manifest in a special case; and, finally, certain effects upon
the environment. Within this second field we may distinguish
roughly between two parts dealing with individual organisms
and with groups of organisms. But it seems doubtful whether
any sharp line can be drawn between these two parts. Compared with the customary classification of science, the first part
would include chiefly psychology, but also some parts of physiology and the humanities. The second part would chiefly include social science and, further, the greater part of the humanities and history, but it has not only to deal with groups of
human beings but also to deal with groups of other organisms.

For the following discussion, the terms 'psychology' and 'social science' will be used as names of the two parts because of lack of better terms. It is clear that both the question of boundary lines and the question of suitable terms for the sections is still in need of much more discussion.

III. Reducibility

The question of the unity of science is meant here as a problem of the logic of science, not of ontology. We do not ask: "Is the world one?" "Are all events fundamentally of one kind?" "Are the so-called mental processes really physical processes or not?" "Are the so-called physical processes really spiritual or not?" It seems doubtful whether we can find any theoretical content in such philosophical questions as discussed by monism, dualism, and pluralism. In any case, when we ask whether there is a unity in science, we mean this as a question of logic, concerning the logical relationships between the terms and the laws of the various branches of science. Since it belongs to the logic of science, the question concerns scientists and logicians alike.

Let us first deal with the question of terms. (Instead of the word 'term' the word 'concept' could be taken, which is more frequently used by logicians. But the word 'term' is more clear, since it shows that we mean signs, e.g., words, expressions consisting of words, artificial symbols, etc., of course with the meaning they have in the language in question. We do not mean 'concept' in its psychological sense, i.e., images or thoughts somehow connected with a word; that would not belong to logic.) We know the meaning (designatum) of a term if we know under what conditions we are permitted to apply it in a concrete case and under what conditions not. Such a knowledge of the conditions of application can be of two different kinds. In some cases we may have a merely practical knowledge, i.e., we are able to use the term in question correctly without giving a theoretical account of the rules for its use. In other cases we may be able to give an explicit formulation of the conditions for the application of the term. If now a certain term x is such that the conditions for its application (as used in the language of science) can be formulated with the help of the terms y, z, etc., we call such a formulation a *reduction statement* for x in terms of y, z, etc., and we call x *reducible* to y, z, etc. There may be several sets of conditions for the application of x; hence x may be reducible to y, z, etc., and also to u, v, etc., and perhaps to other sets. There may even be cases of mutual reducibility, e.g., each term of the set x_1, x_2, etc., is reducible to y_1, y_2, etc.; and, on the other hand, each term of the set y_1, y_2, etc., is reducible to x_1, x_2, etc.

A *definition* is the simplest form of a reduction statement. For the formulation of examples, let us use '$\equiv$' (called the symbol of equivalence) as abbreviation for 'if and only if.' Example of a definition for 'ox': 'x is an ox $\equiv$ x is a quadruped and horned and cloven-footed and ruminant, etc.' This is also a reduction statement because it states the conditions for the application of the term 'ox,' saying that this term can be applied to a thing if and only if that thing is a quadruped and horned, etc. By that definition the term 'ox' is shown to be reducible to—moreover definable by—the set of terms 'quadruped,' 'horned,' etc.

A reduction statement sometimes cannot be formulated in the simple form of a definition, i.e., of an equivalence statement, '. . . . $\equiv$ . . . . ,' but only in the somewhat more complex form 'If . . . . , then: . . . . $\equiv$ . . . . .' Thus a reduction statement is either a simple (i.e., explicit) definition or, so to speak, a conditional definition. (The term 'reduction statement' is generally used in the narrower sense, referring to the second, conditional form.) For instance, the following statement is a reduction statement for the term 'electric charge' (taken here for the sake of simplicity as a nonquantitative term), i.e., for the statement form 'the body x has an electric charge at the time t': 'If a light body y is placed near x at t, then: x has an electric charge at t $\equiv$ y is attracted by x at t.' A general way of procedure which enables us to find out whether or not a certain term can be applied in concrete cases may be called a *method of determination* for the term in question. The method of determination for a quantitative term (e.g., 'temperature') is the method of measurement for that term. Whenever we know an experimental method of determination for a term, we are in a position to formulate a reduction statement for it. To know an experimental method of determination for a term, say 'Q_3,' means to know two things. First, we must know an experimental situation which we have to create, say the state Q_1, e.g., the arrangement of measuring apparatuses and of suitable conditions for their use. Second, we must know the possible experimental result, say Q_2, which, if it occurs, will confirm the presence of the property Q_3. In the simplest case—let us leave aside the more complex cases—Q_2 is also such that its nonoccurrence shows that the thing in question does not have the property Q_3. Then a reduction statement for 'Q_3,' i.e., for the statement form 'the thing (or space-time-point) x is Q_3 (i.e., has the property Q_3) at the time t,' can be formulated in this way: 'If x is Q_1 (i.e., x and the surroundings of x are in the state Q_1) at time t, then: x is Q_3 at $t \equiv x$ is Q_2 at t.' On the basis of this reduction statement, the term 'Q_3' is reducible to 'Q_1,' 'Q_2,' and spatio-temporal terms. Whenever a term 'Q_3' expresses the disposition of a thing to behave in a certain way (Q_2) to certain conditions (Q_1), we have a reduction statement of the form given above. If there is a connection of such a kind between Q_1, Q_2, and Q_3, then in biology and psychology in certain cases the following terminology is applied: 'To the stimulus Q_1 we find the reaction Q_2 as a symptom for Q_3.' But the situation is not essentially different from the analogous one in physics, where we usually do not apply that terminology.

Sometimes we know several methods of determination for a certain term. For example, we can determine the presence of an electric current by observing either the heat produced in the conductor, or the deviation of a magnetic needle, or the quantity of a substance separated from an electrolyte, etc. Thus the term 'electric current' is reducible to each of many sets of other terms. Since not only can an electric current be measured by measuring a temperature but also, conversely, a temperature can be measured by measuring the electric current produced by a thermo-electric element, there is mutual reducibility between the terms of the theory of electricity, on the one hand, and those of the theory of heat, on the other. The same holds for the terms of the theory of electricity and those of the theory of magnetism.

Let us suppose that the persons of a certain group have a certain set of terms in common, either on account of a merely practical agreement about the conditions of their application or with an explicit stipulation of such conditions for a part of the terms. Then a reduction statement reducing a new term to the terms of that original set may be used as a way of introducing the new term into the language of the group. This way of introduction assures conformity as to the use of the new term. If a certain language (e.g., a sublanguage of the language of science, covering a certain branch of science) is such that every term of it is reducible to a certain set of terms, then this language can be constructed on the basis of that set by introducing one new term after the other by reduction statements. In this case we call the basic set of terms a *sufficient reduction basis* for that language.

IV. The Unity of the Language of Science

Now we will analyze the logical relations among the terms of different parts of the language of science with respect to reducibility. We have indicated a division of the whole language of science into some parts. Now we may make another division cutting across the first, by distinguishing in a rough way, without any claims to exactness, between those terms which we use on a prescientific level in our everyday language, and for whose application no scientific procedure is necessary, and scientific terms in the narrower sense. That sublanguage which is the common part of this prescientific language and the physical language may be called physical thing-language or briefly *thing-language*. It is this language that we use in speaking about the properties of the observable (inorganic) things surrounding us. Terms like 'hot' and 'cold' may be regarded as belonging to the thing-language, but not 'temperature' because its determination requires the application of a technical instrument; further, 'heavy' and 'light' (but not 'weight'); 'red,' 'blue,' etc.; 'large,' 'small,' 'thick,' 'thin,' etc.

The terms so far mentioned designate what we may call observable properties, i.e., such as can be determined by a direct observation. We will call them *observable thing-predicates*. Besides such terms the thing-language contains other ones, e.g., those expressing the disposition of a thing to a certain behavior under certain conditions, e.g., 'elastic,' 'soluble,' 'flexible,' 'transparent,' 'fragile,' 'plastic,' etc. These terms—they might be called disposition-predicates—are reducible to observable thing-predicates because we can describe the experimental conditions and the reactions characteristic of such disposition-predicates in terms of observable thing-predicates. Example of a reduction statement for 'elastic': 'If the body x is stretched and then released at the time t, then: x is elastic at the time $t \equiv x$ contracts at t,' where the terms 'stretched,' 'released,' and 'contracting' can be defined by observable thing-predicates. If these predicates are taken as a basis, we can moreover introduce, by iterated application of definition and (conditional) reduction, every other term of the *thing-language*, e.g., designations of substances, e.g., 'stone,' 'water,' 'sugar,' or of processes, e.g., 'rain,' 'fire,' etc. For every term of that language is such that we can apply it either on the basis of direct observation or with the help of an experiment for which we know the conditions and the possible result determining the application of the term in question.

Now we can easily see that every term of the *physical language* is reducible to those of the thing-language and hence finally to observable thing-predicates. On the scientific level, we have the quantitative coefficient of elasticity instead of the qualitative term 'elastic' of the thing-language; we have the quantitative term 'temperature' instead of the qualitative ones 'hot' and 'cold'; and we have all the terms by means of which physicists describe the temporary or permanent states of things or processes. For any such term the physicist knows at least one method of determination. Physicists would not admit into their language any term for which no method of determination by observations were given. The formulation of such a method, i.e., the description of the experimental arrangement to be carried out and of the possible result determining the application of the term in question, is a reduction statement for that term. Sometimes the term will not be directly reduced by the reduction statement to thing-predicates, but first to other scientific terms, and these by their reduction statements again to other scientific terms, etc.; but such a reduction chain must in any case finally lead to predicates of the thing-language and, moreover, to observable thing-predicates because otherwise there would be no way of determining whether or not the physical term in question can be applied in special cases, on the basis of given observation statements.

If we come to *biology* (this term now always understood in the narrower sense), we find again the same situation. For any biological term the biologist who introduces or uses it must know empirical criteria for its application. This applies, of course, only to biological terms in the sense explained before, including all terms used in scientific biology proper, but not to certain terms used sometimes in the philosophy of biology—'a whole,' 'entelechy,' etc. It may happen that for the description of the criterion, i.e., the method of determination of a term, other biological terms are needed. In this case the term in question is first reducible to them. But at least indirectly it must be reducible to terms of the thing-language and finally to observable thing-predicates, because the determination of the term in question in a concrete case must finally be based upon observations of concrete things, i.e., upon observation statements formulated in the thing-language.

Let us take as an example the term 'muscle.' Certainly biologists know the conditions for a part of an organism to be a muscle; otherwise the term could not be used in concrete cases. The problem is: Which other terms are needed for the formulation of those conditions? It will be necessary to describe the functions within the organism which are characteristic of muscles, in other words, to formulate certain laws connecting the processes in muscles with those in their environment, or, again in still other words, to describe the reactions to certain stimuli characteristic of muscles. Both the processes in the environment and those in the muscle (in the customary terminology: stimuli and reactions) must be described in such a way that we can determine them by observations. Hence the term 'muscle,' although not definable in terms of the thing-language, is reducible to them. Similar considerations easily show the reducibility of any other biological term—whether it be a designation of a kind of organism, or of a kind of part of organisms, or of a kind of process in organisms.

The result found so far may be formulated in this way: The terms of the thing-language, and even the narrower class of the observable thing-predicates, supply a sufficient basis for the languages both of physics and of biology. (There are, by the way, many reduction bases for these languages, each of which is much more restricted than the classes mentioned.) Now the question may be raised whether a basis of the kind mentioned is sufficient even for the whole language of science. The affirmative answer to this question is sometimes called *physicalism* (because it was first formulated not with respect to the thing-language but to the wider physical language as a sufficient basis). If the thesis of physicalism is applied to biology only, it scarcely meets any serious objections. The situation is somewhat changed, however, when it is applied to psychology and social science (individual and social behavioristics). Since many of the objections raised against it are based on misinterpretations, it is necessary to make clear what the thesis is intended to assert and what not.

The question of the reducibility of the terms of psychology to those of the biological language and thereby to those of the thing-language is closely connected with the problem of the various methods used in psychology. As chief examples of methods used in this field in its present state, the physiological, the behavioristic, and the introspective methods may be considered. The *physiological approach* consists in an investigation of the functions of certain organs in the organism, above all, of the nervous system. Here, the terms used are either those of biology

55

or those so closely related to them that there will scarcely be any doubt with respect to their reducibility to the terms of the biological language and the thing-language. For the *behavioristic approach* different ways are possible. The investigation may be restricted to the external behavior of an organism, i.e., to such movements, sounds, etc., as can be observed by other organisms in the neighborhood of the first. Or processes within the organism may also be taken into account so that this approach overlaps with the physiological one. Or, finally, objects in the environment of the organism, either observed or worked on or produced by it, may also be studied. Now it is easy to see that a term for whose determination a behavioristic method—of one of the kinds mentioned or of a related kind— is known, is reducible to the terms of the biological language, including the thing-language. As we have seen before, the formulation of the method of determination for a term is a reduction statement for that term, either in the form of a simple definition or in the conditional form. By that statement the term is shown to be reducible to the terms applied in describing the method, namely, the experimental arrangement and the characteristic result. Now, conditions and results consist in the behavioristic method either of physiological processes in the organism or of observable processes in the organism and in its environment. Hence they can be described in terms of the biological language. If we have to do with a behavioristic approach in its pure form, i.e., leaving aside physiological investigations, then the description of the conditions and results characteristic for a term can in most cases be given directly in terms of the thing-language. Hence the behavioristic reduction of psychological terms is often simpler than the physiological reduction of the same term.

Let us take as an example the term 'angry.' If for anger we knew a sufficient and necessary criterion to be found by a physiological analysis of the nervous system or other organs, then we could define 'angry' in terms of the biological language. The same holds if we knew such a criterion to be determined by the observation of the overt, external behavior. But a physiological criterion is not yet known. And the peripheral symptoms known are presumably not necessary criteria because it might be that a person of strong self-control is able to suppress these symptoms. If this is the case, the term 'angry' is, at least at the present time, not definable in terms of the biological language. But, nevertheless, it is reducible to such terms. It is sufficient for the formulation of a reduction sentence to know a behavioristic procedure which enables us—if not always, at least under suitable circumstances—to determine whether the organism in question is angry or not. And we know indeed such procedures; otherwise we should never be able to apply the term 'angry' to another person on the basis of our observations of his behavior, as we constantly do in everyday life and in scientific investigation. A reduction of the term 'angry' or similar terms by the formulation of such procedures is indeed less useful than a definition would be, because a definition supplies a complete (i.e., unconditional) criterion for the term in question, while a reduction statement of the conditional form gives only an incomplete one. But a criterion, conditional or not, is all we need for ascertaining reducibility. Thus the result is the following: If for any psychological term we know either a physiological or a behavioristic method of determination, then that term is reducible to those terms of the thing-language.

In psychology, as we find it today, there is, besides the physiological and the behavioristic approach, the so-called *introspective method*. The questions as to its validity, limits, and necessity are still more unclear and in need of further discussion than the analogous questions with respect to the two other methods. Much of what has been said about it, especially by philosophers, may be looked at with some suspicion. But the facts themselves to which the term 'introspection' is meant to refer will scarcely be denied by anybody, e.g., the fact that a person sometimes knows that he is angry without applying any of those procedures which another person would have to apply, i.e., without looking with the help of a physiological instrument at his nervous system or looking at the play of his facial muscles. The problems of the practical reliability and theoretical validity of the introspective method may here be left aside. For the discussion of reducibility an answer to these problems is not needed. It will suffice to show that in every case, no matter whether the introspective method is applicable or not, the behavioristic method can be applied at any rate. But we must be careful in the interpretation of this assertion. It is not meant as saying: 'Every psychological process can be ascertained by the behavioristic method.' Here we have to do not with the single processes themselves (e.g., Peter's anger yesterday morning) but with kinds of processes (e.g., anger). If Robinson Crusoe is angry and then dies before anybody comes to his island, nobody except himself ever knows of this single occurrence of anger. But anger of the same kind, occurring with other persons, may be studied and ascertained by a behavioristic method, if circumstances are favorable. (Analogy: if an electrically charged raindrop falls into the ocean without an observer or suitable recording instrument in the neighborhood, nobody will ever know of that charge. But a charge of the same kind can be found out under suitable circumstances by certain observations.) Further, in order to come to a correct formulation of the thesis, we have to apply it not to the kinds of processes (e.g., anger) but rather to the terms designating such kinds of processes (e.g., 'anger'). The difference might seem trivial but is, in fact, essential. We do not at all enter a discussion about the question whether or not there are kinds of events which can never have any behavioristic symptoms, and hence are knowable only by introspection. We have to do with psychological terms not with kinds of events. For any such term, say, 'Q,' the psychological language contains a statement form applying that term, e.g., 'The person . . . . is at the time . . . . in the state Q.' Then the utterance by speaking or writing of the statement 'I am now (or: I was yesterday) in the state Q,' is (under suitable circumstances, e.g., as to reliability, etc.) an observable symptom for the state Q. Hence there cannot be a term in the psychological language, taken as an intersubjective language for mutual communication, which designates a kind of state or event without any behavioristic symptom. Therefore, there is a behavioristic method of determination for any term of the psychological language. Hence every such term is reducible to those of the thing-language.

The logical nature of the psychological terms becomes clear by an analogy with those physical terms which are introduced by reduction statements of the conditional form. Terms of both kinds designate a state characterized by the disposition to certain reactions. In both cases the state is not the same as those reactions. Anger is not the same as the movements by which an angry organism reacts to the conditions in his environment, just as the state of being electrically charged is not the same as the process of attracting other bodies. In both cases that state sometimes occurs without these events which are observable from outside; they are consequences of the state according to certain laws and may therefore under suitable circumstances be taken as symptoms for it; but they are not identical with it.

The last field to be dealt with is *social science* (in the wide sense indicated before; also called social behavioristics). Here we need no detailed analysis because it is easy to see that every term of this field is reducible to terms of the other fields. The result of any investigation of a group of men or other organisms can be described in terms of the members, their relations to one another and to their environment. Therefore, the conditions for the application of any term can be formulated in terms of psychology, biology, and physics, including the thing-language. Many terms can even be defined on that basis, and the rest is certainly reducible to it.

It is true that some terms which are used in psychology are such that they designate a certain behavior (or disposition to behavior) within a group of a certain kind or a certain attitude toward a group, e.g., 'desirous of ruling,' 'shy,' and others. It may be that for the definition or reduction of a term of this kind some terms of social science describing the group involved are needed. This shows that there is not a clear-cut line between psychology and social science and that in some cases it is not clear whether a term is better assigned to one or to the other field. But such terms are also certainly reducible to those of the thing-language because every term referring to a group of organisms is reducible to terms referring to individual organisms.

The result of our analysis is that the class of observable thing-predicates is a sufficient reduction basis for the whole of the language of science, including the cognitive part of the everyday language.

V. The Problem of the Unity of Laws

The relations between the terms of the various branches of science have been considered. There remains the task of analyzing the relations between the laws. According to our previous consideration, a biological law contains only terms which are reducible to physical terms. Hence there is a common language to which both the biological and the physical laws belong so that they can be logically compared and connected. We can ask whether or not a certain biological law is compatible with the system of physical laws, and whether or not it is derivable from them. But the answer to these questions cannot be inferred from the reducibility of the terms. At the present state of the development of science, it is certainly not possible to derive the biological laws from the physical ones. Some philosophers believe that such a derivation is forever impossible because of the very nature of the two fields. But the proofs attempted so far for this thesis are certainly insufficient. This question is, it seems, the scientific kernel of the problem of vitalism; some recent discussions of this problem are, however, entangled with rather questionable metaphysical issues. The question of derivability itself is, of course, a very serious scientific problem. But it will scarcely be possible to find a solution for it before many more results of experimental investigation are available than we have today. In the meantime the efforts toward derivation of more and more biological laws from physical laws—in the customary formulation: explanation of more and more processes in organisms with the help of physics and chemistry—will be, as it has been, a very fruitful tendency in biological research.

As we have seen before, the fields of psychology and social science are very closely connected with each other. A clear division of the laws of these fields is perhaps still less possible than a division of the terms. If the laws are classified in some way or other, it will be seen that sometimes a psychological law is derivable from those of social science, and sometimes a law of social science from those of psychology. (An example of the first kind is the explanation of the behavior of adults—e.g., in the theories of A. Adler and Freud—by their position within the family or a larger group during childhood; an example of the second kind is the obvious explanation of an increase of the price of a commodity by the reactions of buyers and sellers in the case of a diminished supply.) It is obvious that, at the present time, laws of psychology and social science cannot be derived from those of biology and physics. On the other hand, no scientific reason is known for the assumption that such a derivation should be in principle and forever impossible.

Thus there is at present *no unity of laws*. The construction of one homogeneous system of laws for the whole of science is an aim for the future development of science. This aim cannot be shown to be unattainable. But we do not, of course, know whether it will ever be reached.

On the other hand, there is a *unity of language* in science, viz., a common reduction basis for the terms of all branches of science, this basis consisting of a very narrow and homogeneous class of terms of the physical thing-language. This unity of terms is indeed less far-reaching and effective than the unity of laws would be, but it is a necessary preliminary condition for the unity of laws. We can endeavor to develop science more and more in the direction of a unified system of laws only because we have already at present a unified language. And, in addition, the fact that we have this unity of language is of the greatest practical importance. The practical use of laws consists in making predictions with their help. The important fact is that very often a prediction cannot be based on our knowledge of only one branch of science. For instance, the construction of automobiles will be influenced by a prediction of the presumable number of sales. This number depends upon the satisfaction of the buyers and the economic situation. Hence we have to combine knowledge about the function of the motor, the effect of gases and vibration on the human organism, the ability of persons to learn a certain technique, their willingness to spend so much money for so much service, the development of the general economic situation, etc. This knowledge concerns particular facts and general laws belonging to all the four branches, partly scientific and partly common-sense knowledge. For very many decisions, both in individual and in social life, we need such a prediction based upon a combined knowledge of concrete facts and general laws belonging to different branches of science. If now the terms of different branches had no logical connection between one another, such as is supplied by the homogeneous reduction basis, but were of fundamentally different character, as some philosophers believe, then it would not be possible to connect singular statements and laws of different fields in such a way as to derive predictions from them. Therefore, the unity of the language of science is the basis for the practical application of theoretical knowledge.

Selected Bibliography

I. LOGICAL ANALYSIS

CARNAP, R. *Philosophy and Logical Syntax*. London, 1935. (Elementary.)
———. *Logical Syntax of Language*. London, 1937. (Technical.)

II. REDUCIBILITY

CARNAP, R. "Testability and Meaning," *Philosophy of Science*, Vols. III (1936) and IV (1937).

III. THE UNITY OF THE LANGUAGE OF SCIENCE; PHYSICALISM

Papers by NEURATH and CARNAP, *Erkenntnis* Vol. II (1932); *ibid.*, Vol. III (1933). Translation of one of these papers: CARNAP, *The Unity of Science*. London, 1934. Concerning psychology: papers by SCHLICK, HEMPEL, and CARNAP, *Revue de synthèse*, Vol. X (1935).

Scientific Empiricism
Charles W. Morris

The mind of Leibniz—which was too comprehensive for any single individual of our time—seemed to have diffused itself over the various sections. This struck me particularly in connection with the project of a scientifically philosophical Encyclopedia, advocated by Dr. Otto Neurath. Leibniz, if he were alive, would no doubt write the whole of it, but in our day different sections of it will have to be undertaken by different men. It must, however, be said that in one point of great importance the modern movement surpasses anything imagined by Leibniz or his contemporaries: I mean the combination of empiricism with mathematical method. In science, this combination has existed since the time of Galileo; but in philosophy, until our time, those who were influenced by mathematical method were anti-empirical, and the empiricists had little knowledge of mathematics. Modern science arose from the marriage of mathematics and empiricism; three centuries later the same union is giving birth to a second child, scientific philosophy, which is perhaps destined to as great a career. For it alone can provide the intellectual temper in which it is possible to find a cure for the diseases of the modern world.

These words of Bertrand Russell appeared in 1936 in the first volume of the *Actes du congrès international de philosophie scientifique* and form part of the statement in which he registered his impression of the meeting recorded in these proceedings—the First International Congress for the Unity of Science (Paris, 1935). They suggest in miniature the context in which the present *Encyclopedia* originates and its possible importance. For that reason they merit commentary.

I. Method in Science

The development of the method of experimental science is possibly the most significant intellectual contribution of Western civilization. The development, like most developments, is a long one, and there is no one moment of absolute origin or culmination. Certainly, neither experimentation nor mathematics had to wait for birth until the flowering of Western science. Nevertheless, in this flowering something of undeniable importance took place: the incorporation of mathematics and experimentation within a single method. Previously they had functioned as rival methods: mathematics as one way to get knowledge of nature, and experimental observation as another. Those scientists who advocated the former were one species of "rationalists," and the advocates of the latter were one species of "empiricists"—even the philosophical opposition of rationalism and empiricism was at bottom a reflection of what were to be taken as different scientific methods for knowing nature. Gradually, and in a way that need not at this point be traced in detail, mathematics came to lose the status of an independent method for the study of nature, while at the same time it supplanted the classical logic as a tool of analysis and as the structural basis for the scientific edifice. The important result was a double shift from a metaphysical to a methodological rationalism, and from a loose-jointed empiricism to an empiricism which utilized the techniques and the form of mathematics. Rationalism and empiricism in this way ceased to be rival methods for knowing nature and became complementary components of experimental science with its one observational-hypothetical-deductive-experimental method.

Not only did this method find place for the rational and empirical factors in the knowledge process, but the emphasis upon experimentation as against mere observation meant the breakdown of the radical opposition of theory and practice, for not only is experimentation itself a kind of practice, but it is of such a kind as to open up the possibility of a novel and systematic control of many kinds of natural processes.

The direction of this double movement within science (the incorporation of the mathematical method within the empiricist temper and the breakdown through experimentation of the dichotomy between theory and practice) is discernible in the Hellenistic period and the late Middle Ages, becomes clearly evident in Galileo, and reaches a definite expression in Newton. By the late seventeenth century the great scientists, whatever their philosophical differences, had found a place within scientific method for careful and systematic observation, mathematical theory, and experimental practice. Since that time no fundamental change in the conception of scientific method has taken place, and science has reaped a rich harvest from its attitude of mathematical experimental empiricism.

II. Generalization of Scientific Method

The attainment of a similar attitude in philosophy came more slowly and has not even yet received wide agreement. As Charles S. Peirce remarked, metaphysics has always been the ape of mathematics, and much that passes for metaphysics rests upon views of mathematics now largely discarded by the mathematicians or upon conceptions of philosophic method once made plausible by the then current conceptions of mathematics. But if philosophic rationalists were slow to see the significance of the changed state which mathematics had undergone in science, the philosophical empiricists were equally blind to the significance of this change. The history of empiricism is not an appropriate theme for an introductory article, but it can safely be said that the main energy of empiricists was spent in opposing the a priori rationalists rather than in contributing to or positively assessing the developing sciences. In fact, these philosophical empiricists at many points became entangled themselves in the speculative nets of their opponents, as is evident in their acceptance of the same superficial subjectivistic, individualistic, and atomistic conception of experience which the rationalists had proudly exhibited, ostensibly on the basis of science but actually because it seemed to show the limitations of the appeal to experience and the consequent need for other foundations for knowledge—hence the protracted and exhausting struggle of past empiricisms against the phantoms of solipsism and idealism.

The philosophical empiricists, in the main, had connection with the biological sciences rather than with mathematics or the physical sciences, and the resulting fact that they were unable satisfactorily to account for mathematics, or to make plausible the rational systematization which the physical sciences were in fact attaining, gave strong advantages to the impressive speculative rationalism of their opponents. The traditional empiricism, in addition to freeing itself from inadequate views of experience, had in fact to be supplemented in two interconnected respects before it could claim to be the philosophical equivalent of the method which science had achieved: it had to be able to assimilate and utilize the logical and mathematical tools of rationalism, and it had to be able to account for the intellectual significance of practice. The first expansion was made by logical empiricism; the second by pragmatism.

The union of formal logic and empiricism is linked with the development of symbolic or mathematical logic—another theme which at the proper place is to receive its separate treatment. This modern version of formal logic developed in the hands of philosophic rationalists who were themselves mathematicians. It arose out of the cross-fertilization of the medieval approach to logic in terms of a general theory of signs and the methods of modern mathematics, a union which is first significantly made by Leibniz[1]—the great Leibniz whose ideals of a universal scientific language, a generalized mathematical science, a calculus applicable to all reasoning, and an encyclopedia showing the logical relation between the concepts of all sciences receive a contemporary form of expression in this *Encyclopedia*. The development of this logic in the period since Leibniz has made available a logic adequate to the relational structure of science and mathematics, and has made possible new and powerful techniques of analysis. The point to be noted in the present connection is that in this development logic, like the mathematics which it generalized, came to be regarded as an instrument free from any speculative accretions, and in particular from the metaphysical (or a priori) rationalism which nourished it, and thus became available for use by empiricists—another instance of the fact mentioned in connection with the development of science that the formal disciplines become compatible with empiricism when they pass from the status of rival methods for the knowledge of nature to that of being formal linguistic structures available to the natural sciences as methodological tools. Logic thus rests, as Peirce[2] maintained, on a general theory of signs, formal logic tracing the relations between signs within a language. So conceived, logic deals with the language in which statements about nature are made, and does not itself make statements about the nonlinguistic world. Hence it is not the rival of the empirical knowledge of nature and becomes assimilable to the temper and program of empiricism.[3] The clear development of this view and the utilization of the methods of the new logic within the framework of empiricism are the significant achievements of logical empiricism as represented by the Vienna Circle (Carnap, Frank, Hahn, Neurath, Schlick) and by Russell, Wittgenstein, and Reichenbach.

This union of empiricism and methodological rationalism requires completion by one further step. Languages are developed and used by living beings operating in a world of objects, and show the influence of both the users and the objects. If, as symbolic logic maintains, there are linguistic forms whose validity is not dependent upon nonlinguistic objects, then their validity must be dependent upon the rules of the language in question, and such rules represent habits actually found in operation or set up by deliberate convention. The introduction of such terms as 'convention,' 'decision,' 'procedure,' and 'rule' involves reference to the users of signs in addition to empirical and formal factors. It has been the function of pragmatism to make explicit the instrumental significance of ideas in general and of scientific results and procedure in particular. Thus Dewey interprets even logical rules as empirical generalizations embodying methods of inquiry which have proved particularly successful for the purpose of inference and which have therefore been transformed by the users into principles accepted for the time being as stipulations for the carrying-on of future inquiry. The introduction of pragmatic considerations avoids the extremes both of empiricism and of conventionalism in logical theory while yet doing justice to both. At the same time, in making explicit the instrumental significance of ideas, it was necessary to determine the scientific usage of such terms as 'idea,' 'meaning,' 'self,' and 'experience' in the light of post-Darwinian biology and sociology;[4] and in doing this, in addition to gaining results of intrinsic significance, pragmatism helped free empiricism itself from certain pitfalls which it had encountered during its former development. The emphasis upon the relational and the functional which the biological emphasis brought with it called attention in general to the previously neglected relational and functional aspects of experience, and the realization of the social context in which mind and knowledge arise and operate made manifest the artificiality of the subjectivistic and individualistic concept of experience with which English empiricists had often operated. Pragmatism accordingly not merely brought to the forefront the pragmatical factor which complements and completes the formal and the empirical factors, but it helped to enrich the empiricist tradition through its conception of radical empiricism.

III. The Viewpoint of Scientific Empiricism

The resulting comprehensive point of view, embracing at once radical empiricism, methodological rationalism, and critical pragmatism, may appropriately be called scientific empiricism.[5] It is the generalized analogue of the point of view which has been effective in science for some centuries. It is willing and able to admit into the scope of its considerations everything involved in the scientific enterprise as such, together with the implications of this enterprise for other human interests. It is an empiricism genuinely oriented around the methods and the results of science and not dependent upon some questionable psychological theory as to the "mental" nature of experience. It is an empiricism which, because of this orientation and the use of powerful tools of logical analysis, has become positive in temper and co-operative in attitude and is no longer condemned to the negative skeptical task of showing defects in the methods and results of its opponents.

Such a point of view, characteristic in the main of this *Encyclopedia* (though, of course, not binding on its contributors) signalizes the widest possible generalization of scientific method. The field of application of this point of view is science itself. In analogy with certain other uses of the prefix 'meta' which are current today, we may introduce the term 'metascience' as a synonym for 'the science of science.'

The attempt to make the scientific enterprise as a whole an object of scientific investigation—i.e., to develop metascience— requires consideration of the three factors involved in this enterprise. Since these factors correspond to the three components of scientific empiricism, this point of view proves to be appropriate to the task. In its most tangible form science exists as a body of written characters and spoken words. It is possible to investigate this linguistic residue of the scientists' activity purely formally, without reference to the relation of these marks and sounds to other objects or to the activity of which they are the residues. There is no mystery as to how such "abstraction" is possible: from a linguistic point of view, to abstract from some of the properties or relations of an object is simply not to talk about them. This type of investigation may, in one sense of the term, be called logical analysis; because of the ambiguity of the term 'logical,' it may be preferable to call it, in the spirit of Carnap, the syntactical investigation of the language of science. Such investigation studies the structure of scientific language: the relation between the terms and the sentences of the same and different sciences. The degree of unity or disunity of science reveals itself here in the degree to which the sciences have or can have a common linguistic structure.

But the signs which constitute scientific treatises have, to some extent at least, a correlation with objects, and the investigation of all aspects of this relation constitutes a second task of metascience. Here belong all the problems as to the nature of this correlation and the analysis of the specific situations under which scientific terms and sentences are applicable. This may be called, in the spirit of the Polish logicians, the semantical investigation of the language of science. The unity of science is here no longer a purely formal unity, for the unity or disunity of the scientific language corresponds to some extent to the semantical relation or lack of relation of the various terms of the sciences—and so to the relations of objects.

A third concern of metascience arises from the fact that the signs which constitute the language of science are parts and products of the activity of scientists. The study of the relation of signs to scientists may be called, in the spirit of pragmatism, the pragmatical investigation of the language of science. Here belong the problems as to how the scientist operates, the connection of science as a social institution with other social institutions, and the relation of scientific activity to other activities. The question as to the unity of science is now the question as to the unity of procedures, purposes, and effects of the various sciences.

Science, as a body of signs with certain specific relations to one another, to objects, and to practice, is at once a language, a knowledge of objects, and a type of activity; the interrelated study of the syntactics, semantics, and pragmatics of the language of science in turn constitutes metascience—the science of science. Discussion of the specific signs of science must be carried on in terms of some theory of signs, and so semiotic, as the science of signs, occupies an important place in the program— indeed, the study of the actual language of science is an instance of applied semiotic. Since the institution of science is a social institution, certain of its features, as Auguste Comte realized, reveal themselves especially well in historical perspective, so that the history of science is of abiding importance within the study of science.

The elaboration of the syntactics, semantics, and pragmatics of science may rightly be regarded as the natural extension and completion of the scientific enterprise itself. It is believed that this program will appeal to scientists and will prove of importance in the development and assessment of science. It is inevitable that, in seeking for its greatest unification, science will make itself an object of scientific investigation. The fulfilment of these related tasks cannot be left to chance if science is to grow to full stature: they must be taken in hand by those familiar with the results and spirit of science—that is, scientists; they must be encouraged by scientific institutions, foundations, and associations; they must be incorporated in educational programs for the training of scientists. It is true that the individual experimenter may not be directly helped in the carrying-out of a particular experiment—though even here he can be justly held as responsible for the careful use of his linguistic tools as he is held for the careful handling of balance, microscope, or telescope. But science has never been content with isolated facts. It has ever pressed on to larger systematizations. This process will continue as long as scientific progress continues. And in this striving for the widest systematization, science inevitably has to study itself and incorporate the results of such study in its systematization. The study of science is not an intellectual luxury for scientists; it is a movement within science itself.

But if the study of science which is here contemplated is science (and so not a domain over and above science), it may equally well be regarded as philosophy. For the three-faceted point of view of scientific empiricism, and of metascience which results from its application to science, can be regarded as embracing the contemporary empiricist equivalents of the traditional fields of philosophy (logic, metaphysics, and theory of value). Logic is grounded on semiotic; metaphysics is replaced by sign analysis and unified science; and axiology becomes the scientific study of values and judgments of values. Within the general orientation of scientific empiricism, science and philosophy relinquish all claims to the possession of distinct methods or subject matters and merge their efforts within a common task: the erection, the analysis, and the assessment of unified science. Such community of effort is an ancient ideal and in part an ancient practice; what is novel today is the scale upon which fruitful co-operation is possible. Science rounds itself out humanly and scientifically in this process, and the relevance and significance which philosophy sometimes had are again regained.

IV. Science and Practice

What has been called the syntactics and the semantics of the language of science will receive immediate and extended treatment in the pages of this *Encyclopedia*. But since this will not be true to the same degree in the case of the pragmatics of the language of science, it is well to pause at this point in order both to see certain implications of the standpoint of scientific empiricism and to avoid certain possible misunderstandings.

The very statement that science walks on three legs of theory, observation, and practice will call out opposition in a certain type of mind—the statement is more frequent with 'practice' omitted. The word 'practice' is admittedly equivocal. The activity which gives rise to the sentences of science is, like any other systematic activity, a practice proceeding in terms of rules or canons. Further, the confirmation of every proposition always involves some instrument, whether this be simply the scientist himself or in addition such instruments as those involved in experimentation—and methodologically there is no important distinction between the two cases. In this (theoretically the most important) sense, all empirical science involves experimentation, and experimentation is an activity, a practice. In the third place, science is part of the practice of the community in which it is an institution, ministering—however indirectly—to the needs of the community and being affected— and very directly—in its development by the community of social institutions of which it is a part.

It is clear that any adequate account of science must take account of these psychological, methodological, and sociological aspects of scientific practice. The present work recognizes that fact. But it should also be clear that 'practice' in all three senses of the word is not an unessential factor added to the theoretical and empirical aspects of the scientific enterprise but an equally essential factor, since, at the minimum, 'confirmation' is a concept which contains irreducible pragmatical features. If this is so, it would be well for scientists to become fully aware of this factor of practice and, in becoming aware of it, to assume the entailed responsibilities.

The same point may be given an alternative formulation in terms of the notion of value. It is often said that science gives only "facts" and has nothing to do with "values." There is an element of truth in such a statement, since the pragmatical factor in language cannot be reduced at a given moment to the empirical, and since life is more than knowledge. But this is hardly the usual import of this statement, which is often made against a background which involves a sharp distinction between the natural sciences and the socio-humanistic sciences. The detailed study of the actual relations must be left for other writers. Nevertheless, it seems clear that, while a program which stresses the unity of science can admit of whatever diversity is in fact found in the various sciences (for unity does not exclude differentiation), it must naturally be skeptical of any such wholesale cleavage. Later treatments of these matters will maintain in harmony with the empiricist attitude that there is no unbridgeable gap within science between the procedures and subject matters of the natural sciences and the socio-humanistic sciences. All knowledge forms in principle one unified whole, and there exists no system of knowledge (such as metaphysics, aesthetics, ethics, religion) alongside of or superior to unified science.

This statement should not be misunderstood. Science is an activity eventuating in a certain sort of product having certain effects; but science is not the only activity of that sort. Art, morality, piety, play, work, and war are also activities with characteristic products and effects, and they must in no sense be confused with the sciences of such activities (aesthetics, ethics, science of religion, etc.). As activities they are co-ordinate with science considered as an activity, but the sciences of these activities fall within the field of unified science. In the first case, they are alternatives to the scientific attitude; in the second case, they are part of science. But an alternative is not necessarily a rival. Indeed, once science is distinguished in terms of its specific goal (reliable knowledge), then science not only does not, in general, clash with other activities but may itself further any other activity in so far as it can be furthered by knowledge.

73

In this respect science is the most practical of human activities. It is in opposition only to such activities as claim to usurp its own cognitive goal or which wither and die when the light of scientific investigation is turned upon them; it is at once both co-ordinate with and instrumental to the realization of the purposes of most other activities.

It is because of this relation of scientific activity to other activities that the scientific habit of mind and scientific results are of such potential promise in society at large and education in particular.[6] For this habit of mind is the best guaranty of an objective consideration of the multiplicity of factors which enter into the complex problems of contemporary man.

V. Scientific Empiricism and Encyclopedism

The standpoint of scientific empiricism is thus ample enough to embrace and to integrate the various factors which must be taken into account in an *Encyclopedia* devoted to unified science —i.e., to the scientific study of the scientific enterprise in its totality. The theory of signs gives the general background for the consideration of the language of science. The investigation of this language breaks up into the distinguishable but interrelated investigations of the syntactics, semantics, and pragmatics of the language of science. In this way, and on a comprehensive scale, science is made an object of scientific investigation; meta-science appears both as a tool for, and as an element within unified science. The attitude of scientific empiricism is simultaneously congenial to the temper of the rationalist, the empiricist, and the pragmatist, and provides the corrective to the one-sidedness of these attitudes when held in isolation. It is from the standpoint of method the complement of encyclopedism, since while it accepts the encyclopedia as the necessary form of human knowledge it yet recognizes that science strives for the greatest degree of systematization compatible with its continual growth.

This *Encyclopedia*, reflecting this inclusive standpoint, rightfully sounds the roll call of those distinguished logicians, scientists, and empiricists whom the traditional history of ideas has so shamefully neglected. But basically it aims to present through extensive co-operation the existing status and the unrealized possibilities for the integration of science. Its existence signalizes the union of scientific and philosophic traditions in a common task. The *Encyclopedia* presents a contemporary version of the ancient encyclopedic ideal of Aristotle, the Scholastics, Leibniz, the Encyclopedists, and Comte. It wishes to give satisfaction to the pervasive human interest in intellectual unity, but its common point of view permits divergences and differences in emphasis and does not blur the fact that an inseparable feature of the institution of science is constant growth. It aims to provide a basis for co-operative activity and not a panacea.

NOTES

1. See the splendid work of Louis Couturat, *La Logique de Leibniz* (Paris, 1901).

2. See especially *Collected Papers* (Cambridge, Mass., 1932), Vol. II.

3. This point was clearly elaborated by H. Hahn (see *Erkenntnis*, II [1931], 135–41; *Logik, Mathematik und Naturerkennen* [Vienna, 1933]). It may be remarked that from this point of view Leibniz' plans for a universal mathematics, a calculus of reasoning, a general characteristic, and a unified science expressed in the form of an encyclopedia all remain valid when interpreted as logical rather than as metaphysical doctrines. Leibniz' rationalistic metaphysics, which came from the simple conversion of formal logic into a metaphysics through the neglect of the criterion of the empirically meaningful, is, in terms of the present conception of the relation of logic to empiricism, no longer the necessary cosmological corollary of his logical doctrines.

4. The writings of George H. Mead are of importance in this connection, especially *Mind, Self, and Society* (Chicago, 1934).

5. This term and certain of the more general features of the point of view are characterized in the author's pamphlet, *Logical Positivism, Pragmatism, and Scientific Empiricism* (Paris: Hermann & Cie, 1937).

6. John Dewey, in particular, has devoted his life to the formulation and assessment of the social, cultural, and educational implications of the scientific habit of mind. See *Philosophy and Civilization* (New York, 1931) and his forthcoming work, *Logic: The Theory of Inquiry.*

Foundations of the Theory of Signs

Charles W. Morris

Foundations of the Theory of Signs

Contents:

Foundations of the Theory of Signs

Charles W. Morris

Nemo autem vereri debet ne characterum contemplatio nos a rebus abducat, imo contra ad intima rerum ducet.—GOTTFRIED LEIBNIZ

I. Introduction

1. Semiotic and Science

Men are the dominant sign-using animals. Animals other than man do, of course, respond to certain things as signs of something else, but such signs do not attain the complexity and elaboration which is found in human speech, writing, art, testing devices, medical diagnosis, and signaling instruments. Science and signs are inseparately interconnected, since science both presents men with more reliable signs and embodies its results in systems of signs. Human civilization is dependent upon signs and systems of signs, and the human mind is inseparable from the functioning of signs—if indeed mentality is not to be identified with such functioning.

It is doubtful if signs have ever before been so vigorously studied by so many persons and from so many points of view. The army of investigators includes linguists, logicians, philosophers, psychologists, biologists, anthropologists, psychopathologists, aestheticians, and sociologists. There is lacking, however, a theoretical structure simple in outline and yet comprehensive enough to embrace the results obtained from different points of view and to unite them into a unified and consistent whole. It is the purpose of the present study to suggest this unifying point of view and to sketch the contours of the science of signs. This can be done only in a fragmentary fashion, partly because of the limitations of space, partly because of the undeveloped state of the science itself, but mainly because of the purpose which such a study aims to serve by its inclusion in this *Encyclopedia*.

Semiotic has a double relation to the sciences: it is both a science among the sciences and an instrument of the sciences. The significance of semiotic as a science lies in the fact that it is a step in the unification of science, since it supplies the foundations for any special science of signs, such as linguistics, logic, mathematics, rhetoric, and (to some extent at least) aesthetics. The concept of sign may prove to be of importance in the unification of the social, psychological, and humanistic sciences in so far as these are distinguished from the physical and biological sciences. And since it will be shown that signs are simply the objects studied by the biological and physical sciences related in certain complex functional processes, any such unification of the formal sciences on the one hand, and the social, psychological, and humanistic sciences on the other, would provide relevant material for the unification of these two sets of sciences with the physical and biological sciences. Semiotic may thus be of importance in a program for the unification of science, though the exact nature and extent of this importance is yet to be determined.

But if semiotic is a science co-ordinate with the other sciences, studying things or the properties of things in their function of serving as signs, it is also the instrument of all sciences, since every science makes use of and expresses its results in terms of signs. Hence metascience (the science of science) must use semiotic as an organon. It was noticed in the essay "Scientific Empiricism" (Vol. I, No. 1) that it is possible to include without remainder the study of science under the study of the language of science, since the study of that language involves not merely the study of its formal structure but its relation to objects designated and to the persons who use it. From this point of view the entire *Encyclopedia*, as a scientific study of science, is a study of the language of science. But since nothing can be studied without signs denoting the objects in the field to be studied, a study of the language of science must make use of signs referring to signs—and semiotic must supply the relevant signs and principles for carrying on this study. Semiotic supplies a general language applicable to any special language or sign, and so applicable to the language of science and specific signs which are used in science.

The interest in presenting semiotic as a science and as part of the unification of science must here be restricted by the practical motive of carrying the analysis only so far and in such directions as to supply a tool for the work of the *Encyclopedia*, i.e., to supply a language in which to talk about, and in so doing to improve, the language of science. Other studies would be necessary to show concretely the results of sign analysis applied to special sciences and the general significance for the unification of science of this type of analysis. But even without detailed documentation it has become clear to many persons today that man—including scientific man—must free himself from the web of words which he has spun and that language—including scientific language—is greatly in need of purification, simplification, and systematization. The theory of signs is a useful instrument for such debabelization.

II. Semiosis and Semiotic

2. The Nature of a Sign

The process in which something functions as a sign may be called *semiosis*. This process, in a tradition which goes back to the Greeks, has commonly been regarded as involving three (or four) factors: that which acts as a sign, that which the sign refers to, and that effect on some interpreter in virtue of which the thing in question is a sign to that interpreter. These three components in semiosis may be called, respectively, the *sign vehicle*, the *designatum*, and the *interpretant;* the *interpreter* may be included as a fourth factor. These terms make explicit the factors left undesignated in the common statement that a sign refers to something for someone.

A dog responds by the type of behavior (*I*) involved in the hunting of chipmunks (*D*) to a certain sound (*S*); a traveler prepares himself to deal appropriately (*I*) with the geographical region (*D*) in virtue of the letter (*S*) received from a friend. In such cases S is the sign vehicle (and a sign in virtue of its functioning), D the designatum, and I the interpretant of the interpreter. The most effective characterization of a sign is the following: S is a sign of D for I to the degree that I takes account of D in virtue of the presence of S. Thus in semiosis something takes account of something else mediately, i.e., by means of a third something. Semiosis is accordingly a mediated-taking-account-of. The mediators are *sign vehicles;* the takings-account-of are *interpretants;* the agents of the process are *interpreters;* what is taken account of are *designata*. There are several comments to be made about this formulation.

It should be clear that the terms 'sign,' 'designatum,' 'interpretant,' and 'interpreter' involve one another, since they are simply ways of referring to aspects of the process of semiosis. Objects need not be referred to by signs, but there are no designata unless there is such reference; something is a sign only because it is interpreted as a sign of something by some interpreter; a taking-account-of-something is an interpretant only in so far as it is evoked by something functioning as a sign; an object is an interpreter only as it mediately takes account of something. The properties of being a sign, a designatum, an interpreter, or an interpretant are relational properties which things take on by participating in the functional process of semiosis. Semiotic, then, is not concerned with the study of a particular kind of object, but with ordinary objects in so far (and only in so far) as they participate in semiosis. The importance of this point will become progressively clearer.

Signs which refer to the same object need not have the same designata, since that which is taken account of in the object may differ for various interpreters. A sign of an object may, at one theoretical extreme, simply turn the interpreter of the sign upon the object, while at the other extreme it would allow the interpreter to take account of all the characteristics of the object in question in the absence of the object itself. There is thus a potential sign continuum in which with respect to every object or situation all degrees of semiosis may be expressed, and the question as to what the designatum of a sign is in any given situation is the question of what characteristics of the object or situation are actually taken account of in virtue of the presence of the sign vehicle alone.

A sign must have a designatum; yet obviously every sign does not, in fact, refer to an actual existent object. The difficulties which these statements may occasion are only apparent difficulties and need no introduction of a metaphysical realm of "subsistence" for their solution. Since 'designatum' is a semiotical term, there cannot be designata without semiosis—but there can be objects without there being semiosis. The designatum of a sign is the kind of object which the sign applies to, i.e., the objects with the properties which the interpreter takes account of through the presence of the sign vehicle. And the taking-account-of may occur without there actually being objects or situations with the characteristics taken account of. This is true even in the case of pointing: one can for certain purposes point without pointing to anything. No contradiction arises in saying that every sign has a designatum but not every sign refers to an actual existent. Where what is referred to actually exists as referred to the object of reference is a *denotatum*. It thus becomes clear that, while every sign has a designatum, not every sign has a denotatum. A designatum is not a thing, but a kind of object or class of objects—and a class may have many members, or one member, or no members. The denotata are the members of the class. This distinction makes explicable the fact that one may reach in the icebox for an apple that is not there and make preparations for living on an island that may never have existed or has long since disappeared beneath the sea.

As a last comment on the definition of sign, it should be noted that the general theory of signs need not commit itself to any specific theory of what is involved in taking account of something through the use of a sign. Indeed, it may be possible to take 'mediated-taking-account-of' as the single primitive term for the axiomatic development of semiotic. Nevertheless, the account which has been given lends itself to treatment from the point of view of behavioristics, and this point of view will be adopted in what follows. This interpretation of the definition of sign is not, however, necessary. It is adopted here because such a point of view has in some form or other (though not in the form of Watsonian behaviorism) become widespread among psychologists, and because many of the difficulties which the history of semiotic reveals seem to be due to the fact that through most of its history semiotic linked itself with the faculty and introspective psychologies. From the point of view of be- havioristics, to take account of D by the presence of S involves responding to D in virtue of a response to S. As will be made clear later, it is not necessary to deny "private experiences" of the process of semiosis or of other processes, but it is necessary from the standpoint of behavioristics to deny that such ex- periences are of central importance or that the fact of their existence makes the objective study of semiosis (and hence of sign, designatum, and interpretant) impossible or even in- complete.

3. Dimensions and Levels of Semiosis

In terms of the three correlates (sign vehicle, designatum, interpreter) of the triadic relation of semiosis, a number of other dyadic relations may be abstracted for study. One may study the relations of signs to the objects to which the signs are applicable. This relation will be called the *semantical dimen- sion of semiosis*, symbolized by the sign 'D_{sem}'; the study of this dimension will be called *semantics*. Or the subject of study may be the relation of signs to interpreters. This relation will be called the *pragmatical dimension of semiosis*, symbolized by 'D_p,' and the study of this dimension will be named *pragmatics*.

One important relation of signs has not yet been introduced: the formal relation of signs to one another. This relationship was not, in the preceding account, explicitly incorporated in the definition of 'sign,' since current usage would not seem to eliminate the possibility of applying the term 'sign' to some- thing which was not a member of a system of signs—such possibilities are suggested by the sign aspects of perception and by various apparently isolated mnemonic and signaling devices.

Nevertheless, the interpretation of these cases is not perfectly clear, and it is very difficult to be sure that there is such a thing as an isolated sign. Certainly, potentially, if not actually, every sign has relations to other signs, for what it is that the sign prepares the interpreter to take account of can only be *stated* in terms of other signs. It is true that this statement need not be made, but it is always in principle capable of being made, and when made relates the sign in question to other signs. Since most signs are clearly related to other signs, since many apparent cases of isolated signs prove on analysis not to be such, and since all signs are potentially if not actually related to other signs, it is well to make a third dimension of semiosis co-ordinate with the other two which have been mentioned. This third dimension will be called the *syntactical dimension of semiosis*, symbolized by 'D_{syn},' and the study of this dimension will be named *syntactics*.

It will be convenient to have special terms to designate certain of the relations of signs to signs, to objects, and to interpreters. '*Implicates*' will be restricted to D_{syn}, '*designates*' and '*denotes*' to D_{sem}, and '*expresses*' to D_p. The word 'table' implicates (but does *not* designate) 'furniture with a horizontal top on which things may be placed,' designates a certain kind of object (furniture with a horizontal top on which things may be placed), denotes the objects to which it is applicable, and expresses its interpreter. In any given case certain of the dimensions may actually or practically vanish: a sign may not have syntactical relations to other signs and so its actual implication becomes null; or it may have implication and yet denote no object; or it may have implication and yet no actual interpreter and so no expression—as in the case of a word in a dead language. Even in such possible cases the terms chosen are convenient to refer to the fact that certain of the possible relations remain unrealized.

It is very important to distinguish between the relations which a given sign sustains and the signs used in talking about such relations—the full recognition of this is perhaps the most important general practical application of semiotic. The functioning of signs is, in general, a way in which certain existences take account of other existences through an intermediate class of existences. But there are levels of this process which must be carefully distinguished if the greatest confusion is not to result. Semiotic as the science of semiosis is as distinct from semiosis as is any science from its subject matter. If x so functions that y takes account of z through x, then we may say that x is a sign, and that x designates z, etc.; but here 'sign,' and 'designates' are signs in a higher order of semiosis referring to the original and lower-level process of semiosis. What is now designated is a certain relation of x and z and not z alone; x is designated, z is designated, and a relation is designated such that x becomes a sign and z a designatum. Designation may therefore occur at various levels, and correspondingly there are various levels of designata; 'designation' reveals itself to be a sign within semiotic (and specifically within semantics), since it is a sign used in referring to signs.

Semiotic as a science makes use of special signs to state facts about signs; it is a language to talk about signs. Semiotic has the three subordinate branches of syntactics, semantics, and pragmatics, dealing, respectively, with the syntactical, the semantical, and the pragmatical dimensions of semiosis. Each of these subordinate sciences will need its own special terms; as previously used 'implicates' is a term of syntactics, 'designates' and 'denotes' are terms of semantics, and 'expresses' is a term of pragmatics. And since the various dimensions are only aspects of a unitary process, there will be certain relations between the terms in the various branches, and distinctive signs will be necessary to characterize these relations and so the process of semiosis as a whole. 'Sign' itself is a strictly semiotical term, not being definable either within syntactics, semantics, or pragmatics alone; only in the wider use of 'semiotical' can it be said that all the terms in these disciplines are semiotical terms.

It is possible to attempt to systematize the entire set of terms and propositions dealing with signs. In principle, semiotic could be presented as a deductive system, with undefined terms and primitive sentences which allow the deduction of other sentences as theorems. But though this is the form of presentation to which science strives, and though the fact that semiotic deals exclusively with relations makes it peculiarly fit for treatment by the new logic of relations, yet it is neither advisable nor possible in the present monograph to attempt this type of exposition. It is true that much has been accomplished in the general analysis of sign relations by the formalists, the empiricists, and the pragmatists, but the results which have been attained seem to be but a small part of what may be expected; the preliminary systematization in the component fields has hardly begun. For such reasons, as well as because of the introductory function of this monograph, it has not seemed advisable to attempt a formalization of semiotic which goes much beyond the existing status of the subject, and which might obscure the role which semiotic is fitted to play in the erection of unified science.

Such a development remains, however, as the goal. Were it obtained it would constitute what might be called *pure semiotic*, with the component branches of pure syntactics, pure semantics, and pure pragmatics. Here would be elaborated in systematic form the metalanguage in terms of which all sign situations would be discussed. The application of this language to concrete instances of signs might then be called *descriptive semiotic* (or syntactics, semantics, or pragmatics as the case may be). In this sense the present *Encyclopedia*, in so far as it deals with the language of science, is an especially important case of descriptive semiotic, the treatment of the structure of that language falling under descriptive syntactics, the treatment of the relation of that language to existential situations falling under descriptive semantics, and the consideration of the relation of that language to its builders and users being an instance of descriptive pragmatics. The *Encyclopedia* as a whole, from the point of view expressed in this monograph, falls within the province of pure and descriptive semiotic.

4. Language

The preceding account is applicable to all signs, however simple or complex. Hence it is applicable to languages as a particular kind of sign system. The term 'language,' in common with most terms which have to do with signs, is ambiguous, since its characterization may be given in terms of the various dimensions. Thus the formalist is inclined to consider any axiomatic system as a language, regardless of whether there are any things which it denotes, or whether the system is actually used by any group of interpreters; the empiricist is inclined to stress the necessity of the relation of signs to objects which they denote and whose properties they truly state; the pragmatist is inclined to regard a language as a type of communicative activity, social in origin and nature, by which members of a social group are able to meet more satisfactorily their individual and common needs. The advantage of the three-dimensional analysis is that the validity of all these points of view can be recognized, since they refer to three aspects of one and the same phenomenon; where convenient the type of consideration (and hence of abstraction) can be indicated by 'L_{syn},' 'L_{sem},' or 'L_p.' It has already been noted that a sign may not denote any actual objects (i.e., have no denotatum) or may not have an actual interpreter. Similarly, there may be languages, as a kind of sign complex, which at a given time are applied to nothing, and which have a single interpreter or even no interpreter, just as an unoccupied building may be called a house. It is not possible, however, to have a language if the set of signs have no syntactical dimension, for it is not customary to call a single sign a language. Even this case is instructive, for in terms of the view expressed (namely, that potentially every sign has syntactical relations to those signs which would state its designatum, that is, the kind of situation to which it is applicable) even an isolated sign is potentially a linguistic sign. It could also be said that an isolated sign has certain relations to itself, and so a syntactical dimension, or that having a null syntactical dimension is only a special case of having a syntactical dimension. These possibilities are important in showing the degree of independence of the various dimensions and consequently of L_{syn}, L_{sem}, and L_p. They also show that there is no absolute cleft between single signs, sentential signs, and languages—a point which Peirce especially stressed.

A language, then, as a system of interconnected signs, has a syntactical structure of such a sort that among its permissible sign combinations some can function as statements, and sign vehicles of such a sort that they can be common to a number of interpreters. The syntactical, semantical, and pragmatical features of this characterization of language will become clearer when the respective branches of semiotic are considered. It will also become clear that just as an individual sign is completely characterized by giving its relation to other signs, objects, and its users, so a language is completely characterized by giving what will later be called the syntactical, semantical, and pragmatical rules governing the sign vehicles. For the moment it should be noted that the present characterization of language is a strictly semiotical one, involving reference to all three dimensions; much confusion will be avoided if it is recognized that the word 'language' is often used to designate some aspect of what is language in the full sense. The simple formula, $L = L_{syn} + L_{sem} + L_p$, helps to clarify the situation.

Languages may be of various degrees of richness in the complexity of their structure, the range of things they designate, and the purposes for which they are adequate. Such natural languages as English, French, German, etc., are in these respects the richest languages and have been called *universal languages*, since in them everything can be represented. This very richness may, however, be a disadvantage for the realization of certain purposes. In the universal languages it is often very difficult to know within which dimension a certain sign is predominantly functioning, and the various levels of symbolic reference are not clearly indicated. Such languages are therefore ambiguous and give rise to explicit contradictions—facts which in some connections (but not in all!) are disadvantageous. The very devices which aid scientific clarity may weaken the potentialities for the aesthetic use of signs, and vice versa. Because of such considerations it is not surprising that men have developed certain special and restricted languages for the better accomplishment of certain purposes: mathematics and formal logic for the exhibition of syntactical structure, empirical science for more accurate description and prediction of natural processes, the fine and applied arts for the indication and control of what men have cherished. The everyday language is especially weak in devices to talk about language, and it is the task of semiotic to supply a language to meet this need. For the accomplishment of their own ends these special languages may stress certain of the dimensions of sign-functioning more than others; nevertheless, the other dimensions are seldom if ever completely absent, and such languages may be regarded as special cases falling under the full semiotical characterization of language which has been suggested.

The general origin of systems of interconnected signs is not difficult to explain. Sign vehicles as natural existences share in the connectedness of extraorganic and intraorganic processes. Spoken and sung words are literally parts of organic responses, while writing, painting, music, and signals are the immediate products of behavior. In the case of signs drawn from materials other than behavior or the products of behavior—as in the sign factors in perception—the signs become interconnected because the sign vehicles are interconnected. Thunder becomes a sign of lightning and lightning a sign of danger just because thunder and lightning and danger are, in fact, interconnected in specific ways. If w expects x on the presence of y, and z on the presence of x, the interconnectedness of the two expectations makes it very natural for w to expect z on the presence of y. From the interconnectedness of events on the one hand, and the interconnectedness of actions on the other, signs become interconnected, and language as a system of signs arises. That the syntactical structure of language is, in general, a function both of objective events and of behavior, and not of either alone, is a thesis which may be called *the dual control of linguistic structure*. This thesis will receive elaboration later, but it should be already evident that it gives a way of avoiding the extremes of both conventionalism and the traditional empiricism in accounting for linguistic structure. For the reasons given, sets of signs tend to become systems of signs; this is as true in the case of perceptual signs, gestures, musical tones, and painting as it is in the case of speech and writing. In some cases the systematization is relatively loose and variable and may include subsystems of various degrees of organization and interconnectedness; in others it is relatively close and stable, as in the case of mathematical and scientific languages. Given such sign structures, it is possible to subject them to a three-dimensional analysis, investigating their structure, their relation to what they denote, and their relations to their interpreters. This will now be done in general terms, discussing in turn the syntactics, semantics, and pragmatics of language, but keeping in mind throughout the relation of each dimension, and so each field of semiotic, to the others. Later, after making use of the abstractions involved in this treatment, we will specifically stress the unity of semiotic.

III. Syntactics

5. The Formal Conception of Language

Syntactics, as the study of the syntactical relations of signs to one another in abstraction from the relations of signs to objects or to interpreters, is the best developed of all the branches of semiotic. A great deal of the work in linguistics proper has been done from this point of view, though often unconsciously and with many confusions. Logicians have from the earliest times been concerned with inference, and this, though historically overlaid with many other considerations, involves the study of the relations between certain combinations of signs within a language. Especially important has been the early presentation by the Greeks of mathematics in the form of a deductive or axiomatic system; this has kept constantly before men's attention the pattern of a closely knit system of signs such that by means of operations upon certain initial sets all the other sets of signs are obtained. Such formal systems presented the material whose considerations made inevitable the development of syntactics. It was in Leibniz the mathematician that linguistic, logical, and mathematical considerations jointly led to the conception of a general formal art (*speciosa generalis*) which included the general characteristic art (*ars characteristica*), essentially a theory and art of so forming signs that all consequences of the corresponding "ideas" could be drawn by a consideration of the signs alone, and the general combinatory art (*ars combinatoria*), a general calculus giving a universal formal method of drawing the consequences from signs. This unification and generalization of mathematical form and method has received since Leibniz' time a remarkable extension in symbolic logic, through the efforts of Boole, Frege, Peano, Peirce, Russell, Whitehead, and others, while the theory of such syntactical relations has received its most elaborate contemporary development in the logical syntax of Carnap. For present purposes only the most general aspect of this point of view need be mentioned, especially since Carnap treats this question in Volume I, Numbers 1 and 3.

Logical syntax deliberately neglects what has here been called the semantical and the pragmatical dimensions of semiosis to concentrate upon the logico-grammatical structure of language, i.e., upon the syntactical dimension of semiosis. In this type of consideration a "language" (i.e., L_{syn}) becomes any set of things related in accordance with two classes of rules: *formation rules*, which determine permissible independent combinations of members of the set (such combinations being called sentences), and *transformation rules*, which determine the sentences which can be obtained from other sentences. These may be brought together under the term '*syntactical rule*.' Syntactics is, then, the consideration of signs and sign combinations in so far as they are subject to syntactical rules. It is not interested in the individual properties of the sign vehicles or in any of their relations except syntactical ones, i.e., relations determined by syntactical rules.

Investigated from this point of view, languages have proved to be unexpectedly complex, and the point of view unexpectedly fruitful. It has been possible accurately to characterize primitive, analytic, contradictory, and synthetic sentences, as well as demonstration and derivation. Without deserting the formal point of view, it has proved possible to distinguish logical and descriptive signs, to define synonymous signs and equipollent sentences, to characterize the content of a sentence, to deal with the logical paradoxes, to classify certain types of expressions, and to clarify the modal expressions of necessity, possibility, and impossibility. These and many other results have been partially systematized in the form of a language, and most of the terms of logical syntax may be defined in terms of the notion of consequence. The result is that there is today available a more precise language for talking about the formal dimension of languages than has ever before existed. Logical syntax has given results of high intrinsic interest and furnished a powerful analytical tool; it will be used extensively in the analysis of the language of science in this *Encyclopedia.*

Our present interest, however, is solely with the relation of logical syntax to semiotic. It is evident that it falls under syntactics; it has indeed suggested this name. All the results of logical syntax are assimilable by syntactics. Further, it is without doubt the most highly developed part of syntactics, and so of semiotic. In its spirit and method it has much to contribute to semantics and pragmatics, and there is evidence that its influence is at work in these fields.

Many of its specific results have analogues in the other branches of semiotic. As an illustration let us use the term *'thing-sentence,'* to designate any sentence whose designatum does not include signs; such a sentence is about things and may be studied by semiotic. On this usage none of the sentences of the semiotical languages are thing-sentences. Now Carnap has made clear the fact that many sentences which are apparently thing-sentences, and so about objects which are not signs, turn out under analysis to be pseudo thing-sentences which must be interpreted as syntactical statements about language. But in analogy to these quasi-syntactical sentences there are corresponding quasi-semantical and quasi-pragmatical sentences which appear to be thing-sentences but which must be interpreted in terms of the relation of signs to designata or the relation of signs to interpreters.

Syntactics is in some respects easier to develop than its coordinate fields, since it is somewhat easier, especially in the case of written signs, to study the relations of signs to one another as determined by rule than it is to characterize the existential situations under which certain signs are employed or what goes on in the interpreter when a sign is functioning. For this reason the isolation of certain distinctions by syntactical investigation gives a clue for seeking their analogues in semantical and pragmatical investigations.

In spite of the importance thus ascribed to logical syntax, it cannot be equated with syntactics as a whole. For it (as the term 'sentence' shows) has limited its investigation of syntactical structure to the type of sign combinations which are dominant in science, namely, those combinations which from a semantical point of view are called statements, or those combinations used in the transformation of such combinations. Thus on Carnap's usage commands are not sentences, and many lines of verse would not be sentences. 'Sentence' is not, therefore, a term which in his usage applies to every independent sign combination permitted by the formation rules of a language—and yet clearly syntactics in the wide sense must deal with all such combinations. There are, then, syntactical problems in the fields of perceptual signs, aesthetic signs, the practical use of signs, and general linguistics which have not been treated within the framework of what today is regarded as logical syntax and yet which form part of syntactics as this is here conceived.

6. Linguistic Structure

Let us now consider more carefully linguistic structure, invoking semantics and pragmatics where they may be of help in clarifying the syntactical dimension of semiosis.

Given a plurality of signs used by the same interpreter, there is always the possibility of certain syntactical relations between the signs. If there are two signs, S_1 and S_2, so used that S_1 (say 'animal') is applied to every object to which S_2 (say 'man') is applied, but not conversely, then in virtue of this usage the semiosis involved in the functioning of S_1 is included in that of S_2; an interpreter will respond to an object denoted by 'man' with the responses he would make to an object denoted by 'animal,' but in addition there are certain responses which would not be made to any animal to which 'man' was not applicable and which would not be made to an animal to which certain other terms (such as 'amoeba') were applicable. In this way terms gain relations among themselves corresponding to the relations of the responses of which the sign vehicles are a part, and these modes of usage are the pragmatical background of the formation and transformation rules. The syntactical structure of a language is the interrelationship of signs caused by the interrelationship of the responses of which the sign vehicles are products or parts. The formalist substitutes for such responses their formulation in signs; when he begins with an arbitrary set of rules, he is stipulating the interrelationship of responses which possible interpreters must have before they can be said to be using the language under consideration.

In so far as a single sign (such as a particular act of pointing) can denote only a single object, it has the status of an index; if it can denote a plurality of things (such as the term 'man'), then it is combinable in various ways with signs which explicate or restrict the range of its application; if it can denote everything (such as the term 'something'), then it has relations with every sign, and so has universal implication, that is to say, it is implicated by every sign within the language. These three kinds of signs will be called, respectively, *indexical signs*, *characterizing signs*, and *universal signs*.

Signs may thus differ in the degree to which they determine definite expectations. To say 'something is being referred to' does not give rise to definite expectations, does not allow taking account of what is being referred to; to use 'animal' with no further specification awakens certain sets of response, but they are not particularized sufficiently to deal adequately with a specific animal; it is an improvement in the situation to use 'man,' as is evident in the contrast between knowing that an animal is coming and that a man is coming; finally, the use of 'this' in an actual situation with the supplementary help of bodily orientation directs behavior upon a specific object but gives a minimum of expectations concerning the character of what is denoted. Universal signs may have a certain importance in allowing one to talk in general of the designata of signs without having to specify the sign or designatum; the difficulty of attempting to avoid such terms as 'object,' 'entity,' and 'something' shows the value of such terms for certain purposes. More important, however, is the combination of indexical and characterizing signs (as in 'that horse runs') since such a combination gives the definiteness of reference of the indexical sign plus the determinateness of the expectation involved in the characterizing sign. It is the complex forms of such combinations that are dealt with formally in the sentences of logical and mathematical systems, and to which (considered semantically) the predicates of truth and falsity apply. This importance is reflected in the fact that all formal systems show a differentiation of two kinds of signs corresponding to indexical and characterizing signs. Further, the fact that the determinateness of expectation can be increased by the use of additional signs is reflected in the fact that linguistic structures provide a framework which permits of degrees of specification and makes clear the sign relations involved.

To use terms suggested by M. J. Andrade, it may be said that every sentence contains a *dominant sign* and certain *specifiers*, these terms being relative to each other, since what is a dominant sign with respect to certain specifiers may itself be a specifier with respect to a more general dominant sign—thus 'white' may make the reference to horses more specific, while 'horse' may itself be a specifier with respect to 'animal.' Since an adequate taking-account-of-something demands an indication of both its location and (relevant) properties, and since the relevant degree of specification is obtained by a combination of characterizing signs, a sentence capable of truth and falsity involves indexical signs, a dominant characterizing sign with possibly characterizing specifiers, and some signs to show the relation of the indexical and characterizing signs to one another and to the members of their own class. Hence the general formula of such a sentence:

Dominant characterizing sign [characterizing specifiers (indexical signs)]

In such a sentence as 'That white horse runs slowly,' spoken in an actual situation with indexical gestures, 'runs' may be taken as the dominant sign, and 'slowly' as a characterizing specifier specifies 'runs'; 'horse' similarly specifies the possible cases of 'runs slowly,' 'white' carries the specification further, and 'that' in combination with the indexical gesture serves as an indexical sign to locate the object to which the dominant sign as now specified is to be applied. The conditions of utterance might show that 'horse' or some other sign is to be taken as the dominant sign, so that pragmatical considerations determine what, in fact, is the dominant sign. The dominant sign may even be more general than any which have been mentioned: it may be a sign to show that what follows is a declaration or a belief held with a certain degree of conviction. Instead of the use of the indexical sign in an actual situation, characterizing signs might be so used as to inform the hearer how to supply the indexical sign: 'Find the horse such that . . . . ; it is that horse to which reference is being made'; or 'Take any horse; then that horse. . . . .' In case a set of objects is referred to, the reference may be to all of the set, to a portion, or to some specified member or members; terms such as 'all,' 'some,' 'three,' together with indexical signs and descriptions, perform this function of indicating which of the possible denotata of a characterizing sign are referred to. There need not be only a single indexical sign; in such a sentence as '*A* gave *B* to *C*,' there are three correlates of the triadic relation to be specified by indexical signs, either used alone or in connection with other devices.

The sign 'to' in the sentence '*A* gave *B* to *C*' serves as an occasion for stressing an important point: to have intelligible sign combinations it is necessary to have special signs within the language in question to indicate the relation of other signs, and such signs, being in the language in question, must be distinguished from those signs in the language of syntactics which designate these relations. In the English examples which have been given, the 's' in 'runs,' the 'ly' in 'slowly,' the position of 'that' and 'white' with reference to the position of 'horse,' the positions of '*A*' and '*B*' before and after the dominant sign 'gives,' the position of 'to' before '*C*' all furnish indications as to which sign specifies which other sign, or which indexical sign denotes which correlate of the relation, or which signs are indexical signs and which are characterizing signs. Pauses, speech melodies, and emphasis help to perform such functions in spoken language; punctuation marks, accents, parentheses, italics, size of letter, etc., are similar aids in written and printed languages. Such signs within the language perform primarily a pragmatical function, but the term 'parenthesis' and its implicates occur in the metalanguage. The metalanguage must not be confused with a language to which it refers, and in the language itself a distinction must be made between those signs whose designata fall outside the language and those signs which indicate the relation of other signs.

All the distinctions which have been recognized as involved in the functioning of language in the full semiotical sense are reflected in the features of language which syntactics has thus far studied. Syntactics recognizes classes of signs, such as individual constants and variables, and predicate constants and variables, which are the formal correlates of various kinds of indexical and characterizing signs; the operators correspond to class specifiers; dots, parentheses, and brackets are devices within the language for indicating certain relations between the signs; terms such as 'sentence,' 'consequence,' and 'analytic' are syntactical terms for designating certain kinds of sign combinations and relations between signs; sentential (or "propositional") functions correspond to sign combinations lacking certain indexical specifiers necessary for complete sentences ("propositions"); the formation and transformation rules correspond to the way in which signs are combined or derived from one another by actual or possible users of the language. In this way the formalized languages studied in contemporary logic and mathematics clearly reveal themselves to be the formal structure of actual and possible languages of the type used in making statements about things; at point after point they reflect the significant features of language in actual use. The deliberate neglect by the formalist of other features of language, and the ways in which language changes, is an aid in isolating a particular object of interest: linguistic structure. The formal logician differs from the grammarian only in his greater interest in the types of sentences and transformation rules operative in the language of science. The logician's interest needs to be supplemented by the grammarian's type of interest and by attention to sign combinations and transformations in fields other than science if the whole domain of syntactics is to be adequately explored.

IV. Semantics

7. The Semantical Dimension of Semiosis

Semantics deals with the relation of signs to their designata and so to the objects which they may or do denote. As in the case of the other disciplines dealing with signs, a distinction may be made between its pure and descriptive aspects, pure semantics giving the terms and the theory necessary to talk about the semantical dimension of semiosis, descriptive semantics being concerned with actual instances of this dimension. The latter type of consideration has historically taken precedence over the former; for centuries linguists have been concerned with the study of the conditions under which specific words were employed, philosophical grammarians have tried to find the correlates in nature of linguistic structures and the differentiation of parts of speech, philosophical empiricists have studied in more general terms the conditions under which a sign can be said to have a denotatum (often in order to show that the terms of their metaphysical opponents did not meet these conditions), discussions of the term 'truth' have always involved the question of the relation of signs to things—and yet, in spite of the length of this history, relatively little has been done in the way of controlled experimentation or in the elaboration of a suitable language to talk about this dimension. The experimental approach made possible by behavioristics offers great promise in determining the actual conditions under which certain signs are employed; the development of the language of semantics has been furthered by recent discussions of the relation of formal linguistic structures to their "interpretations," by attempts (such as those of Carnap and Reichenbach) to formulate more sharply the doctrine of empiricism, and by the efforts of the Polish logicians (notably Tarski) to define formally in a systematic fashion certain terms of central importance within semantics. Nevertheless, semantics has not yet attained a clarity and systematization comparable to that obtained by certain portions of syntactics.

Upon consideration, this situation is not surprising, for a rigorous development of semantics presupposes a relatively highly developed syntactics. To speak of the relation of signs to the objects they designate presupposes, in order to refer both to signs and to objects, the language of syntactics and the thing-language. This reliance upon syntactics is particularly evident in discussing languages, for here a theory of formal linguistic structure is indispensable. For example, the constantly recurring question as to whether the structure of language is the structure of nature cannot properly be discussed until the terms 'structure' and 'structure of a language' are clear; the unsatisfactoriness of historical discussions of this question are certainly in part due to the lack of such preliminary clarification as syntactics has today supplied.

A sign combination such as ' 'Fido' designates A ' is an instance of a sentence in the language of semantics. Here ' 'Fido' ' denotes Fido' (i.e., the sign or the sign vehicle and not a non-linguistic object), while 'A' is an indexical sign of some object (it might be the word 'that' used in connection with some directive gesture). ' 'Fido' ' is thus a term in the metalanguage denoting the sign 'Fido' in the object language; 'A' is a term in the thing-language denoting a thing. 'Designates' is a semantical term, since it is a characterizing sign designating a relation between a sign and an object. Semantics presupposes syntactics but abstracts from pragmatics; whether dealing with simple signs or complex ones (such as a whole mathematical system), semantics limits itself to the semantical dimension of semiosis.

In considering this dimension, the most important addition to the preceding account lies in the term *'semantical rule.'* Unlike the formation and transformation rules, which deal with certain sign combinations and their relations, 'semantical rule' designates within semiotic a rule which determines under which conditions a sign is applicable to an object or situation; such rules correlate signs and situations denotable by the signs. A sign denotes whatever conforms to the conditions laid down in the semantical rule, while the rule itself states the conditions of designation and so determines the designatum (the class or kind of denotata). The importance of such rules has been stressed by Reichenbach as definitions of co-ordination, and by Ajdukiewicz as empirical rules of meaning; the latter insists that such rules are necessary to characterize uniquely a language, since with different semantical rules two persons might share the same formal linguistic structure and yet be unable to understand each other. Thus, in addition to the syntactical rules, the characterization of a language requires the statement of the semantical rules governing the sign vehicles singly and in combination (it will later become clear that the full semiotical characterization of a language demands in addition the statement of what will be called pragmatical rules).

Rules for the use of sign vehicles are not ordinarily formulated by the users of a language, or are only partially formulated; they exist rather as habits of behavior, so that only certain sign combinations in fact occur, only certain sign combinations are derived from others, and only certain signs are applied to certain situations. The explicit formulation of rules for a given language requires a higher order of symbolization and is a task of descriptive semiotic; it would be a very difficult task to formulate, for instance, the rules of English usage, as may be seen if one even tries to formulate the conditions under which the

101

words 'this' and 'that' are used. It is natural, therefore, that attention has been chiefly devoted to fragments of the common languages and to languages which have been deliberately constructed.

A sign has a semantical dimension in so far as there are semantical rules (whether formulated or not is irrelevant) which determine its applicability to certain situations under certain conditions. If this usage is stated in terms of other signs, the general formula is as follows: The sign vehicle 'x' designates the conditions a, b, c . . . . under which it is applicable. The statement of those conditions gives the semantical rule for 'x.' When any object or situation fulfils the required conditions, then it is denoted by 'x.' The sign vehicle itself is simply one object, and its denotation of other objects resides solely in the fact that there are rules of usage which correlate the two sets of objects.

The semantical rule for an indexical sign such as pointing is simple: the sign designates at any instant what is pointed at. In general, an indexical sign designates what it directs attention to. An indexical sign does not characterize what it denotes (except to indicate roughly the space-time co-ordinates) and need not be similar to what it denotes. A characterizing sign characterizes that which it can denote. Such a sign may do this by exhibiting in itself the properties an object must have to be denoted by it, and in this case the characterizing sign is an *icon;* if this is not so, the characterizing sign may be called a *symbol*. A photograph, a star chart, a model, a chemical diagram are icons, while the word 'photograph,' the names of the stars and of chemical elements are symbols. A "concept" may be regarded as a semantical rule determining the use of characterizing signs. The semantical rule for the use of icons is that they denote those objects which have the characteristics which they themselves have—or more usually a certain specified set of their characteristics. The semantical rule for the use of symbols must be stated in terms of other symbols whose rules or usages are not in question, or by pointing out specific objects which serve as models (and so as icons), the symbol in question then being employed to denote objects similar to the models.

It is the fact that the semantical rule of usage for a symbol can be stated in terms of other symbols which makes possible (to use Carnap's term) the reduction of one scientific term to others (or, better, the construction of one term upon others) and thus the systematization of the language of science. It is because indexical signs are indispensable (for symbols ultimately involve icons, and icons indices) that such a program of systematization as physicalism proposes is forced to terminate the process of reduction by the acceptance of certain signs as primitive terms whose semantical rules of usage, determining their applicability to things indicated by indices, must be taken for granted but cannot, within that particular systematization, be stated.

The semantical rule for the use of a sentence involves reference to the semantical rules of the component sign vehicles. A sentence is a complex sign to the effect that the designatum of the indexical component is also a designatum of the component which is a characterizing sign. The designatum of a sentence is thus the designatum-of-an-indexical-sign-as-the-designatum-of-a-characterizing-sign; when the situation conforms to the semantical rule of a sentence, the situation is a denotatum of that sentence (and the sentence may then be said to be true of that situation).

The difference between indices, icons, and symbols (sentences being compounds of other signs) is accounted for by different kinds of semantical rules. Things may be regarded as the designata of indexical signs, properties as the designata of one-place characterizing signs, relations as the designata of two- (or more) place characterizing signs, facts or state of affairs as designata of sentences, and entities or beings as the designata of all signs whatsoever.

It is because a sign may have a rule of usage to determine what it can denote without actually being so used that there can be signs which in fact denote nothing or have null denotation. It was previously noted that the very notion of sign involves that of designatum, but not that there be actually existing objects which are denoted. The designatum of a sign is such things which the sign *can* denote, i.e., such objects or situations which according to the semantical rule of usage could be correlated to the sign vehicle by the semantical relation of denotation. It is now clear, as formerly it could not be, that the *statement* of what would constitute a designatum of a certain sign must itself make use of terms with syntactical relations, since the semantical rule of usage states what the sign in question signifies by using the sign in relation to other signs. 'Designatum' is clearly a semiotical term, while the question as to whether there are objects of such and such a kind is a question to be answered by considerations which go beyond semiotic. The failure to keep separate the statements of semiotic from thing-sentences has led to many pseudo thing-sentences. To say that there is a "realm of subsistence" in addition to, but on a par with, the realm of existences, since "When we think, we must think about something," is a quasi-semantical statement: it seems to speak about the world in the same way that physics does, but actually the statement is an ambiguous form of a semantical sentence, namely, the sentence that for every sign that can denote something a semantical rule of usage can be formulated which will state the conditions under which the sign is applicable. This statement, analytically correct within semantics, does not in any sense imply that there are objects denoted by every such sign—objects which are "subsistential" when not existential.

8. Linguistic and Nonlinguistic Structures

One of the oldest and most persistent theories is that languages mirror (correspond with, reflect, are isomorphic with) the realm of nonlinguistic objects. In the classical tradition it was often held that this mirroring was threefold: thought reflected the properties of objects; and spoken language, composed of sounds which had been given a representative function by mind, in turn reflected the kinds and relations of mental phenomena and so the realm of nonmental objects.

It goes without saying that such a persistent tradition as lies behind the doctrine in question must have something to commend it; it is, nevertheless, significant that this tradition has progressively weakened and has even been repudiated by some of its most vigorous former champions. What light can the general semiotical point of view throw on the situation? In attempting to answer this question, it will be seen that the heart of the matter lies in the fact that the only relevant correlation which exists between signs and other objects is that established by semantical rules.

It seems plausible that the excesses and difficulties of the attempt to find a complete semantical correlation between linguistic signs and other objects lies in the neglect or oversimplification of the syntactical and pragmatical dimensions of semiosis. It has been noted that the very possibility of language requires that there be some special signs to indicate the syntactical relations of other signs in the language. Examples of such signs are pauses, intonations, order of signs, prepositions, affixes, suffixes, etc. Such signs function predominantly in the syntactical and pragmatical dimensions; in so far as they have a semantical dimension, they denote sign vehicles and not nonlinguistic objects. It need not be denied that such signs might help to establish some kind of isomorphism between the remaining signs and nonlinguistic objects, for such isomorphism might be much more complicated than the relation of a model to that of which it is a model. Spatial relations of signs might not correspond to spatial relations between things, but there might be a correlating relation such that for every spatial relation between signs there holds some other relation between the objects denoted by the signs. Such possibilities are open to investigation and should be specifically explored; if they do not hold for all signs, they may hold for certain of them, namely, for such as have semantical rules correlating them with nonlinguistic situations. Nevertheless, the defenders of isomorphism have not shown that such is the case, or that such must be the case if language is to be possible.

The unconvincingness of the general theory increases if notice is taken of such signs as 'all,' 'some,' 'the,' 'not,' 'point at infinity,' '-1.' The first three terms indicate how much of the class determined by some characterizing sign is to be taken account of. The term 'not' is primarily of practical importance, since it allows reference to something other than what is specifically referred to without specifying what the other is. So clarified semantically, the practical importance of the term is obvious, but it is not theoretically necessary in a language, and certainly no existential "negative facts" need be invoked to correspond to it. The mathematical terms mentioned are commonly regarded as signs added to the language so that certain operations, otherwise impossible in certain cases, are always possible, and certain formulas, otherwise needing qualification, can be stated in their full generality.

There are also many signs in a common language which indicate the reaction of the user of the signs to the situation being described (as the 'fortunately' in 'Fortunately, he came'), or even to the signs he is himself using in the description (as in expressing his degree of confidence in a statement). Such terms within discourse have a semantical dimension only at a higher level of semiosis, since the pragmatical dimension of a process of semiosis is not denoted in that process but only in one of a higher level. As in the case of the predominantly syntactical features of a language, the predominantly pragmatical features should not be confounded with those elements correlated by means of semantical rules with the nonlinguistic objects which are being denoted. The traditional versions of isomorphism failed to distinguish the various dimensions of semiosis and the various levels of languages and designata. To what extent some qualified version of the thesis may be held can only be determined after it is formulated. But it is clear that, when a language as a whole is considered, its syntactical structure is a function of both pragmatic and empirical considerations and is not a bare mirroring of nature considered in abstraction from the users of the language.

The main point of the discussion is not to deny that all the signs in a language may have designata and so a semantical dimension but rather to call attention to the fact that the designata of signs in a given discourse (and so the objects denoted, if there are such) do not stand at the same level: the designata of some signs must be sought at the level of semiotic rather than at the level of the thing-language itself; in the given discourse such signs simply indicate (but do not designate) relations of the other signs to one another or to the interpreter—in Scholastic terms they bring something of material and simple supposition into the functioning of terms in personal supposition. The strata of signs are as complex and as difficult to unravel as geological strata; the scientific and psychological effects of unraveling them may be as great in the former case as it has been in the latter.

So much for a bare indication of the field of semantics. The precise analysis of semantical terms, their formal systematization, and the question of the applicability of semantics to domains other than the language of science (for instance, to aesthetic signs) obviously are not possible in an introductory account. If pragmatical factors have appeared frequently in pages belonging to semantics, it is because the current recognition that syntactics must be supplemented by semantics has not been so commonly extended to the recognition that semantics must in turn be supplemented by pragmatics. It is true that syntactics and semantics, singly and jointly, are capable of a relatively high degree of autonomy. But syntactical and semantical rules are only the verbal formulations within semiotic of what in any concrete case of semiosis are habits of sign usage by actual users of signs. 'Rules of sign usage,' like 'sign' itself, is a semiotical term and cannot be stated syntactically or semantically.

V. Pragmatics

9. The Pragmatical Dimension of Semiosis

The term 'pragmatics' has obviously been coined with reference to the term 'pragmatism.' It is a plausible view that the permanent significance of pragmatism lies in the fact that it has directed attention more closely to the relation of signs to their users than had previously been done and has assessed more profoundly than ever before the relevance of this relation in understanding intellectual activities. The term 'pragmatics' helps to signalize the significance of the achievements of Peirce, James, Dewey, and Mead within the field of semiotic. At the same time, 'pragmatics' as a specifically semiotical term must receive its own formulation. By 'pragmatics' is designated the science of the relation of signs to their interpreters. 'Pragmatics' must then be distinguished from 'pragmatism,' and 'pragmatical' from 'pragmatic.' Since most, if not all, signs have as their interpreters living organisms, it is a sufficiently accurate characterization of pragmatics to say that it deals with the biotic aspects of semiosis, that is, with all the psychological, biological, and sociological phenomena which occur in the functioning of signs. Pragmatics, too, has its pure and descriptive aspects; the first arises out of the attempt to develop a language in which to talk about the pragmatical dimension of semiosis; the latter is concerned with the application of this language to specific cases.

Historically, rhetoric may be regarded as an early and restricted form of pragmatics, and the pragmatical aspect of science has been a recurrent theme among the expositors and interpreters of experimental science. Reference to interpreter and interpretation is common in the classical definition of signs. Aristotle, in the *De interpretatione*, speaks of words as conventional signs of thoughts which all men have in common. His words contain the basis of the theory which became traditional: The interpreter of the sign is the mind; the interpretant is a thought or concept; these thoughts or concepts are common to all men and arise from the apprehension by mind of objects and their properties; uttered words are then given by the mind the function of directly representing these concepts and indirectly the corresponding things; the sounds chosen for this purpose are arbitrary and vary from social group to social group; the relations between the sounds are not arbitrary but correspond to the relations of concepts and so of things. In this way throughout much of its history the theory of signs was linked with a particular theory of thought and mind, so much so that logic, which has always been affected by current theories of signs, was often conceived as dealing with concepts—a view made precise in the

Scholastic doctrine of logical terms as terms of second intention. Even Leibniz' insistence upon the empirical study of the sign vehicle as determined by rule was not a repudiation of the dominant tradition but merely an insistence that in this way a new and better technique could be obtained for analyzing concepts than by the attempt to inspect thought directly.

In the course of time most of the tenets of this traditional version of pragmatics were questioned, and today they would be accepted only with serious qualifications. The change in point of view has been most rapid as a result of the implications for psychology of the Darwinian biology—implications which received an early interpretation in pragmatism. Charles S. Peirce, whose work is second to none in the history of semiotic, came to the conclusion that in the end the interpretant of a symbol must reside in a habit and not in the immediate physiological reaction which the sign vehicle evoked or in the attendant images or emotions—a doctrine which prepared the way for the contemporary emphasis on rules of usage. William James stressed the view that a concept was not an entity but a way in which certain perceptual data functioned representatively and that such "mental" functioning, instead of being a bare contemplation of the world, is a highly selective process in which the organism gets indications as to how to act with reference to the world in order to satisfy its needs or interests. George H. Mead was especially concerned with the behavior involved in the functioning of linguistic signs and with the social context in which such signs arise and function. His work is the most important study from the point of view of pragmatism of these aspects of semiosis. John Dewey's instrumentalism is the generalized version of the pragmatists' emphasis upon the instrumental functioning of signs or "ideas."

If from pragmatism is abstracted the features of particular interest to pragmatics, the result may be formulated somewhat as follows: The interpreter of a sign is an organism; the interpretant is the habit of the organism to respond, because of the sign vehicle, to absent objects which are relevant to a present problematic situation as if they were present. In virtue of semiosis an organism takes account of relevant properties of absent objects, or unobserved properties of objects which are present, and in this lies the general instrumental significance of ideas. Given the sign vehicle as an object of response, the organism expects a situation of such and such a kind and, on the basis of this expectation, can partially prepare itself in advance for what may develop. The response to things through the intermediacy of signs is thus biologically a continuation of the same process in which the distance senses have taken precedence over the contact senses in the control of conduct in higher animal forms; such animals through sight, hearing, and smell are already responding to distant parts of the environment through certain properties of objects functioning as signs of other properties. This process of taking account of a constantly more remote environment is simply continued in the complex processes of semiosis made possible by language, the object taken account of no longer needing to be perceptually present.

With this orientation, certain of the terms which have previously been used appear in a new light. The relation of a sign vehicle to its designatum is the actual taking-account in the conduct of the interpreter of a class of things in virtue of the response to the sign vehicle, and what are so taken account of are designata. The semantical rule has as its correlate in the pragmatical dimension the habit of the interpreter to use the sign vehicle under certain circumstances and, conversely, to expect such and such to be the case when the sign is used. The formation and transformation rules correspond to the actual sign combinations and transitions which the interpreter uses, or to stipulations for the use of signs which he lays down for himself in the same way in which he attempts to control deliberately other modes of behavior with reference to persons and things. Considered fron the point of view of pragmatics, a linguistic structure is a system of behavior: corresponding to analytical sentences are the relations between sign responses to the more inclusive sign responses of which they are segments; corresponding to synthetical sentences are those relations between sign responses which are not relations of part to whole. The indexical signs (or their substitutes) in a sign combination direct the attention of the interpreter to parts of the environment; the dominant characterizing sign determines some general response (expectation) to these parts; the characterizing specifiers delimit the general expectation, the degree of specification and the choice of the dominant sign being determined with respect to the problem at hand. If the indexical and characterizing functions are both performed, the interpreter is judging and the sign combination is a judgment (corresponding to the sentence of syntactics and the statement or proposition of semantics). To the degree that what is expected is found as expected the sign is confirmed; expectations are, in general, only partially confirmed; there may be, in addition, various degrees of indirect confirmation that what is indexically referred to has the properties it was expected to have. In general, from the point of view of behavior, signs are "true" in so far as they correctly determine the expectations of their users, and so release more fully the behavior which is implicitly aroused in the expectation or interpretation.

Such statements go somewhat beyond pragmatics proper into the strictly semiotical question as to the interrelation of the dimensions—a topic yet to be specifically discussed. Pragmatics itself would attempt to develop terms appropriate to the study of the relation of signs to their users and to order systematically the results which come from the study of this dimension of semiosis. Such terms as 'interpreter,' 'interpretant,' 'convention' (when applied to signs), 'taking-account-of' (when a function of signs), 'verification,' and 'understands' are terms of pragmatics, while many strictly semiotical terms such as 'sign,' 'language,' 'truth,' and 'knowledge' have important pragmatical components. In a systematic presentation of semiotic, pragmatics presupposes both syntactics and semantics, as the latter in turn presupposes the former, for to discuss adequately the relation of signs to their interpreters requires knowledge of the relation of signs to one another and to those things to which they refer their interpreters. The unique elements within pragmatics would be found in those terms which, while not strictly semiotical, cannot be defined in syntactics or semantics; in the clarification of the pragmatical aspect of various semiotical terms; and in the statement of what psychologically, biologically, and sociologically is involved in the occurrence of signs. Attention may now be turned to some aspects of this latter problem.

10. Individual and Social Factors in Semiosis

The topic in question may be approached, and a possible objection forestalled, by asking why there is any need of adding pragmatics to semantics; since semantics deals with the relation of signs to objects, and since interpreters and their responses are natural objects studied by the empirical sciences, it would seem as if the relation of signs to interpreters fell within semantics. The confusion here arises from the failure to distinguish levels of symbolization and to separate—in the use of 'object'— semiotical from nonsemiotical terms. Everything that is designatable is subject matter for a (in principle) unified science, and in this sense all the semiotical sciences are parts of unified science. When descriptive statements are made about any dimension of semiosis, the statements are in the semantical dimension of a higher level of semiosis and so are not necessarily of the same dimension that is being studied. Statements in pragmatics about the pragmatical dimension of specific signs are functioning predominantly in the semantical dimension. The fact that the pragmatical dimension becomes a designatum for a higher-level process of description does not signify that the interpretant of a sign at any given level is a designatum of that particular sign. The interpretant of a sign is the habit in virtue of which the sign vehicle can be said to designate certain kinds of objects or situations; as the method of determining the set of objects the sign in question designates, it is not itself a member of that set. Even the language of a unified science which would contain an account of the pragmatical dimension would not at the moment of use denote its own pragmatical dimension, though at a higher level of usage the account given of the pragmatical dimension may be found applicable to the pragmatical dimension of the lower level. Since the pragmatical dimension is involved in the very existence of the relation of designation, it cannot itself be put within the semantical dimension. Semantics does not deal with all the relations of signs to objects but, as a semiotical science, deals with the relation of signs to their designata; pragmatics, dealing with another relation of signs, cannot be put within semantics alone or in combination with syntactics. This conclusion is completely independent of the relation of physical and biological existences; the distinction of the semantical and pragmatical dimensions is a semiotical distinction and has nothing to do with the relation of biology and physics.

The point can perhaps be made sharper if we introduce the term *'pragmatical rule.'* Syntactical rules determine the sign relations between sign vehicles; semantical rules correlate sign vehicles with other objects; pragmatical rules state the conditions in the interpreters under which the sign vehicle is a sign. Any rule when actually in use operates as a type of behavior, and in this sense there is a pragmatical component in all rules. But in some languages there are sign vehicles governed by rules over and above any syntactical or semantical rules which may govern those sign vehicles, and such rules are pragmatical rules. Interjections such as 'Oh!,' commands such as 'Come here!,' value terms such as 'fortunately,' expressions such as 'Good morning!,' and various rhetorical and poetical devices occur only under certain definite conditions in the users of the language; they may be said to express such conditions, but they do not denote them at the level of semiosis in which they are actually employed in common discourse. The statement of the conditions under which terms are used, in so far as these cannot be formulated in terms of syntactical and semantical rules, constitutes the pragmatical rules for the terms in question.

The full characterization of a language may now be given: *A language in the full semiotical sense of the term is any intersubjective set of sign vehicles whose usage is determined by syntactical, semantical, and pragmatical rules.*

113

Interpretation becomes especially complex, and the individual and social results especially important, in the case of linguistic signs. In terms of pragmatics, a linguistic sign is used in combination with other signs by the members of a social group; a language is a social system of signs mediating the responses of members of a community to one another and to their environment. To understand a language is to employ only those sign combinations and transformations not prohibited by the usages of the social group in question, to denote objects and situations as do the members of this group, to have the expectations which the others have when certain sign vehicles are employed, and to express one's own states as others do—in short, to understand a language or to use it correctly is to follow the rules of usage (syntactical, semantical, and pragmatical) current in the given social community.

There is a further stipulation often made in connection with the linguistic sign: it must be capable of voluntary use for the function of communicating. Such terms as 'voluntary' and 'communication' need more extended analysis than is here possible, but Mead's account, in *Mind, Self, and Society*, of the linguistic sign (which he calls the significant symbol) seems to cover the point intended in this stipulation. According to Mead, the primary phenomenon out of which language in the full human sense emerges is the gesture, especially the vocal gesture. The gesture sign (such as a dog's snarl) differs from such a nongestural sign as thunder in the fact that the sign vehicle is an early phase of a social act and the designatum a later phase of this act (in this case the attack by the dog). Here one organism prepares itself for what another organism—the dog—is to do by responding to certain acts of the latter organism as signs; in the case in question the snarl is the sign, the attack is the designatum, the animal being attacked is the interpreter, and the preparatory response of the interpreter is the interpretant. The utility of such gesture signs is limited by the fact that the sign is not a sign to the producer as it is to the receiver: the dog which snarls does not respond to his snarl as does his opponent; the sign is not held in common and so is not a linguistic sign.

On the other hand, the important characteristic of the vocal gesture lies precisely in the fact that the emitter of the sound himself hears the sound just as others do. When such sounds become connected with social acts (such as a fight, a game, a festival), the various participants in the act have through this common sign, and in spite of their differentiated functions within the act, a common designatum. Each participant in the common activity stimulates himself by his vocal gestures as he stimulates others. Couple this with what Mead termed the temporal dimension of the nervous system (namely, an earlier but more slowly aroused activity may initiate a later and more rapid activity which in turn furthers or checks the complete arousal of the first activity), and one obtains a possible explanation of how linguistic signs serve for voluntary communication. To use one of Mead's frequent examples, we may consider the situation of a person noticing smoke in a crowded theater. Smoke is a nongestural sign of fire, and its perception calls out to some degree responses appropriate to fire. But further, the spoken word 'fire,' as a response which is connected with a whole set of responses to fire, tends to be uttered. Since this is a linguistic sign, the utterer begins to respond toward this tendency toward utterance as other members of his social group would respond—to run toward an exit, to push, and perhaps trample over, others blocking the way, etc. But the individual, in virtue of certain fundamental attitudes, will respond either favorably or unfavorably to these tendencies and will thus check or further the tendency to say 'Fire!'

In such a case it is said that the man "knew what he was about," that he "deliberately used (or did not use) a certain sign to communicate to others," that he "took account of others." Mead would generalize from such common usages: from his point of view "to have a mind" or "to be conscious of something" was equivalent to "using linguistic signs." It is through such signs that the individual is able to act in the light of consequences to himself and to others, and so to gain a certain amount of control over his own behavior; the presentation of possible consequences of action through the production of linguistic signs becomes a factor in the release or inhibition of the action which has (or seems to have) such consequences. It is in such processes that the term 'choice' gains its clarification—and also whatever distinction is to be made between senders and receivers of linguistic signs. Since the linguistic sign is socially conditioned, Mead, from the standpoint of his social behaviorism, regarded the individual mind and self-conscious self as appearing in a social process when objective gestural communication becomes internalized in the individual through the functioning of vocal gestures. Thus it is through the achievements of the community, made available to the individual by his participation in the common language, that the individual is able to gain a self and mind and to utilize those achievements in the furtherance of his interests. The community benefits at the same time in that its members are now able to control their behavior in the light of the consequences of this behavior to others and to make available to the whole community their own experiences and achievements. At these complex levels of semiosis, the sign reveals itself as the main agency in the development of individual freedom and social integration.

11. Pragmatic Use and Abuse of Signs

When a sign produced or used by an interpreter is employed as a means of gaining information about the interpreter, the point of view taken is that of a higher process of semiosis, namely, that of descriptive pragmatics. Psychoanalysis among the psychologies, pragmatism among the philosophies, and now the sociology of knowledge among the social sciences have made this way of looking at signs a common possession of educated persons. Newspaper statements, political creeds, and philosophical systems are increasingly being looked at in terms of the interests which are expressed and served by the production and use of the signs in question. The psychoanalyist is interested in dreams for the light they throw upon the dreamer; the sociologist of knowledge is interested in the social conditions under which doctrines and systems of doctrine are current. In neither case is the interest in the question whether the dreams or doctrines are true in the semantical sense of the term, i.e., whether there are situations which the dreams and the doctrines may be said to denote. Such studies, together with many others, have confirmed over a wide range the general thesis of pragmatism as to the instrumental character of ideas.

Any sign whatever may be looked at in terms of the psychological, biological, and sociological conditions of its usage. The sign expresses but does not denote its own interpretant; only at a higher level is the relation of the sign to the interpreter itself made a matter for designation. When this is done and a correlation found, the sign becomes of individual and social diagnostic value, and so a new sign at a higher level of semiosis. Signs as well as things not signs can become diagnostic signs: the fact that a patient has a fever shows certain things about his condition; equally well the fact that a certain sign is used by someone expresses that person's condition, for the interpretant of the sign is part of the conduct of the individual. In such cases the same sign vehicle may be functioning as two signs, interpreted by the patient as referring to its denotata and by the diagnostician as referring to the interpretant involved in the patient's sign.

Not only may all signs be regarded in terms of pragmatics, but it is also perfectly legitimate for certain purposes to use signs simply in order to produce certain processes of interpretation, regardless of whether there are objects denoted by the signs or even whether the sign combinations are formally possible in terms of the formation and transformation rules of the language in which the sign vehicles in question are normally used. Some logicians seem to have a generalized fear of contradictions, forgetting that, while contradictions frustrate the normal uses of deduction, they may be perfectly compatible with other interests. Even linguistic signs have many other uses than that of communicating confirmable propositions: they may be used in many ways to control the behavior of one's self or of other users of the sign by the production of certain inter-

117

pretants. Commands, questions, entreaties, and exhortations are of this sort, and to a large degree the signs used in the literary, pictorial, and plastic arts. For aesthetic and practical purposes the effective use of signs may require rather extensive variations from the use of the same sign vehicles most effective for the purposes of science. Scientists and logicians may be excused if they judge signs in terms of their own purposes, but the semiotician must be interested in all the dimensions and all the uses of signs; the syntactics, semantics, and pragmatics of the signs used in literature, the arts, morality, religion, and in value judgments generally are as much his concern as studies of the signs used in science. In one case as in the other the usage of the sign vehicle varies with the purpose to be served.

If semiotic must defend the legitimacy for certain purposes of a concern for the effect of the sign on those who will interpret it, it must equally set itself the task of unmasking confusion of these various purposes which signs serve, whether the confusion be unintentional or deliberate. Just as properly syntactical or semantical statements may masquerade in a form which causes them to appear as statements about nonlinguistic objects, so may pragmatical statements thus masquerade; they then become, as quasi-pragmatical statements, one particular form of pseudo thing-sentences. In the clearly dishonest cases a purpose is accomplished by giving the signs employed the characteristics of statements with syntactical or semantical dimensions, so that they seem to be rationally demonstrated or empirically supported when in fact they are neither. An intellectual intuition, superior to scientific method, may be invoked to bolster up the validity of what is apparently affirmed. The masquerading may not be of one dimension in terms of others but within the pragmatical dimension itself; a purpose that cannot fully stand the light of scrutiny expresses itself in a form suitable to other purposes: aggressive acts of individuals and social groups often drape themselves in the mantle of morality, and the declared purpose is often not the real one. A peculiarly intellectualistic justification of dishonesty in the use of signs is to deny that truth has any other component than the pragmatical, so that any sign which furthers the interest of the user is said to be true. In terms of the preceding analysis it should be clear that 'truth' as commonly used is a semiotical term and cannot be used in terms of any one dimension unless this usage is explicitly adopted. Those who like to believe that 'truth' is a strictly pragmatical term often refer to the pragmatists in support of their view and naturally fail to note (or to state) that pragmatism as a continuation of empiricism is a generalization of scientific method for philosophical purposes and could not hold that the factors in the common usage of the term 'truth' to which attention was being drawn rendered nonexistent previously recognized factors. Certain of James's statements taken in isolation might seem to justify this perversion of pragmatism, but no one can seriously study James without seeing that his doctrine of truth was in principle semiotical: he clearly recognized the need of bringing in formal, empirical, and pragmatic factors; his main difficulty was in integrating these factors, since he lacked the base which a developed theory of signs provides. Dewey has specifically denied the imputed identification of truth and utility. Pragmatism has insisted upon the pragmatical and pragmatic aspects of truth; the perversion of this doctrine into the view that truth has only such aspects is an interesting case of how the results of a scientific analysis may be distorted to lend credibility to quasi-pragmatical statements.

Pseudo thing-sentences of the quasi-pragmatical type are not for the most part deliberate deception of others by the use of signs but cases of unconscious self-deception. Thus a philosopher with certain imperious needs may from a relatively small empirical base construct an elaborate sign system, perhaps in mathematical form, and yet the great majority of terms may be without semantical rules of usage; the impression that the system is about the world, and perhaps superior in truth to science, comes from the confusion of analytic and synthetic sentences and from the illusion that the congenial attitudes evoked by the signs constitute semantical rules. A somewhat similar manifestation is found in mythology, but without the evident influence of scientific types of expression.

119

A particularly interesting aberration of the semiotical processes takes place in certain phenomena studied by psychopathology. Signs normally take the place of objects they designate only to a limited extent; but if for various reasons interests cannot be satisfied in the objects themselves, the signs come more and more to take the place of the object. In the aesthetic sign this development is already evident, but the interpreter does not actually confuse the sign with the object it designates: the described or painted man is called a man, to be sure, but with more or less clear recognition of the sign status—it is only a painted or described man. In the magical use of signs the distinction is less clearly made; operations on the sign vehicle take the place of operations on the more elusive object. In certain kinds of insanity the distinction between the designatum and denotata vanishes; the troublesome world of existences is pushed aside, and the frustrated interests get what satisfaction they can in the domain of signs, oblivious in varying degrees to the restrictions of consistency and verifiability imposed by the syntactical and semantical dimensions. The field of psychopathology offers great opportunities for applications of, and contributions to, semiotic. A number of workers in this field have already recognized the key place which the concept of sign holds. If, following the lead of the pragmatist, mental phenomena be equated with sign responses, consciousness with reference by signs, and rational (or "free") behavior with the control of conduct in terms of foreseen consequences made available by signs, then psychology and the social sciences may recognize what is distinctive in their tasks and at the same time see their place within a unified science. Indeed, it does not seem fantastic to believe that the concept of sign may prove as fundamental to the sciences of man as the concept of atom has been for the physical sciences or the concept of cell for the biological sciences.

VI. The Unity of Semiotic

12. Meaning

We have been studying certain features of the phenomenon of sign-functioning by making use of the abstractions involved in distinguishing syntactics, semantics, and pragmatics—just as biologists study anatomy, ecology, and physiology. While we have recognized explicitly the abstractions involved and have constantly correlated the three subdisciplines of semiotic, we must now draw even more explicitly the unity of semiotic into the focus of attention.

In a wide sense, any term of syntactics, semantics, or pragmatics is a semiotical term; in a narrow sense, only those terms are semiotical which cannot be defined in any of the component fields alone. In the strict sense 'sign,' 'language,' 'semiotic,' 'semiosis,' 'syntactics,' 'truth,' 'knowledge,' etc., are semiotical terms. What of the term 'meaning'? In the preceding discussion the term 'meaning' has been deliberately avoided. In general it is well to avoid this term in discussions of signs; theoretically, it can be dispensed with entirely and should not be incorporated into the language of semiotic. But since the term has had such a notorious history, and since in its consideration certain important implications of the present account can be made clear, the present section is devoted to its discussion.

The confusion regarding the "meaning of 'meaning' " lies in part in the failure to distinguish with sufficient clarity the dimension of semiosis which is under consideration, a situation which also obtains in the confusions as to the terms 'truth' and 'logic.' In some cases 'meaning' refers to designata, in other cases to denotata, at times to the interpretant, in some cases to what a sign implicates, in some usages to the process of semiosis as such, and often to significance or value. Similar confusions are found in the common usages of 'designates,' 'signifies,' 'indicates,' 'expresses,' and in various attempts by linguists to define such terms as 'sentence,' 'word,' and 'part of speech.' The most charitable interpretation of such confusions is to suggest that for the major purposes which the everyday languages serve it has not been necessary to denote with precision the various factors in semiosis—the process is merely referred to in a vague way by the term 'meaning.' When, however, such vague usages are taken over into domains where an understanding of semiosis is important, then confusion results. It then becomes necessary to either abandon the term 'meaning' or to devise ways to make clear the usage in question. Semiotic does not rest upon a theory of "meaning"; the term 'meaning' is rather to be clarified in terms of semiotic.

Another factor in the confusion is a psychological-linguistic one: men in general find it difficult to think clearly about complex functional and relational processes, a situation reflected in the prevalence of certain linguistic forms. Action centers around handling things with properties, and the fact that these things and properties appear only in complex contexts is a much later and more difficult realization. Hence the naturalness of what Whitehead has called the fallacy of simple location. In the present case this takes the form of looking for meanings as one would look for marbles: a meaning is considered as one thing among other things, a definite something definitely located somewhere. This may be sought for in the designatum, which thus becomes transformed in certain varieties of·"realism" into a special kind of object—a "Platonic idea" inhabiting the "realm of subsistence," perhaps grasped by a special faculty for intuiting "essences"; or it may be sought for in the interpretant, which then becomes transformed in conceptualism into a concept or idea inhabiting a special domain of mental entities whose relation to the "psychical states" of individual interpreters becomes very difficult to state; or in desperation caused by contemplation of the previous alternatives it may be sought in the sign vehicle—though historically few if any "nominalists" have held this position. As a matter of fact, none of these positions has proved satisfactory and none of them is demanded. As semiotical terms, neither 'sign vehicle,' 'designatum,' nor 'interpretant' can be defined without reference to one another; hence they do not stand for isolated existences but for things or properties of things in certain specifiable functional relations to other things or properties. A "psychical state," or even a response, is not as such an interpretant but becomes such only in so far as it is a "taking-account-of-something" evoked by a sign vehicle. No object is as such a denotatum but becomes one in so far as it is a member of the class of objects designatable by some sign vehicle in virtue of the semantical rule for that sign vehicle. Nothing is intrinsically a sign or a sign vehicle but becomes such only in so far as it permits something to take account of something through its mediation. Meanings are not to be located as existences at any place in the process of semiosis but are to be characterized in terms of this process as a whole. 'Meaning' is a semiotical term and not a term in the thing-language; to say that there are meanings in nature is not to affirm that there is class of entities on a par with trees, rocks, organisms, and colors, but that such objects and properties function within processes of semiosis.

This formulation also avoids another persistent stumbling block, namely, the belief that meaning is in principle personal, private, or subjective. Such a view historically owes much to the assimilation of the conceptualistic position within an associational psychology which itself uncritically accepted the current metaphysical view of the subjectivity of experience. Persons such as Ockham and Locke were well aware of the importance of habit in the functioning of signs, but as the associational psychology came more and more to reduce mental phenomena to combinations of "psychical states," and to conceive these states as within the individual's "mind" and only accessible to that mind, meaning itself came to be considered in the same terms. Meanings were inaccessible to observation from without, but individuals somehow managed to communicate these private mental states by the use of sounds, writing, and other signs.

The notion of the subjectivity of experience cannot be here analyzed with the detail the problem merits. It is believed, however, that such an analysis would show that 'experience' itself is a relational term masquerading as a thing-name. x is an experience if and only if there is some y (the experiencer) which stands in the experience relation to x. If E is an abbreviation for 'experience relation,' then the class of y's such that y stands in the relation of E to something or other is the class of *experiencers*, and the x's to which something or other stands in the relation E constitute the class of *experiences*. An experience is not, then, a special class of objects on a par with other objects, but objects in a certain relation. The relation E will not here be exhaustively characterized (that is a central task for empiricism), but as a first approximation it can be said that to experience something is to take account of its properties by appropriate conduct; the experience is *direct* to the degree that this is done by direct response to the something in question, and *indirect* to the degree that it is done through the intermediacy of signs. For y_1 to experience x_1 it is sufficient that y_1Ex_1 holds; there is *conscious experience* if y_1Ex_1 is an experience (e.g., if $y_1E[y_1Ex_1]$ holds), otherwise the experience is *unconscious*. An experience x_1 is *de facto subjective* with respect to y_1 if y_1 is the only one who stands in the relation E to x_1; an experience x_1 is *intrinsically subjective* with respect to y_1, relative to a certain state of knowledge, if the known laws of nature permit the deduction that no other y can stand in this relation to x_1. An experience is *de facto intersubjective* if it is not *de facto* subjective, and it is *potentially intersubjective* if it is not intrinsically subjective. It should be noted that with such usages a person may not be able directly to experience aspects of himself that others can directly experience, so that the line between subjective and intersubjective experience in no sense coincides with the distinction between experiencers and external objects.

What bearing does this (tentative and preliminary) analysis have on the question of meaning? It may be admitted, if the facts warrant it, that there are certain experiences which are *de facto* subjective as far as direct experience is concerned and that this may even be true of the direct experience of the process of semiosis; there would be nothing surprising in the conclusion that, if I am the interpreter of a particular sign, there are then aspects of the process of interpretation which I can directly experience but which others cannot. The important point is that

such a conclusion would not be in opposition to the thesis of
the potential intersubjectivity of every meaning. The fact that y_1
and y_2 do not stand in the relation of direct experience to each
other's respective direct experience of x_1 does not prevent them
both from directly experiencing x_1, or from indirectly designating (and so indirectly experiencing) by the use of signs the
experience relations in which the other stands—for under certain circumstances an object which cannot be directly experienced can, nevertheless, be denoted. Applying this result to
the case of a particular sign, y_1 and y_2 may differ in their direct
experience of the meaning situation and yet have the same
meaning in common and, in general, be able to decide what the
other means by a particular sign and the degree to which the
two meanings are the same or different. For the determination
of the meaning of S_1 (where S_1 is a sign vehicle) to y_1 it is not
necessary that an investigator become y_1 or have his experiences
of S_1: it is sufficient to determine how S_1 is related to other signs
used by y_1, under what situations y_1 uses S_1 for purposes of
designation, and what expectations y_1 has when he responds to
S_1. To the degree that the same relations hold for y_2 as for y_1,
then S_1 has the same meaning to y_1 and y_2; to the degree that
the relations in question differ for y_1 and y_2, then S_1 has a
different meaning.

In short, since the meaning of a sign is exhaustively specified
by the ascertainment of its rules of usage, the meaning of any
sign is in principle exhaustively determinable by objective investigation. Since it is then possible, if it seems wise, to stand-
ardize this usage, the result is that the meaning of every sign is
potentially intersubjective. Even where the sign vehicle is intrinsically subjective there can be indirect confirmation that
there is such a sign vehicle with such and such meaning. It is
true that in practice the determination of meaning is difficult
and that the differences in sign usages among persons of even
the same social group may be rather great. But it is theoretically important to realize that the subjectivity of certain experiences, and even experiences of semiosis, is compatible with the

possibility of an objective and exhaustive determination of any meaning whatsoever.

Having introduced the term 'meaning' only provisionally in order to bring out the implications of the position here taken, the use of the term will now be discontinued—it adds nothing to the set of semiotical terms. It may be pointed out that the preceding argument shows the agreement of what will be called *sign analysis* with the requirements of scientific investigation. Sign analysis is the determination of the syntactical, semantical, and pragmatical dimensions of specific processes of semiosis; it is the determination of the rules of usage of given sign vehicles. Logical analysis is, in the widest sense of the term 'logic,' identical with sign analysis; in narrower usages, logical analysis is some part of sign analysis, such as the study of the syntactical relations of the sign vehicle in question. Sign analysis (i.e., descriptive semiotic) can be carried on in accordance with all recognized principles of scientific procedure.

13. Universals and Universality

Certain aspects of the "universality" (or generality) of signs have long attracted attention, and their explanation has been a source of many philosophical disputes. By viewing the phenomena vaguely referred to under the overworked terms 'universals' and 'universality' through the prism of semiotical analysis, the various components of the problems may be separated and their relations seen.

The subject may be approached in terms of Peirce's distinction between a *sinsign* and a *legisign:* a sinsign is a particular something functioning as a sign, while a legisign is a "law" functioning as a sign. A particular series of marks at a specific place, such as 'house,' is a sinsign; such a specific set of marks is not, however, the English word *house*, for this word is "one," while its instances or replicas are as numerous as the various employments of the word. It is a law or habit of usage, a "universal" as over against its particular instances. Peirce was very much impressed by this situation and made the difference basic in his classification of signs; it gave an instance in the domain of signs of the phenomena of law (habit, Thirdness, mediation) upon whose objectivity Peirce was so insistent.

The account which has here been given is compatible with this general emphasis; the preceding section should have made clear that semiosis, as a functional process, is just as real and objective as are the component factors which function in the process. It must also be admitted that in a given instance of semiosis in which, say, 'house' functions as a sign vehicle, this sinsign or this particular instance of semiosis is not identical with the legisign *house*. What, then, is a legisign and where in semiosis are "universals" and "universality" to be found? In general, the answer must be that there is an element of universality or generality in all the dimensions and that confusion results here as elsewhere when these are not distinguished and when statements in the metalanguage are confounded with statements in the thing-language.

It is experimentally confirmable that in a given process of semiosis various sign vehicles may be substituted for the original sign vehicle without the occurrence of any relevant change in the remainder of the process. The metronome beat to which an animal is conditioned may move faster or slower within certain limits without the response of the animal undergoing change; the spoken word 'house' may be uttered at different times by the same or different persons, with various tonal changes, and yet will awaken the same response and be used to designate the same objects. If the word is written, the sizes may vary greatly, the letters may differ in style, the media used may be of various colors. The question of the limits of such variation and what remains constant within this range is in a given case very difficult to determine even by the use of the most careful experimental techniques, but of the fact of variability there is no doubt possible. Strictly speaking, the sign vehicle is only that aspect of the apparent sign vehicle in virtue of which semiosis takes place; the rest is semiotically irrelevant. To say that a given sign vehicle is "universal" (or general) is merely to say that it is one of a class of objects which have the property or properties necessary to arouse certain expectations, to combine in specified ways with other sign vehicles, and to denote certain objects, i.e., that it is one member of a class of objects all of which are subject to the same rules of sign usage. Thus 'house' and 'HOUSE' may be the same sign vehicles, but 'house' and 'Haus' are not; the fact that 'the house is red' conforms to the rules of English while 'the Haus is red' does not, shows that the sign vehicles are not the same, since the rules of usage are (in part) different. None of the disciplines concerned with signs is interested in the complete physical description of the sign vehicle but is concerned with the sign vehicle only in so far as it conforms to rules of usage.

In any specific case of semiosis the sign vehicle is, of course, a definite particular, a sinsign; its "universality," its being a legisign, consists only in the fact, statable in the metalanguage, that it is one member of a class of objects capable of performing the same sign function.

Another component of the problem enters in connection with the semantical dimension. The designatum of a sign is the class of objects which a sign can denote in virtue of its semantical rule. The rule may allow the sign to be applied to only one object, or to many but not to all, or to everything. Here "universality" is simply the potentiality of denoting more than one object or situation. Since such a statement is semantical, a statement can be made in terms of the converse of the relation of denotation: it can then be said that objects have the property of universality when denotable by the same sign. In so far as a number of objects or situations permit of a certain sign being applied, they conform to the conditions laid down in the semantical rule; hence there is something equally true of all of them, and in this respect or to this degree they are the same— whatever differences they may have are irrelevant to the particular case of semiosis. 'Universality (or generality) of objects' is a semantical term, and to talk as if 'universality' were a term in the thing-language, designating entities ("universals") in the world, is to utter pseudo thing-sentences of the quasi-semantical type. This fact was recognized in the Middle Ages in the doctrine that 'universality' was a term of second intention rather

128

than of first; in contemporary terms, it is a term within semiotic and not a term in the thing-language. In the thing-language there are simply terms whose rules of usage make them applicable to a plurality of situations; expressed in terms of objects it can only be said that the world is such that often a number of objects or situations can be denoted by a given sign.

A similar situation appears in syntactics, where the relations of sign vehicles are studied in so far as these relations are determined by formation or transformation rules. A combination of sign vehicles is a particular, but it may share its form with other combinations of sign vehicles, i.e., a number of combinations of different sign vehicles may be instances of the same formation or transformation rule. In this case the particular sign combination has a formal or syntactical universality.

From the standpoint of pragmatics two considerations are relevant to the problem in hand. One is the correlative of the semantical situation which has already been described. The fact that certain sign vehicles may denote many objects corresponds to the fact that expectations vary in determinateness, so that a number of objects may satisfy an expectation. One expects a nice day tomorrow—and a number of weather conditions will meet the expectation. Hence, while a response in a particular situation is specific, it is a true statement within pragmatics that similar responses are often called out by a variety of sign vehicles and are satisfied by a variety of objects. From this point of view the interpretant (in common with any habit) has a character of "universality" which contrasts to its particularity in a specific situation. There is a second aspect of sign universality distinguishable in pragmatics, namely, the social universality which lies in the fact that a sign may be held in common by a number of interpreters.

It is accordingly necessary to distinguish in the universality appropriate to semiosis five types of universality. Since the term 'universality' has such a variety of usages, and is clearly inappropriate in some of the five cases, the term 'generality' will be used instead. There are, then, five types of sign generality: *generality of sign vehicle, generality of form, generality of denotation*, *generality of the interpretant*, and *social generality*. The central point is that each of these kinds of generality can be stated only within semiotic; generality is accordingly a relational concept, since all the branches of semiotic investigate only relations. To speak of something as a "general" or a "universal" is merely to use a pseudo thing-sentence instead of the unambiguous semiotical expression; such terms can only signify that the something in question stands to something or other in one of the relations embodied in the five kinds of sign generality which have been distinguished. In this way there is kept what is significant in the historical emphases of nominalism, realism, and conceptualism, while yet avoiding the last traces of the substantive or entitive conception of generality by recognizing the level of discourse appropriate to discussions of generality and the relational character of the terms employed at this level.

14. Interrelation of the Semiotical Sciences

Since the current tendency is in the direction of specialized research in syntactics, semantics, or pragmatics, it is well to stress emphatically the interrelations of these disciplines within semiotic. Indeed, semiotic, in so far as it is more than these disciplines, is mainly concerned with their interrelations, and so with the unitary character of semiosis which these disciplines individually ignore.

One aspect of the interrelation is indicated in the fact that while each of the component disciplines deals in one way or another with signs, none of them can define the term 'sign' and, hence, cannot define themselves. 'Syntactics' is not a term within syntactics but is a strictly semiotical term—and the same is true of 'semantics' and 'pragmatics.' Syntactics speaks of formation and transformation rules, but rules are possible modes of behavior and involve the notion of interpreter; 'rule' is, therefore, a pragmatical term. Semantics refers explicitly only to signs as designating objects or situations, but there is no such relation without semantical rules of usage, and so again the notion of interpreter is implicitly involved. Pragmatics deals directly only with signs as interpreted, but 'interpreter' and 'interpretant' cannot be defined without the use of 'sign vehicle' and 'designatum'—so that all of these terms are strictly semiotical terms. Such considerations—themselves only a few among many possible ones—show that, while the component semiotical disciplines do not as sciences refer to one another, yet they can be characterized and distinguished only in terms of the wider science of which they are components.

It is also true that a person who studies some dimension of semiosis uses terms which have all three dimensions and employs the results of the study of the other dimensions. The rules which govern the sign vehicles of the language being studied must be understood, and 'understanding' is a pragmatical term. The rules for combining and transforming possible sign vehicles cannot be composed merely of possible sign vehicles but must actually function as signs. In descriptive syntactics there must be signs to denote the sign vehicles being studied, and the aim must be to make true statements about these sign vehicles—but 'denote' and 'true' are not syntactical terms. Semantics will study the relation of a sign combination to what it denotes or can denote, but this involves the knowledge of the structure of the sign combination and the semantical rules in virtue of which the relation of denotation may obtain. Pragmatics cannot go far without taking account of the formal structures for which it should seek the pragmatical correlate, and of the relation of signs to objects which it seeks to explain through the notion of habit of usage. Finally, the languages of syntactics, semantics, and pragmatics have all three dimensions: they designate some aspect of semiosis, they have a formal structure, and they have a pragmatical aspect in so far as they are used or understood.

The intimate relation of the semiotical sciences makes semiotic as a science possible but does not blur the fact that the subsciences represent three irreducible and equally legitimate points of view corresponding to the three objective dimensions of semiosis. Any sign whatsoever may be studied from any of the three standpoints, though no one standpoint is adequate to the full nature of semiosis. Thus in one sense there is no limit to either point of view, i.e., no place at which an investigator must desert one standpoint for another. This is simply because they are studies of semiosis from different points of view; in fastening attention upon one dimension, each deliberately neglects the aspects of the process discernible in terms of the other standpoints. Syntactics, semantics, and pragmatics are components of the single science of semiotic but mutually irreducible components.

VII. Problems and Applications

15. Unification of the Semiotical Sciences

There remains the task of briefly showing the problems which remain open within semiotic and the possible fields of application. These may be roughly grouped under three headings: unification of the semiotical sciences, semiotic as organon of the sciences, and humanistic implications of semiotic. The remarks which follow aim merely to be suggestive—to indicate directions rather than solutions.

The account which has been given has been adapted to the purposes of an introduction. Large areas of the field were ignored, exactitude in statement was often sacrificed to avoid lengthy preliminary analysis, and the consideration of the examples which were introduced was carried only so far as to illuminate the point at issue. Even though the larger outlines of semiotic be correct, it is still far from the condition of an advanced science. Progress will require collaboration by many investigators. There is need both for fact-finders and for systematizers. The former must make clear the conditions under which semiosis occurs and what precisely takes place in the process; the latter must in the light of available facts develop a precise systematized theoretical structure which future fact-finders can in turn use. One theoretical problem of importance lies in the relation of the various kinds of rules. The theory of signs which has been given opens up many points of contact with the concrete work of biologists, psychologists, psychopathologists, linguists, and social scientists. Systematization can profitably make use of symbolic logic; for, since semiotic deals throughout with relations, it is peculiarly amenable to treatment in terms of the logic of relations. The work of fact-finders and systematizers is equally important and must go hand in hand; each provides material for the other.

Semioticians should find the history of semiotic useful both as a stimulus and as a field of application. Such hoary doctrines as the categories, the transcendentals, and the predicables are early sallies into semiotical domains and should be clarified by the later developments. Hellenistic controversies over the admonitive and the indicative sign, and the medieval doctrines of intention, imposition, and supposition are worth reviving and interpreting. The history of linguistics, rhetoric, logic, empiricism, and experimental science offers rich supplementary material. Semiotic has a long tradition, and in common with all sciences it should keep alive its history.

In the development of semiotic the disciplines which now are current under the names of logic, mathematics, and linguistics can be reinterpreted in semiotical terms. The logical paradoxes, the theory of types, the laws of logic, the theory of probability, the distinction of deduction, induction, and hypothesis, the logic of modality—all such topics permit of discussion within the theory of signs. In so far as mathematics is knowledge of linguistic structures, and not simply identified with some (or all) of such structures, it too may be considered as part of semiotic. Linguistics clearly falls within semiotic, dealing at present with certain aspects of the complex sign structures which constitute languages in the full semiotical sense of that term. It is possible that the admittedly unsatisfactory situation with respect to such terms as 'word,' 'sentence,' and 'part of speech' can be clarified in terms of the sign functions which various linguistic devices serve. Ancient projects of a universal grammar take on a new and defensible form when translated into the study of the way all languages perform similar sign functions by the use of different devices.

Logic, mathematics, and linguistics can be absorbed in their entirety within semiotic. In the case of certain other disciplines this may occur only in part. Problems which are often classed as epistemological or methodological fall in large part under semiotic: thus empiricism and rationalism are at heart theories as to when the relation of denotation obtains or may be said to obtain; discussions of truth and knowledge are inseparably linked with semantics and pragmatics; a discussion of the procedures of scientists, when more than a chapter in logic, psychology, or sociology, must relate these procedures to the cognitive status of the statements which result from their application. In so far as aesthetics studies a certain functioning of signs (such as iconic signs whose designata are values), it is a semiotical discipline with syntactical, semantical, and pragmatical components, and the distinction of these components offers a base for aesthetic criticism. The sociology of knowledge is clearly part of pragmatics, and so is rhetoric; semiotic is the framework in which to fit the modern equivalents of the ancient trivium of logic, grammar, and rhetoric. It has already been suggested that psychology and the human social sciences may find part (if not the entire) basis of their distinction from other biological and social sciences in the fact that they deal with responses mediated by signs. The development of semiotic is itself a stage in the unification of sciences dealing in whole or in part with signs; it may also play an important role in bridging the gap between the biological sciences, on the one hand, and the psychological and human social sciences, on the other, and in throwing a new light upon the relation of the so-called "formal" and "empirical" sciences.

16. Semiotic as Organon of the Sciences

Semiotic holds a unique place among the sciences. It may be possible to say that every empirical science is engaged in finding data which can serve as reliable signs; it is certainly true that every science must embody its results in linguistic signs. Since this is so, the scientist must be as careful with his linguistic tools as he is in the designing of apparatus or in the making of observations. The sciences must look to semiotic for the concepts and general principles relevant to their own problems of sign analysis. Semiotic is not merely a science among sciences but an organon or instrument of all the sciences.

This function can be performed in two ways. One is by making training in semiotic a regular part of the equipment of the scientist. In this way a scientist would become critically conscious of his linguistic apparatus and develop careful habits in its use. The second way is by specific investigations of the languages of the special sciences. The linguistically expressed results of all the sciences is part of the subject matter of descriptive semiotic. Specific analyses of certain basic terms and problems in the various sciences will show the working scientist whatever relevance semiotic has in these fields more effectively than any amount of abstract argument. Other essays in the *Encyclopedia* may be regarded as contributing such studies. Current scientific formulations embody many pseudo problems which arise from the confusion of statements in the language of semiotic and the thing-language—recent discussions of indeterminism and complementarity in the physical sciences abound in illustrations. Empirical problems of a nonlinguistic sort are not solved by linguistic considerations, but it is important that the two kinds of problems not be confused and that nonlinguistic problems be expressed in such a form as aids their empirical solution. The classical logic thought of itself as the organon of the sciences but was, in fact, unable to play the role it set itself; contemporary semiotic, embodying in itself the newer logical developments and a wide variety of approaches to sign phenomena, may again attempt to assume the same role.

17. Humanistic Implications of Semiotic

Signs serve other purposes than the acquisition of knowledge, and descriptive semiotic is wider than the study of the language of science. Corresponding to the various purposes which signs serve, there have developed more or less specialized languages which follow to some extent the various dimensions of semiosis. Thus the mathematical form of expression is well adapted to stress the interrelation of terms in a language, letting the relation to objects and interpreters recede into the background; the language of empirical science is especially suitable for the description of nature; the languages of morality, the fine arts, and the applied arts are especially adapted to the control of behavior, the presentations of things or situations as objects of interest, and the manipulation of things to effect desired eventuations. In none of these cases are any of the dimensions of semiosis absent; certain of them are simply subordinated and partially transformed by the emphasis upon one of the dimensions. Mathematical propositions may have an empirical aspect (many indeed were discovered empirically), and mathematical problems may be set by problems in other fields, but the language of mathematics subordinates these factors in order to better accomplish the task it is developed to fulfil. Empirical science is not really concerned with simply getting all true statements possible (such as the statement of the area of each mark on this page) but in getting important true statements (i.e., statements that, on the one hand, furnish a secure base for prediction and, on the other hand, that aid in the creation of a systematic science)—but the language of empirical science is adapted to expressing the truth and not the importance of its statements. Lyric poetry has a syntax and uses terms which designate things, but the syntax and the terms are so used that what stand out for the reader are values and evaluations. The maxims of the applied arts rest on true propositions relevant to the accomplishment of certain purposes ("to accomplish x, do so and so"); moral judgments may similarly have an empirical component but, in addition, assume the desirability of reaching a certain end and aim to control conduct ("You ought to have your child vaccinated," i.e., "Taking the end of health for granted, vaccination is in the present situation the surest way of realizing that end, so have it done").

Semiotic provides a basis for understanding the main forms of human activity and their interrelationship, since all these activities and relations are reflected in the signs which mediate the activities. Such an understanding is an effective aid in avoiding confusion of the various functions performed by signs. As Goethe said, "One cannot really quarrel with any form of representation"—provided, of course, that the form of representation does not masquerade as what it is not. In giving such understanding, semiotic promises to fulfil one of the tasks which traditionally has been called philosophical. Philosophy has often sinned in confusing in its own language the various functions which signs perform. But it is an old tradition that philosophy should aim to give insight into the characteristic forms of human activity and to strive for the most general and the most systematic knowledge possible. This tradition appears in a modern form in the identification of philosophy with the theory of signs and the unification of science, that is, with the more general and systematic aspects of pure and descriptive semiotic.

Selected Bibliography

AJDUKIEWICZ, K. "Sprache und Sinn," *Erkenntnis*, Vol. IV (1934).

BENJAMIN, A. C. *The Logical Structure of Science*, chaps. vii, viii, and ix. London, 1936.

CARNAP, R. *Philosophy and Logical Syntax*. London, 1935.

———. *Logical Syntax of Language*. Vienna, 1934; London, 1937.

———. "Testability and Meaning," *Philosophy of Science*. Vol. III (1936); *ibid*., Vol. IV (1937).

CASSIRER, E. *Die Philosophie der symbolischen Formen*. 3 vols. Berlin, 1923 ff.

EATON, R. M. *Symbolism and Truth*. Cambridge, Mass., 1925.

GÄTSCHENBERGER, R. *Zeichen*. Stuttgart, 1932.

HUSSERL, E. *Logische Untersuchungen*, Vol. II, Part I. 4th ed. Halle, 1928.

KOKOSZYNSKA, M. "Über den absoluten Wahrheitsbegriff und einige andere semantische Begriffe," *Erkenntnis*, Vol. VI (1936).

MEAD, G. H. *Mind, Self, and Society*. Chicago, 1934.

———. *The Philosophy of the Act*. Chicago, 1938.

MORRIS, C. W. *Logical Positivism, Pragmatism, and Scientific Empiricism*. Paris, 1937.

OGDEN, C. K., and RICHARDS, I. A. *The Meaning of 'Meaning.'* London, 1923.

PEIRCE, C. S. *Collected Papers*, esp. Vol. II. Cambridge, Mass., 1931 ff.

REICHENBACH, H. *Experience and Prediction*, chaps. i and ii. Chicago, 1938.

SCHLICK, M. *Gesammelte Aufsätze, 1926–1936*. Vienna, 1938.

TARSKI, A. "Grundlegung der wissenschaftlichen Semantik," *Actes du congres international de philosophe scientifique*. Paris, 1936.

———. "Der Wahrheitsbegriff in den formalisierten Sprachen," *Studia philosophica*, Vol. I (1935).

WITTGENSTEIN, L. *Tractatus logico-philosophicus*. London, 1922.

Foundations of Logic
and Mathematics

Rudolf Carnap

Foundations of Logic and Mathematics

Contents:

Contents

Foundations of Logic and Mathematics

Rudolf Carnap

I. Logical Analysis of Language: Semantics and Syntax

1. Theoretical Procedures in Science

The activities of a scientist are in part practical: he arranges experiments and makes observations. Another part of his work is theoretical: he formulates the results of his observations in sentences, compares the results with those of other observers, tries to explain them by a theory, endeavors to confirm a theory proposed by himself or somebody else, makes predictions with the help of a theory, etc. In these theoretical activities, deduction plays an important part; this includes calculation, which is a special form of deduction applied to numerical expressions. Let us consider, as an example, some theoretical activities of an astronomer. He describes his observations concerning a certain planet in a report, O_1. Further, he takes into consideration a theory T concerning the movements of planets. (Strictly speaking, T would have to include, for the application to be discussed, laws of some other branches of physics, e.g., concerning the astronomical instruments used, refraction of light in the atmosphere, etc.) From O_1 and T, the astronomer deduces a prediction, P; he calculates the apparent position of the planet for the next night. At that time he will make a new observation and formulate it in a report O_2. Then he will compare the prediction P with O_2 and thereby find it either confirmed or not. If T was a new theory and the purpose of the procedure described was to test T, then the astronomer will take the confirmation of P by O_2 as a partial confirmation for T; he will apply the same procedure again and again and thereby obtain either an increasing degree of confirmation for T or else a disconfirmation. The same deduction of P from O_1 and T is made in the case where T is already scientifically acknowledged on the

143

basis of previous evidence, and the present purpose is to obtain a prediction of what will happen tomorrow. There is a third situation in which a deduction of this kind may be made. Suppose we have made both the observations described in O_1 and in O_2; we are surprised by the results of the observation described in O_2 and therefore want an explanation for it. This explanation is given by the theory T; more precisely, by deducing P from O_1 and T and then showing that O_2 is in accordance with P ("What we have observed is exactly what we had to expect").

These simple examples show that the chief theoretical procedures in science—namely, testing a theory, giving an explanation for a known fact, and predicting an unknown fact—involve as an essential component deduction and calculation; in other words, the application of logic and mathematics. (These procedures will later be discussed more in detail, especially in §§ 15, 19, and 23.) It is one of the chief tasks of this essay to make clear the role of logic and mathematics as applied in empirical science. We shall see that they furnish instruments for deduction, that is, for the transformation of formulations of factual, contingent knowledge. However, logic and mathematics not only supply rules for transformation of factual sentences but they themselves contain sentences of a different, non-factual kind. Therefore, we shall have to deal with the question of the nature of logical and mathematical theorems. It will become clear that they do not possess any factual content. If we call them true, then another kind of truth is meant, one not dependent upon facts. A theorem of mathematics is not tested like a theorem of physics, by deriving more and more predictions with its help and then comparing them with the results of observations. But what else is the basis of their validity? We shall try to answer these questions by examining how theorems of logic and mathematics are used in the context of empirical science.

The material on which the scientist works in his theoretical activities consists of reports of observations, scientific laws and theories, and predictions; that is, formulations in language which describe certain features of facts. Therefore, an analysis of theoretical procedures in science must concern itself with language and its applications. In the present section, in preparing for the later task, we shall outline an analysis of language and explain the chief factors involved. Three points of view will be distinguished, and accordingly three disciplines applying them, called pragmatics, semantics, and syntax. These will be illustrated by the analysis of a simple, fictitious language. In the later sections the results of these discussions will be applied in an analysis of the theoretical procedure of science, especially from the point of view of calculi, their interpretation, and their application in empirical science.

2. Analysis of Language

A language, as, e.g., English, is a system of activities or, rather, of habits, i.e., dispositions to certain activities, serving mainly for the purposes of communication and of co-ordination of activities among the members of a group. The elements of the language are signs, e.g., sounds or written marks, produced by members of the group in order to be perceived by other members and to influence their behavior. Since our final interest in this essay concerns the language of science, we shall restrict ourselves to the theoretical side of language, i.e., to the use of language for making assertions. Thus, among the different kinds of sentences, e.g., commands, questions, exclamations, declarations, etc., we shall deal with declarative sentences only. For the sake of brevity we shall call them here simply *sentences*.

This restriction to declarative sentences does not involve, in the investigation of processes accompanying the use of language, a restriction to theoretical thinking. Declarative sentences, e.g., 'This apple is sour', are connected not only with the theoretical side of behavior but also with emotional, volitional, and other factors. If we wish to investigate a language as a human activity, we must take into consideration all these factors connected with speaking activities. But the sentences, and the signs (e.g., words) occurring in them, are sometimes involved in still another relation. A sign or expression may concern or designate or describe something, or, rather, he who uses the expression may intend to refer to something by it, e.g., to an object or a property or a state of affairs; this we call the *designatum* of the expression. (For the moment, no exact definition for 'designatum' is intended; this word is merely to serve as a convenient, common term for different cases—objects, properties, etc.—whose fundamental differences in other respects are not hereby denied.) Thus, three components have to be distinguished in a situation where language is used. We see these in the following example: (1) the action, state, and environment of a man who speaks or hears, say, the German word 'blau'; (2) the word 'blau' as an element of the German language (meant here as a specified acoustic [or visual] design which is the common property of the many sounds produced at different times, which may be called the tokens of that design); (3) a certain property of things, viz., the color blue, to which this man—and German-speaking people in general—intends to refer (one usually says, "The man means the color by the word", or "The word means the color for these people", or ". . . . within this language").

The complete theory of language has to study all these three components. We shall call *pragmatics* the field of all those investigations which take into consideration the first component, whether it be alone or in combination with the other components. Other inquiries are made in abstraction from the speaker and deal only with the expressions of the language and their relation to their designata. The field of these studies is called *semantics*. Finally, one may abstract even from the designata and restrict the investigation to formal properties—in a sense soon to be explained—of the expressions and relations among them. This field is called *logical syntax*. The distinction between the three fields will become more clear in our subsequent discussions.

That an investigation of language has to take into consideration all the three factors mentioned was in recent times made clear and emphasized especially by C. S. Peirce, by Ogden and Richards, and by Morris (see Vol. I, No. 2). Morris made it the basis for the three fields into which he divides semiotic (i.e., the general theory of signs), namely, pragmatics, semantics, and syntactics. Our division is in agreement with his in its chief features. For general questions concerning language and its use compare also Bloomfield, Volume I, No. 4.

3. Pragmatics of Language B

In order to make clear the nature of the three fields and the differences between them, we shall analyze an example of a language. We choose a fictitious language B, very poor and very simple in its structure, in order to get simple systems of semantical and syntactical rules.

Whenever an investigation is made about a language, we call this language the *object-language* of the investigation, and the language in which the results of the investigation are formulated the *metalanguage*. Sometimes object-language and metalanguage are the same, e.g., when we speak in English about English. The theory concerning the object-language which is formulated in the metalanguage is sometimes called metatheory. Its three branches are the pragmatics, the semantics, and the syntax of the language in question. In what follows, B is our object-language, English our metalanguage.

Suppose we find a group of people speaking a language B which we do not understand; nor do they understand ours. After some observation, we discover which words the people use, in which forms of sentences they use them, what these words and sentences are about, on what occasions they are used, what activities are connected with them, etc. Thus we may have obtained the following results, numbered here for later reference.

Pragm. 1.—Whenever the people utter a sentence of the form '... ist kalt', where '...' is the name of a thing, they intend to assert that the thing in question is cold.

Pragm. 2a.—A certain lake in that country, which has no name in English, is usually called 'titisee'. When using this name, the people often think of plenty of fish and good meals.

Pragm. 2b.—On certain holidays the lake is called 'rumber';

when using this name, the people often think—even during good weather—of the dangers of storm on the lake.

Pragm. 3.—The word 'nicht' is used in sentences of the form 'nicht . . .', where '. . .' is a sentence. If the sentence '. . .' serves to express the assertion that such and such is the case, the whole sentence 'nicht . . .' is acknowledged as a correct assertion if such and such is not the case.

In this way we slowly learn the designata and mode of use of all the words and expressions, especially the sentences; we find out both the cause and the effect of their utterance. We may study the preferences of different social groups, age groups, or geographical groups in the choice of expressions. We investigate the role of the language in various social relations, etc.

The pragmatics of language B consists of all these and similar investigations. Pragmatical observations are the basis of all linguistic research. We see that pragmatics is an empirical discipline dealing with a special kind of human behavior and making use of the results of different branches of science (principally social science, but also physics, biology, and psychology).

4. Semantical Systems

We now proceed to restrict our attention to a special aspect of the facts concerning the language B which we have found by observations of the speaking activities within the group who speak that language. We study the relations between the expressions of B and their designata. On the basis of those facts we are going to lay down a system of rules establishing those relations. We call them *semantical rules.* These rules are not unambiguously determined by the facts. Suppose we have found that the word 'mond' of B was used in 98 per cent of the cases for the moon and in 2 per cent for a certain lantern. Now it is a matter of our decision whether we construct the rules in such a way that both the moon and the lantern are designata of 'mond' or only the moon. If we choose the first, the use of 'mond' in those 2 per cent of cases was right—with respect to our rules; if we choose the second, it was wrong. The facts do not determine whether the use of a certain expression is right or wrong but only how often it occurs and how often it leads to the effect intended, and the like. A question of right or wrong must always refer to a system of rules. Strictly speaking, the rules which we shall lay down are not rules of the factually given language B; they rather constitute a language system corresponding to B which we will call the *semantical system B-S*. The language B belongs to the world of facts; it has many properties, some of which we have found, while others are unknown to us. The language system B-S, on the other hand, is something constructed by us; it has all and only those properties which we establish by the rules. Nevertheless, we construct B-S not arbitrarily but with regard to the facts about B. Then we may make the empirical statement that the language B is to a certain degree in accordance with the system B-S. The previously mentioned pragmatical facts are the basis—in the sense explained—of some of the rules to be given later (Pragm. 1 for SD 2a and SL 1, Pragm. 2a,b for SD 1a, Pragm. 3 for SL 2).

We call the elements of a semantical system *signs;* they may be words or special symbols like '0', '+', etc. A sequence consisting of one or several signs is called an *expression*. As signs of the system B-S we take the words which we have found by our observations to be words of B or, rather, only those words which we decide to accept as "correct." We divide the signs of B-S—and, in an analogous way, those of any other semantical system—into two classes: *descriptive* and *logical* signs. As descriptive signs we take those which designate things or properties of things (in a more comprehensive system we should classify here also the relations among things, functions of things, etc.). The other signs are taken as logical signs: they serve chiefly for connecting descriptive signs in the construction of sentences but do not themselves designate things, properties of things, etc. Logical signs are, e.g., those corresponding to English words like 'is', 'are', 'not', 'and', 'or', 'if', 'any', 'some', 'every', 'all'. These unprecise explanations will suffice here. Our later discussions will show some of the differentiae of the two classes of signs.

Semantics as an exact discipline is quite new; we owe it to the very fertile school of contemporary Polish logicians. After some of this group, especially Lesniewski and Ajdukiewicz, had discussed semantical questions, Tarski, in his treatise on truth, made the first comprehensive systematic investigation in this field, giving rise to very important results.

5. Rules of the Semantical System B-S

In order to show how semantical rules are to be formulated and how they serve to determine truth conditions and thereby give an interpretation of the sentences, we are going to construct the semantical rules for the system B-S. As preliminary steps for this construction we make a classification of the signs and lay down rules of formation. Each class is defined by an enumeration of the signs belonging to it. The signs of B-S are divided into descriptive and logical signs. The descriptive signs of B-S are divided into names and predicates. Names are the words 'titisee', 'rumber', 'mond', etc. (here a complete list of the names has to be given). Predicates are the words 'kalt', 'blau', 'rot', etc. The logical signs are divided into logical constants ('ist', 'nicht', 'wenn', 'so', 'fuer', 'jedes') and variables ('x', 'y', etc.). For the general description of forms of expressions we shall use blanks like '. . .', '- - -', etc. They are not themselves signs of B-S but have to be replaced by expressions of B-S. If nothing else is said, a blank stands for any expression of B-S. A blank with a subscript 'n', 'p', 's', or 'v' (e.g., '. . .$_n$') stands for a name, a predicate, a sentence, or a variable, respectively. If the same blank occurs several times within a rule or a statement, it stands at all places for the same expression.

The rules of formation determine how sentences may be constructed out of the various kinds of signs.

Rules of formation.—An expression of B-S is called a *sentence* (in the semantical sense) or a *proposition* of B-S, if and only if it has one of the following forms, F 1–4. F 1: '. . .$_n$ ist - - -$_p$' (e.g., 'mond ist blau'); F 2: 'nicht. . .$_s$' (e.g., 'nicht mond ist blau'); F 3: 'wenn . . .$_s$, so - - -$_s$' (e.g., 'wenn titisee ist rot, so mond ist kalt'); F 4: 'fuer jedes . .$_v$, - . . -', where '- . . -' stands for an expression which is formed out of a sentence not containing a variable by replacing one or several names by the variable

'. .,' (e.g., 'fuer jedes x, x ist blau'; 'fuer jedes y, wenn y ist blau, so y ist kalt'). The partial sentence in a sentence of the form F 2 and the two partial sentences in a sentence of the form F 3 (indicated above by blanks) are called *components* of the whole sentence. In order to indicate the components of a sentence in case they are themselves compound, commas and square brackets are used when necessary.

Rules B-SD. Designata of descriptive signs:

SD 1. The *names* designate things, and especially
  a) each of the thing-names 'titisee' and 'rumˀᴊer' designates the lake at such and such a longitude and latitude.
  b) 'mond' designates the moon.
  Etc. [Here is to be given a complete list of rules for all the names of B-S.]

SD 2. The *predicates* designate properties of things, and especially
  a) 'kalt' designates the property of being cold.
  b) 'blau' designates the property of being blue.
  c) 'rot' designates the property of being red.
  Etc. [for all predicates].

Rules B-SL. Truth conditions for the sentences of B-S. These rules involve the *logical signs*. We call them the L-semantical rules of B-S.

SL 1. 'ist', form F 1. A sentence of the form '. . .ₙ ist - - -ₚ' is true if and only if the thing designated by '. . .ₙ' has the property designated by '- - -ₚ'.

SL 2. 'nicht', form F 2. A sentence of the form 'nicht . . .ₛ' is true if and only if the sentence '. . .ₛ' is not true.

SL 3. 'wenn' and 'so', form F 3. A sentence of the form 'wenn . . .ₛ, so - - -ₛ' is true if and only if '. . .ₛ' is not true or '- - -ₛ' is true.

SL 4. 'fuer jedes', form F 4. A sentence of the form 'fuer jedes . .ᵥ, - . . . -', where '- . . . -' is an expression formed out of a sentence by replacing one or several names by the variable '. .ᵥ', is true if and only if all sentences of the following kind are true: namely, those sentences constructed out of the expression '- . . -' by replacing the variable '. .,' at all places where it occurs within that expression by a name, the same for all places; here names of any things may be taken, even of those for which there is no name in the list of names in B-S. (Example: The sentence 'fuer jedes *x*, *x* ist blau' is true if and only if every sentence of the form '. . ., ist blau' is true; hence, according to SL 1, if and only if everything is blue.)

The rule SL 1, in combination with SD, provides direct truth conditions for the sentences of the simplest form; direct, since the rule does not refer to the truth of other sentences. SL 2–4 provide indirect truth conditions for the compound sentences by referring to other sentences and finally back to sentences of the simplest form. Hence the rules B-SD and SL together give a general definition of '*true* in B-S' though not in explicit form. (It would be possible, although in a rather complicated form, to formulate an explicit definition of 'true in B-S' on the basis of the rules given.) A sentence of B-S which is not true in B-S is called *false* in B-S.

If a sentence of B-S is given, one can easily construct, with the help of the given rules, a direct *truth-criterion* for it, i.e., a necessary and sufficient condition for its truth, in such a way that in the formulation of this condition no reference is made to the truth of other sentences. Since to know the truth conditions of a sentence is to know what is asserted by it, the given semantical rules determine for every sentence of B-S what it asserts—in usual terms, its "meaning"—or, in other words, how it is to be translated into English.

Examples: (1) The sentence 'mond ist blau' is true if and only if the moon is blue. (2) The sentence 'fuer jedes *x*, wenn *x* ist blau, so *x* ist kalt' is true if and only if every thing—not only those having a name in B-S—either is not blue or is cold; in other words, if all blue things are cold. Hence, this sentence asserts that all blue things are cold; it is to be translated into the English sentence 'all blue things are cold'.

Therefore, we shall say that we *understand* a language system, or a sign, or an expression, or a sentence in a language system, if we know the semantical rules of the system. We shall also say that the semantical rules give an *interpretation* of the language system.

We have formulated the semantical rules of the descriptive signs by stating their designata, for the logical signs by stating truth conditions for the sentences constructed with their help. We may mention here two other ways of formulating them which are often used in the practice of linguistics and logic. The first consists in giving *translations* for the signs and, if necessary, for the complex expressions and sentences, as it is done in a dictionary. The second way consists in stating *designata* throughout, not only for the descriptive signs as in SD, but also for expressions containing the logical signs, corresponding to SL. Example (corresponding to SL 1): A sentence of the form '. . .$_n$ ist - - -$_p$' designates (the state of affairs) that the thing designated by '. . .$_n$' has the property designated by '- - -$_p$'.

6. Some Terms of Semantics

We shall define some more terms which belong to the metalanguage and, moreover, to the semantical part of the metalanguage (as is seen from the fact that the definitions refer to the semantical rules). Any semantical term is relative to a semantical system and must, in strict formulation, be accompanied by a reference to that system. In practice the reference may often be omitted without ambiguity (thus we say, e.g., simply 'synonymous' instead of 'synonymous in B-S').

Two expressions are said to be semantically synonymous, or briefly, *synonymous*, with each other in a semantical system S if they have the same designatum by virtue of the rules of S. Hence, according to SD 1*a*, the signs 'titisee' and 'rumber' are semantically synonymous with one another in B-S. They are, however, not what we might call pragmatically synonymous in B, as is shown by Pragm. 2*a,b*. Since the transition from pragmatics to semantics is an abstraction, some properties drop out of consideration and hence some distinctions disappear. Because of the semantical synonymity of the names mentioned, the sentences 'titisee ist kalt' and 'rumber ist kalt' are also semantically synonymous. These two sentences have the same truth conditions, although different pragmatical conditions of application. Suppose that the lake is cold and hence the sentence 'titisee ist kalt' is true. Then the sentence 'rumber is kalt' is also true, even if sinfully spoken on a working day. If this happened by mistake, people would tell the speaker that he is right in his belief but that he ought to formulate it—i.e., the same belief—in another way.

We shall apply the semantical terms to be defined not only to sentences but also to classes of sentences. In what follows we shall use 'S_1', 'S_2', etc., for sentences; 'C_1', 'C_2', etc., for classes of sentences; 'T_1', 'T_2', etc., stand both for sentences and for classes of sentences. (These 'S' and 'C' with subscripts have nothing to do with the same letters without subscripts, which we use for semantical systems and calculi, e.g., 'B-S' and 'B-C'.) We understand the assertion of a class of sentences C_1 as a simultaneous assertion of all the sentences belonging to C_1; therefore, we make the following definition: a *class* of sentences C_1 is called *true* if all sentences of C_1 are true; false, if at least one of them is false. T_1 and T_2 (i.e., two sentences, or two classes of sentences, or one sentence and one class) are called *equivalent* with each other, if either both are true or both are false. T_2 is called an *implicate* of T_1, if T_1 is false or T_2 is true. T_1 is said to *exclude* T_2 if not both are true.

7. L-Semantical Terms

Let us compare the following two sentences: 'Australia is large' (S_1) and 'Australia is large or Australia is not large' (S_2). We see that they have a quite different character; let us try to give an exact account of their difference. We learn S_1 in geography but S_2 in logic. In order to find out for each of these sentences whether it is true or false, we must, of course, first understand the language to which it belongs. Then, for S_1 we have to know, in addition, some facts about the thing whose name occurs in it, i.e., Australia. Such is not the case for S_2. Whether Australia is large or small does not matter here; just by understanding S_2 we become aware that it must be right. If we agree to use the same term 'true' in both cases, we may express their difference by saying that S_1 is factually (or empirically) true while S_2 is logically true. These unprecise explanations can easily be transformed into precise definitions by replacing the former reference to understanding by a reference to semantical rules. We call a sentence of a semantical system S (logically true or) *L-true* if it is true in such a way that the semantical rules of S suffice for establishing its truth. We call a sentence (logically false or) *L-false* if it is false in such a way that the semantical rules suffice for finding that it is false. The two terms just defined and all other terms defined on their basis we call *L-semantical terms*. If a sentence is either L-true or L-false, it is called *L-determinate*, otherwise (L-indeterminate or) *factual*. (The terms 'L-true', 'L-false', and 'factual' correspond to the terms 'analytic', 'contradictory', and 'synthetic', as they are used in traditional terminology, usually without exact definitions.) If a factual sentence is true, it is called (factually true or) *F-true;* if it is false, (factually false or) *F-false*. Every sentence which contains only logical signs is L-determinate. This is one of the chief characteristics distinguishing logical from descriptive signs. (Example: 'For every object x and every property F, if x is an F then x is an F' is L-true. There are no sentences of this kind in the system B-S.)

Classification of sentences of a semantical system:

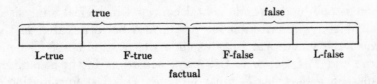

Examples of sentences in B-S: (1) We found earlier (§ 5) that the sentence 'mond ist blau' (S_1) is true in B-S if and only if the moon is blue. Hence, in order to find out whether S_1 is true or false, not only must we know the rules of B-S but we have to make observations of the moon. Hence S_1 is not L-determinate but factual. (2) Let us analyze the sentence 'wenn mond ist blau, so mond is blau' (S_2). According to rule SL 3, a 'wenn-so' sentence is true if its first component is not true or its second component is true. Now, if S_1 is true, the second component of S_2 is true, and hence S_2 is true; and if S_1 is not true, then the first component of S_2 is not true, and hence S_2 is again true. Thus S_2 is true in any case, independently of the facts concerning the moon; it is true merely in virtue of rule SL 3. Therefore S_2 is L-true. (3) The sentence 'nicht, wenn mond ist blau, so mond ist blau' (S_3) has S_2 as its com-

155

ponent; and we found S_2 to be true on the basis of SL 3. Therefore, according to *SL 2*, S_3 is not true but false. And, moreover, it is false not because some fact happens to be the case but merely by virtue of the rules SL 3 and 2. Hence, S_3 is L-false.

Terminological remark.—The use of the word 'true' in everyday language and in philosophy is restricted by some to factual sentences, while some others use it in a wider sense, including analytic sentences. We adopted here the wider use; it is more customary in modern logic (e.g., 'truth function', 'truth-value-table'), and it turns out to be much more convenient. Otherwise, we should always have to say in the semantical rules and in most of the semantical theorems 'true or analytic' instead of 'true'. Semantical rules stating truth-conditions in the sense of 'F-true' would become very complicated and indeed indefinite.

The definitions given can easily be transferred to classes of sentences. C_1 is called L-true if it is possible to find out that C_1 is true with the help of the semantical rules alone, hence if all sentences of C_1 are L-true. C_1 is called L-false if it is possible to find out with the help of the semantical rules that C_1 is false, i.e., that at least one sentence of C_1 is false (in this case, however, all sentences of C_1 may be factual). If C_1 is either L-true or L-false, it is called L-determinate, otherwise factual.

If the semantical rules suffice to show that T_2 is an implicate of T_1, we call T_2 an *L-implicate* of T_1. This relation of L-implication is one of the fundamental concepts in logical analysis of language. The criterion for it can also be formulated in this way: the semantical rules exclude the possibility of T_1 being true and T_2 false; or in this way: according to the semantical rules, if T_1 is true, T_2 must be true. This last formulation of the criterion shows that L-implication, as defined here, is essentially the same as what is usually called logical consequence or deducibility or strict implication or entailment, although the form of the definitions of these terms may be different. Our definition is a semantical one as it refers to the semantical rules. Later we shall discuss the possibility of defining a corresponding syntactical term.

Examples: (1) 'mond ist rot' (S_1); 'wenn mond ist rot, so titisee ist kalt' (S_2); 'titisee ist kalt' (S_3). We shall see that S_3 is an L-implicate of the class C_1 consisting of S_1 and S_2. According to the definition of 'implicate' (§ 6), if S_3 is true, S_3 is an implicate of C_1. The same holds if S_1 is false because C_1 is then also false. The only remaining case is that S_1 is true and S_3 is false. In this case, according to rule SL 3 (§ 5), S_2 is false and, hence, C_1 is false too, and S_3 is an implicate of C_1. Thus we have found, without examining the facts described by the sentences, and merely by referring to the semantical rules, that S_3 is an implicate of C_1. Therefore, S_3 is an L-implicate of C_1. (2) 'fuer jedes x, x ist blau' (S_4); 'mond ist blau' (S_5). We shall see that S_5 is an L-implicate of S_4. If S_5 is true, S_5 is an implicate of S_4. And if S_5 is not true, then according to SL 4 (§ 5), S_4 is not true, and, hence, S_5 is again an implicate of S_4. We found this result by merely referring to a semantical rule. Therefore, S_5 is an L-implicate of S_4.

T_1 and T_2 are said to be *L-equivalent* if the semantical rules suffice to establish their equivalence, in other words, if T_1 and T_2 are L-implicates of each other. L-equivalent sentences have the same truth conditions; therefore, they say the same thing, although the formulations may be quite different.

Example: 'mond ist kalt' (S_1); 'nicht, mond ist kalt' (S_2); 'nicht, nicht, mond ist kalt' (S_3). These sentences are factual; the semantical rules do not suffice for finding out their truth or falsity. But they suffice for showing that S_1 and S_3 are equivalent. If S_1 is true, S_2 is, according to SL 2 (§ 5), false, and hence S_3 true. Therefore, in this case, S_1 and S_3 are equivalent. And, if S_1 is false, then S_2 is true and S_3 is false; hence, S_1 and S_3 are again equivalent. Thus, on the basis of the semantical rules, S_1 and S_3 cannot be other than equivalent. Therefore they are L-equivalent.

If S_1 is an L-true sentence, then the truth of S_1 can be established without any regard to the facts, e.g., to the properties of the things whose names occur in S_1. Therefore, S_1 does not convey any information about facts; this is sometimes formulated by saying that an L-true sentence has no factual content. Suppose S_2 to be an L-implicate of the class of sentences C_1. Then S_2 is an implicate of C_1, and hence, if the sentences of C_1 are true, S_2 is also true; and, moreover, this relation between C_1 and S_2 can be found to hold without taking into account any facts. Therefore, S_2 does not furnish any new information concerning facts that were not already given by C_1. This is sometimes expressed by saying that logical deduction does not increase the factual content of the premises. The two characteristics just explained of L-truth and L-implication (which have been especially emphasized by Wittgenstein) are very important for a clear understanding of the relation between logic and empirical

157

knowledge. We shall see later that they hold also for mathematical theorems and mathematical deductions even if applied in empirical science (§ 19).

8. Logical Syntax

We distinguished three factors in the functioning of language: the activities of the speaking and listening persons, the designata, and the expressions of the language. We abstracted from the first factor and thereby came from pragmatics to semantics. Now we shall abstract from the second factor also and thus proceed from semantics to syntax. We shall take into consideration only the expressions, leaving aside the objects, properties, states of affairs, or whatever may be designated by the expressions. The relation of designation will be disregarded entirely. As this relation is the basis of the whole semantical system, it might seem as if nothing would be left. But we shall soon see that this is not the case.

A definition of a term in the metalanguage is called *formal* if it refers only to the expressions of the object-language (or, more exactly, to the kinds of signs and the order in which they occur in the expressions) but not to any extralinguistic objects and especially not to the designata of the descriptive signs of the object-language. A term defined by a formal definition is also called formal, as are questions, proofs, investigations, etc., in which only formal terms occur. We call the formal theory of an object-language, formulated in the metalanguage, the *syntax* of the object-language (or the logical syntax, whenever it seems necessary to distinguish this theory from that part of linguistics which is known as syntax but which usually is not restricted to formal terms). A formal definition, term, analysis, etc., is then also called syntactical.

The definitions of all semantical terms refer directly or indirectly to designata. But some of these terms—e.g., 'true', 'L-true', 'L-implicate'—are attributed not to designata but only to expressions; they designate properties of, or relations between, expressions. Now our question is whether it is possible to define within syntax, i.e., in a formal way, terms which correspond more or less to those semantical terms, i.e., whose extensions coincide partly or completely with theirs. The development of syntax—chiefly in modern symbolic logic—has led to an affirmative answer to that question. Especially is the possibility of defining in a formal way terms which completely correspond to 'L-true' and 'L-implicate' of fundamental importance. This shows that logical deduction can be completely formalized.

A *syntactical system* or *calculus* (sometimes also called a formal deductive system or a formal system) is a system of formal rules which determine certain formal properties and relations of sentences, especially for the purpose of formal deduction. The simplest procedure for the construction of a calculus consists in laying down some sentences as primitive sentences (sometimes called postulates or axioms) and some rules of inference. The primitive sentences and rules of inference are used for two purposes, for the construction of proofs and of derivations. We shall call the sentences to which the proofs lead *C-true* sentences (they are often called provable or proved sentences or theorems of the calculus). A derivation leads from any not necessarily C-true sentences, called the premisses, to a sentence, called the conclusion. We shall call the conclusion a *C-implicate* of the class of premisses (it is sometimes called derivable or derived or [formally] deducible or deduced from the premisses or a [formal] consequence of the premisses). A calculus may (but usually does not) also contain rules which determine certain sentences as *C-false*. If the rules of a calculus determine some sentence as both C-true and C-false, the calculus is called *inconsistent;* otherwise *consistent*. (If, as is usually done, no rules for 'C-false' are given, the calculus cannot be inconsistent.) In order to explain this procedure, we shall construct the calculus B-C as an example.

Logical syntax has chiefly grown out of two roots, one being formal logic, founded by Aristotle, the other the axiomatic method, initiated by Euclid. The general idea of operations with calculi goes back to Leibniz; since the middle of the last century it has been developed in the systems of symbolic logic into a comprehensive discipline. Among the founders of symbolic logic, or logistic, Boole (1854) is especially to be mentioned. More comprehensive systems (including the higher functional calculus [see § 14]) were created by Schroeder (1890), Frege (1893), Peano (1895), and Whitehead and Russell (1910). Frege was the first to formulate explicitly and to fulfil strictly the requirement of formality, i.e., of a formulation of rules of logic without any reference to designata. Hilbert considerably developed the axiomatic method, in its application both to geometry (see § 21) and to classical mathematics (see §§ 18 and 20).

9. The Calculus B-C

While the sentences of a semantical system are interpreted, assert something, and therefore are either true or false, within a calculus the sentences are looked at from a purely formal point of view. In order to emphasize this distinction, we sometimes call sentences as elements of a semantical system *propositions* and as elements of a calculus *formulas*.

We constructed earlier a semantical system B-S on the basis of the language B, but not, as we have seen, uniquely determined by B. Analogously, we shall now construct a calculus B-C on the basis of B. As preliminary steps for the construction of the syntactical rules proper, which we shall then call rules of transformation, we have to make a *classification* of the signs of B-C and to lay down *syntactical rules of formation* F_C 1–4. But they correspond exactly to the classification and the rules of formation F 1–4 of B-S (§ 5); these rules were already formal. Therefore we shall not write them down again.

Calculus B-C. Rules of Transformation:

PS. A sentence of B-C is called a *primitive sentence* of B-C, if it has one of the following forms, PS 1–4:

PS 1. 'wenn . . . , so [wenn nicht . . . , so - - -]'.

PS 2. 'wenn [wenn nicht . . . , so . . .], so . . .'.

PS 3. 'wenn [wenn . . . , so - - -], so [wenn [wenn - - -, so . - . -], so [wenn . . . , so . - . -]]'.

PS 4. 'wenn [fuer jedes . . , - . . -], so - . - . -'; here '. .' is a variable, '- . - . -' is a sentence which does not contain 'fuer jedes' but contains a name '. - .' one or several times, and '- . . -' is an expression constructed out of '- . - . -' by replacing '. - .' at one or several (not necessarily all) places by the variable '. .'. (Examples: [1] 'wenn [fuer jedes x, x ist rot], so mond ist rot'; [2] see sentence (3) in the first example of a derivation, at the end of this section.)

R. Rules of Inference: The relation of direct derivability holds if and only if one of the following conditions is fulfilled.

R 1. Rule of Implication: From 'wenn . . . , so - - -' and '. . .', '- - -' is directly derivable in B-C.

R 2. Rule of Synonymity: The words 'titisee' and 'rumber' may be exchanged at any place (i.e., if S_2 is constructed out of S_1 by replacing one of those words at one place by the other one, then S_2 is directly derivable from S_1 in B-C).

A *proof* in B-C is a sequence of sentences of B-C such that each of them is either a primitive sentence or directly derivable from one or two sentences preceding it in the sequence. A sentence S_1 of B-C is called *provable* in B-C if it is the last sentence of a proof in B-C. A sentence of B-C is called *C-true* in B-C if and only if it is provable in B-C; a sentence '. . .' is called *C-false* in B-C if and only if 'nicht . . .' is provable in B-C. (For B-C, provability and C-truth coincide, and likewise derivability and C-implication; for other calculi, this is in general not the case, as we shall see.)

A *derivation* in B-C with a class C_1 of premises is a sequence of sentences of B-C such that each of them is either a sentence of C_1 or a primitive sentence or directly derivable from one or two sentences preceding it in the sequence. The last sentence of a derivation is called its *conclusion*. S_2 is called *derivable* from C_1 and also a *C-implicate* of C_1 if it is the conclusion of a derivation with the class of premises C_1.

Both the rules of formation and the rules of transformation of B-C do not in any way refer to designata; they are strictly formal. Nevertheless, they have been chosen with regard to B-S in such a way that the extension of the terms 'C-true', 'C-false', and 'C-implicate' in B-C coincides with that of 'L-true', 'L-false', and 'L-implicate', respectively, in B-S. There are an infinite number of other possible choices of primitive sentences and rules of inference which would lead to the same result. This result gives the practical justification for our choice of the rules of B-C. A calculus in itself needs no justification; this point will be discussed later.

The calculus B-C corresponds to a restricted form of the so-called lower functional calculus, as constructed by Hilbert and Bernays. PS 1–3 and R 1 correspond to the so-called sentential calculus. That the lower functional calculus is complete, i.e., that it exhausts the extension of L-truth and L-implication, has been shown by Gödel.

Example of a proof in B-C. If in the following sequence the blank '. . .' is always replaced by the same sentence, e.g., 'titisee ist blau', the sequence fulfils the conditions—as shown by the remarks on the left side—and therefore is a proof. Hence any sentence of the form 'wenn . . ., so . . .' is provable and C-true in B-C, e.g., 'wenn titisee ist blau, so titisee ist blau'.

PS 1   wenn . . ., so [wenn nicht . . ., so . . .]   (1)
PS 2   wenn [wenn nicht . . ., so . . .], so . . .   (2)
PS 3   wenn [wenn . . ., so [wenn nicht . . ., so . . .]],
          so [wenn [wenn [wenn nicht . . ., so . . .], so . . .],
          so [wenn . . ., so . . .]]   (3)
(here, 'wenn nicht . . ., so . . .' has been taken for '- - -', and
'. . .' for '. - .-')
(1)(3) R 1   wenn [wenn [wenn nicht . . ., so . . .], so . . .],
                so [wenn . . ., so . . .]   (4)
(2)(4) R 1   wenn . . ., so . . .   (5)

First example of a derivation in B-C:

Premisses {titisee ist blau   (1)
            {fuer jedes x, [wenn x ist blau, so x ist kalt]   (2)
PS 4   wenn [fuer jedes x, [wenn x ist blau, so x
            ist kalt]], so [wenn titisee ist blau, so
            titisee ist kalt]   (3)
(2)(3) R 1 wenn titisee ist blau, so titisee ist kalt   (4)
(1)(4) R 1 *Conclusion:* titisee ist kalt   (5)

If we interpret these sentences as in B-S, (1) says that a certain object is blue, (2) says that all blue things are cold (see example [2] at the end of § 5), (5) says that that object is cold. Here, however, the conclusion is derived from the premisses in a formal way, i.e., without making use of an interpretation.

Second example of a derivation in B-C:

Premisses {wenn mond ist blau, so mond ist kalt   (1)
            {nicht mond ist kalt   (2)
Provable: wenn [wenn mond ist blau, so mond ist kalt], so
             [wenn nicht mond ist kalt, so nicht mond ist blau]   (3)

(1)(3) R 1 wenn nicht mond ist k. lt, so nicht mond ist blau (4)

(2)(4) R 1 *Conclusion:* nicht mona ist blau (5)

(3) is a provable sentence. To save space, we do not give its proof here. Suppose that the proof of (3) has been constructed earlier, then the example shows how its result can be used in a deriva on. According to the definitions previously given for 'proof' and 'derivation' any proof may also occur as a part of a derivation. If this happens, we can abbreviate the derivation; we write in the derivation not all the sentences of the proof, whose last sentence we intend to use, but only this one sentence, as we have done in the example given with sentence (3). In this way a sentence which has been proved once can be used in derivations again and again. Later, in the discussion of the application of calculi in empirical science we shall come back to this application of proved sentences in derivations (§ 19).

II. Calculus and Interpretation

10. Calculus and Semantical System

We shall investigate the relations which may hold between a calculus and a semantical system. Sometimes we shall use as examples the calculus B-C and the semantical system B-S as discussed before. Suppose a calculus is given—it may be designated by 'Z-C' or briefly 'C'—and a semantical system—designated by 'Z-S' or 'S'. We call S an *interpretation* of C if the rules of S determine truth criteria for all sentences of C; in other words, if to every formula of C there is a corresponding proposition of S; the converse is not required.

Suppose S fulfils the following condition: for any T_1, T_2, T_3, and T_4, if T_2 is a C-implicate of T_1 in C, T_2 is an implicate of T_1 in S; if T_3 is C-true in C, it is true in S; if T_4 is C-false in C, it is false in S. If an interpretation S of C fulfils the condition stated, we call it a *true interpretation* of C; otherwise a *false interpretation*. If the semantical rules suffice to show that S is a true interpretation of C, then we call S an *L-true interpretation* of C. In this case C-implication becomes L-implication; every C-true sentence becomes L-true, and every C-false sentence becomes L-false. If, on the other hand, these semantical rules suffice to show that S is a false interpretation, we call S an *L-false interpretation*. If S is an interpretation but neither an

L-true nor an L-false interpretation of C, we call S a *factual interpretation* of C. In this case, in order to find out whether the interpretation is true, we have to find out whether some factual sentences are true; for this task we have to carry out empirical investigations about facts. An interpretation S of C is called a *logical interpretation* if all sentences of C become logical sentences of S (i.e., sentences containing logical signs only), otherwise a *descriptive interpretation*. A logical interpretation is always L-determinate. Applying these definitions to the system of our former example: B-S is a true and, moreover, L-true, and descriptive interpretation of B-C.

The class of the sentences which are C-true in C is, interpreted by S, a class of assertions; we call it the *theory correlated* to C by S. If the interpretation is true, L-true or logical, respectively, the correlated theory is likewise true, L-true or logical, respectively; the converse does not hold generally.

Previously we had a semantical system B-S and then constructed a calculus B-C "in accordance with" B-S. What was meant by this can now be formulated: we intended to construct B-C in such a way that B-S is a true interpretation of B-C. It is easy to see that for any given semantical system S it is possible to construct a calculus C of that kind. All we have to do is to select partial domains, as small as we wish, of the extensions of 'implicate in S', 'true in S', and 'false in S' (usually the null class), and then lay down formal definitions of 'C-implicate', 'C-true', and possibly 'C-false', in such a way that their extensions correspond to these partial domains. On the other hand, it is an important problem whether it is possible to construct for a given system S a calculus C such that C is not only in accordance with S, in the sense explained, but that the extensions of 'C-implicate', 'C-true', and (if defined at all) 'C-false' coincide with those of 'L-implicate', 'L-true', and possibly 'L-false,' respectively. If this is the case, we call C an *L-exhaustive calculus* with respect to S. Thus B-C is L-exhaustive with respect to B-S. (We do not define a term for the case that the extensions of 'C-implicate', 'C-true', and 'C-false' coincide with those of 'implicate', 'true', and 'false' because that would be impossible for any somewhat richer language system, e.g., for any language system of a branch of science.)

In order to answer the question of the possibility of an L-exhaustive calculus, we have to distinguish two fundamentally different kinds of rules of transformation, which we call finite and transfinite rules. By *finite rules* we understand those of the customary kind: primitive sentences and rules of inference each of which refers to a finite number of premisses (in most cases one or two). Almost all rules used by logicians up to the present time are finite. Finite rules are applied in the construction of proofs and derivations of the usual kind, which are finite sequences of sentences, as we have seen in the examples in B-C. A rule of transformation is called *transfinite* if it refers to an infinite number of premisses. Because of this number being infinite, a transfinite rule cannot be used within a proof or derivation; a procedure of deduction of an entirely new kind is necessary. We call a calculus finite if all its rules of transformation are finite, otherwise transfinite. It may be remarked that some logicians reject transfinite rules.

We shall make the following terminological distinction: the terms 'C-implicate' and 'C-true' are applied generally with respect both to finite and to transfinite calculi. On the other hand, we shall restrict the corresponding terms 'derivable' and 'provable' to finite calculi. Thus we call T_2 a C-implicate of T_1 in C, if it is possible to obtain T_2 from the premisses T_1 by a procedure of deduction of any kind in C; and we call T_3 C-true if it is possible to obtain T_3 by a procedure of deduction without premisses. If C is a finite calculus— as, e.g., B-C—the deduction takes the form of a finite sequence of sentences, either a derivation or a proof. In this case T_2 is called, moreover, derivable from T_1, and T_3 is called, moreover, provable.

Now we come back to the problem whether it is possible to construct for a given semantical system S an L-exhaustive calculus C. The answer can now be formulated (but not proved here). The answer depends upon the degree of complexity of S; more precisely, it depends upon whether there are in S a sentence S_2 and an infinite class of sentences C_1 such that S_2 is an L-implicate of C_1 but not an L-implicate of any finite subclass of C_1. (Example. S contains a name for every object of an infinite domain: 'a_1', 'a_2', 'a_3', etc. 'P' is a descriptive predicate. C_1 is the [infinite] class of all sentences of the form '. . . is a P' where '. . .' is one of the object names. S_2 is the sentence 'for every x, x is a P'.) If this is not the case, then there is a finite L-exhaustive calculus C. If, however, it is the case, an L-exhaustive calculus C can be constructed if and only if transfinite rules are admitted. For, because C_1 is infinite, S_2 cannot be derivable from C_1. If we decide in a given case to admit transfinite rules, we have to accept the complications and methodological difficulties connected with them. It was first shown by Gödel that a calculus of the ordinary kind (in our terminology, a finite calculus) cannot be constructed for the whole of arithmetic.

11. On the Construction of a Language System

We found earlier that the pragmatical description of a language gives some suggestions for the construction of a corresponding semantical system without, however, determining it. Therefore, there is a certain amount of freedom for the selection and formulation of the semantical rules. Again, if a semantical system S is given and a calculus C is to be constructed in accordance with S, we are bound in some respects and free in others. The rules of formation of C are given by S. And in the construction of the rules of transformation we are restricted by the condition that C must be such that S is a true interpretation of C, as discussed before. But this still leaves some range of choice. We may, for instance, decide that the class of C-true sentences is to be only a proper subclass of the class of L-true sentences, or that it is to coincide with that class (as we did in constructing B-C), or that it is to go beyond that class and comprehend some factual sentences, e.g., some physical laws. When the extensions of 'C-true' and 'C-implicate' are decided, there is still some possibility of choice in the construction of the rules, e.g., primitive sentences and rules of inference, leading to those extensions. This choice, however, is not of essential importance, as it concerns more the form of presentation than the result.

If we are concerned with a historically given language, the pragmatical description comes first, and then we may go by abstraction to semantics and (either from semantics or immediately from pragmatics) to syntax. The situation is quite different if we wish to construct a language (or rather a language system, because we lay down rules), perhaps with the intention of practical application, as for making communications or formulating a scientific theory. Here we are not bound by a previous use of language, but are free to construct in accordance with our wishes and purposes. The construction of a language system Z may consist in laying down two kinds of rules, the semantical rules (Z-S or briefly S) and the syntactical rules (calculus Z-C or C). As a common basis for both, according to our former discussion, we have to make a classification of the signs which we intend to use and lay down rules of formation Z-F. Z-S consists of two parts, rules for the descriptive signs (Z-SD or SD) and rules for the logical signs (Z-SL or SL).

In constructing the system Z, we can proceed in two different ways—different as to the order of S and C. Here the order is not unessential, for, if we have chosen some rules arbitrarily, we are no longer free in the choice of others.

The first method consists in first constructing S and then constructing C. We start with a classification of the kinds of signs which we want, and rules F determining the forms of sentences which we intend to use. Then we lay down the rules SD; we choose objects, properties, etc., for which we wish to have direct designations, and then signs to designate these objects, properties, etc. Next we construct the rules SL; we choose signs to be used as logical signs and state for each of them the conditions of the truth of the sentences constructed with its help. (As mentioned before, we may also proceed by indicating the translations of the sentences containing logical signs, or giving their designata.) After this we proceed to syntax and construct the calculus C, e.g., by stating primitive sentences and rules of inference. It has been explained already that, if S is given or constructed, we are limited in constructing C in some essential respects, because C must be such that S is a true interpretation of C; but we are free in other respects.

The *second method* for constructing Z is first to construct C and then S. We begin again with a classification of signs and a system F of syntactical rules of formation, defining 'sentence in C' in a formal way. Then we set up the system C of syntactical rules of transformation, in other words, a formal definition of 'C-true' and 'C-implicate'. Since so far nothing has been determined concerning the single signs, we may choose these definitions, i.e., the rules of formation and of transformation, in any way we wish. With respect to a calculus to be constructed there is only a question of expedience or fitness to purposes chosen, but not of correctness. This will be discussed later.

Then we add to the uninterpreted calculus C an interpretation S. Its function is to determine truth conditions for the sentences of C and thereby to change them from formulas to propositions. We proceed in the following way. It is already determined by the rules F which expressions are formulas in C. Now we have to stipulate that each of them is also a proposition in S. By the syntactical classification of the signs it is not yet completely settled which signs are logical and which descriptive. In many cases there is still a considerable amount of freedom of choice in this respect, as we shall see later in some examples. After having stated which signs are to be logical and which descriptive, we construct the rules SL for the logical signs. Here our choice is restricted to some extent by the requirement that the interpretation must be true.

Finally we establish the rules SD for the descriptive signs. Here we have to take into account the classification of signs. We choose the designata for each kind of signs and then for each sign of that kind. We may begin with individual names. First we choose a field of objects with which we wish to deal in the language to be constructed, e.g., the persons of a certain group, the towns of a certain country, the colors, geometrical structures, or whatever else. Then we determine for each individual name, as its designatum, one object of the class chosen. Then, for each predicate, we choose a possible property of those objects, etc. In this way, a designatum for every descriptive sign is chosen. If we decide to make S an L-true interpretation of C, we have a great amount of freedom for the choice of the rules SD. Otherwise, we find some essential restrictions. If some of the C-true formulas are to become factual propositions, they must be factually true. Therefore, in this case, on the basis of our factual knowledge about the objects which we have chosen as subject matter of Z, we have to take care that the interpretations for the descriptive names, predicates, etc., i.e., their designata, are chosen in such a way that those factual C-true sentences are actually true.

12. Is Logic a Matter of Convention?

There has been much controversial discussion recently on the question whether or not logic is conventional. Are the rules on which logical deduction is based to be chosen at will and, hence, to be judged only with respect to convenience but not to correctness? Or is there a distinction between objectively right and objectively wrong systems so that in constructing a system of rules we are free only in relatively minor respects (as, e.g., the way of formulation) but bound in all essential respects? Obviously, the question discussed refers to the rules of an interpreted language, applicable for purposes of communication; nobody doubts that the rules of a pure calculus, without regard to any interpretation, can be chosen arbitrarily. On the basis of our former discussions we are in a position to answer the question. We found the possibility—which we called the second method—of constructing a language system in such a way that first a calculus C is established and then an interpretation is given by adding a semantical system S. Here we are free in choosing the rules of C. To be sure, the choice is not irrelevant; it depends upon C whether the interpretation can yield a rich language or only a poor one.

We may find that a calculus we have chosen yields a language which is too poor or which in some other respect seems unsuitable for the purpose we have in mind. But there is no question of a calculus being right or wrong, true or false. A true interpretation is possible for any given consistent calculus (and hence for any calculus of the usual kind, not containing rules for 'C-false'), however the rules may be chosen.

On the other hand, those who deny the conventional character of logic, i.e., the possibility of a free choice of the logical rules of deduction, are equally right in what they mean if not in what they say. They are right under a certain condition, which presumably is tacitly assumed. The condition is that the "meanings" of the logical signs are given before the rules of deduction are formulated. They would, for instance, insist that the rule R 1 of B-C ('from 'wenn . . . , so - - -' and '. . .', '- - -' is directly derivable' [§ 9]) is necessary; that it would be wrong to change it arbitrarily, e.g., into R 1*: 'from 'wenn . . ., so - - -' and 'nicht . . .', '- - -' is directly derivable'. What they presumably mean is that the rule R 1* is incorrect on the basis of

169

the presupposed "meaning" of the signs 'wenn', 'so', and 'nicht'. Thus they have in mind the procedure which we called the first method (§ 11): we begin by establishing the semantical rules SL or assume them as given—obviously this is meant by saying that the "meaning" is given—and then we ask what rules of deduction, i.e., syntactical rules of transformation, would be in accordance with the presupposed semantical rules. In this order of procedure, we are, as we have seen, indeed bound in the choice of the rules in all essential respects. Thus we come to a reconciliation of the opposing views. And it seems to me that an agreement should easily be attainable in the other direction as well. The anti-conventionalists would certainly not deny that the rule R 1* can also be chosen and can lead to correct results, provided we interpret the logical signs in a different way (in the example given, we could interpret 'wenn . . . , so - - -', e.g., as '. . . or - - -').

The result of our discussion is the following: logic or the rules of deduction (in our terminology, the syntactical rules of transformation) can be chosen arbitrarily and hence are conventional if they are taken as the basis of the construction of the language system and if the interpretation of the system is later superimposed. On the other hand, a system of logic is not a matter of choice, but either right or wrong, if an interpretation of the logical signs is given in advance. But even here, conventions are of fundamental importance; for the basis on which logic is constructed, namely, the interpretation of the logical signs (e.g., by a determination of truth conditions) can be freely chosen.

It is important to be aware of the conventional components in the construction of a language system. This view leads to an unprejudiced investigation of the various forms of new logical systems which differ more or less from the customary form (e.g., the intuitionist logic constructed by Brouwer and Heyting, the systems of logic of modalities as constructed by Lewis and others, the systems of plurivalued logic as constructed by Lukasiewicz and Tarski, etc.), and it encourages the construction of further new forms. The task is not to decide which of the different systems is "the right logic" but to examine their formal properties and the possibilities for their interpretation and application in science. It might be that a system deviating from the ordinary form will turn out to be useful as a basis for the language of science.

III. Calculi and Their Application in Empirical Science

13. Elementary Logical Calculi

For any given calculus there are, in general, many different possibilities of a true interpretation. The practical situation, however, is such that for almost every calculus which is actually interpreted and applied in science, there is a certain interpretation or a certain kind of interpretation used in the great majority of cases of its practical application. This we will call the *customary interpretation* (or kind of interpretation) for the calculus. In what follows we shall discuss some calculi and their application. We classify them according to their customary interpretation in this way: logical calculi (in the narrower sense), mathematical, geometrical, and (other) physical calculi. The customary interpretation of the logical and mathematical calculi is a logical, L-determinate interpretation; that of the geometrical and physical calculi is descriptive and factual. The mathematical calculi are a special kind of logical calculi, distinguished merely by their greater complexity. The geometrical calculi are a special kind of physical calculi. This classification is rather rough and is only meant to serve a temporary, practical purpose.

To the logical calculi (in the narrower sense) belong most of the calculi of elementary structure used in symbolic logic, above all, the so-called sentential calculus and the so-called lower functional calculus. The *sentential calculus* has approximately the structure of B-C with F 4 and PS 4 omitted. The customary interpretation corresponds to the rules B-SL 2, 3. The form mostly used contains, however, only those signs which are logical in the customary interpretation, corresponding to the English words 'not', 'if', 'or', 'and', and the like, and sentential variables. The *lower functional calculus* (or predicate calculus) contains the sentential calculus and, in addition, general sentences with individual variables, namely, universal sentences (interpretation: 'for every x, ... ') and existential sentences (interpretation: 'there is an x such that ... '). Within symbolic logic, this calculus too is mostly used without descriptive signs but with three kinds of variables: sentential variables, individual variables (as in B-C), and predicate variables. The customary interpretation is a logical one, as given by B-SL. In the case of the logical calculi here explained the customary interpretation is the only one which is ever used practically. (If the calculi are supplemented in a certain way, it is even the only possible true interpretation.) Therefore, we shall call it the *normal interpretation* of the logical calculus.

If a calculus C is constructed with the intention of using it mostly or exclusively with a certain interpretation S, it may often seem convenient to use as signs of C not artificial symbols but those words of the word-language whose ordinary use is approximately in acccord with the interpretation intended (a word with exact accordance will usually not be available). Then we have in C the same sentences as in the interpreted language S, which is perhaps to be applied in science; "the same sentences" as to the wording, but in C they are formulas, while they are propositions in S. This procedure is mostly chosen in geometrical and other physical calculi (for examples see end of § 17, beginning of § 22).

In what follows we shall do the same for the logical calculus (where, for good reasons, it is usually not done). Thus, instead of symbols, we shall use the words 'not', 'if', etc. It has been shown (by H. M. Sheffer) that two primitive signs are sufficient, namely, 'excludes' (to be interpreted later) and 'for every'. It is not necessary to take as many primitive signs as we did in B-C, corresponding to 'not', 'if—then', 'for every'. The other logical signs of the logical calculus can be introduced by definitions. The primitive signs mentioned and all signs defined with their help are called logical constants. We shall use three kinds of variables: sentential variables ('p', 'q', etc.), individual variables ('x', 'y', etc., as in B-C), and predicate variables ('F',

'*G*', etc.). For a sentential variable a sentence may be substituted, for an individual variable an individual name, for a predicate variable a predicate, and for '*Fx*' an expression of sentential form containing the variable '*x*'.

A *definition* is a rule of a calculus which serves for introducing a new sign. In simpler cases the rule states that the new sign is to be taken as an abbreviation for a certain expression consisting only of old signs (i.e., primitive signs or signs defined earlier). In other cases the rule states that sentences containing the new sign and old signs are to be taken as abbreviations for certain sentences containing old signs only. Rules of the first kind are called explicit definitions (e.g., Defs. 11, 12, and 13 in § 14); those of the second kind are called definitions in use (e.g., Defs. 1–7, below); we shall use still another kind of definition, the so-called recursive definitions frequently found in arithmetic (e.g., Defs. 14 and 15 in § 14). The definitions in a calculus are, so to speak, additional rules of transformation, either primitive sentences or rules of inference, according to their formulation; they are added in order to provide shorter expressions. If a calculus C contains definitions and the interpretation S contains semantical rules for the primitive signs of C, the interpretation of the defined signs need not be given explicitly. The definitions, together with those rules of S, determine the truth conditions of the sentences containing the defined signs and thereby the interpretation of these signs.

We shall formulate the definitions here in this form: ' '...' for '- - -' '. This means that '...' is to serve as an abbreviation for '- - -', i.e., that '...' and '- - -', and likewise two expressions constructed out of '...' and '- - -' by the same substitutions, may always be replaced by each other. In this calculus, we take as simplest form of sentences in the beginning '*Fx*' (e.g., 'city Chicago' instead of 'Chicago is a city'); the usual form with 'is a' is introduced later by Definition 7.

The expressions included in parentheses serve merely to facilitate understanding; in the exact formulation they have to be omitted. The brackets and commas, however, are essential; they indicate the structure of the sentence (cf. § 5).

173

Def. 1. 'not *p*' for '*p* excludes *p*'.
Def. 2. '*p* or *q*' for 'not *p*, excludes, not *q*'.
Def. 3. '*p* and *q*' for 'not [*p* excludes *q*]'.
Def. 4. 'if *p* then *q*' for 'not *p*, or *q*'.
Def. 5. '*p* if and only if *q*' for '[if *p* then *q*] and [if *q* then *p*]'.
Def. 6. 'for some *x*, *Fx*' for 'not [for every *x*, not *Fx*]'.
Def. 7. '*x* is an *F*' for '*Fx*'.

The rules of transformation of the sentential calculus and the functional calculus will not be given here. They are not essentially different from those of B-C. It has been shown (by J. Nicod) that, if 'excludes' is taken as primitive sign, one primitive sentence is sufficient for the sentential calculus. For the lower functional calculus we have to add one more primitive sentence for 'for every', analogous to PS 4 in B-C.

The *normal interpretation* for the logical calculus is a logical one. Therefore, if interpreted, it is, so to speak, a skeleton of a language rather than a language proper, i.e., one capable of describing facts. It becomes a factual language only if supplemented by descriptive signs. These are then interpreted by SD-rules, and the logical constants by SL-rules. As SL-rules for the lower functional calculus we can state the following two rules for the two primitive signs. For the sentential calculus the first rule suffices.

1. A sentence of the form '. . . excludes - - -' is true if and only if not both '. . .' and '- - -' are true.
2. A sentence of the form 'for every . . . , - - -' is true if and only if all individuals have the property designated by '- - -' with respect to the variable '. . .'. (The individuals are the objects of the domain described, which is to be determined by an SD-rule.)

The interpretation of the defined signs 'not', etc., is determined by rule (1) and Definition 1, etc. The interpretation of 'not' and 'if—then' is easily seen to be the same as that of 'nicht', and 'wenn—so' in B-SL. (The truth conditions here given by rule [1] and Definitions 1–5 are the same as those which in symbolic logic usually are stated with the help of truth-value tables for the corresponding symbols, the so-called connectives.)

14. Higher Logical Calculi

The lower functional calculus can be enlarged to the higher functional calculus by the addition of predicates of higher levels. The predicates occurring in the lower functional calculus are now called predicates of first level; they designate properties of first level, i.e., properties of individuals. Now we introduce predicates of second level, which designate properties of second level, i.e., properties of properties of first level; predicates of third level designating properties of third level, etc. Further, new kinds of variables for these predicates of higher levels are introduced. (In the subsequent definitions we shall use as variables for predicates of second level '*m*' and '*n*', for predicates of third level '*K*'.) Expressions of the form 'for every . . .', and analogously 'for some . . .' (Def. 6), are now admitted not only for individual variables but also for predicate variables of any level. Some new rules of transformation for these new kinds of variables have to be added. We shall not give them here. Some of them are still controversial.

The *normal interpretation* of the higher functional calculus can again be given by two semantical rules. Rule (1) is kept, as the sentential calculus remains the basis for the higher functional calculus. Rule (2) must be replaced by the subsequent rule (2*), because of the extended use of 'for every'. For individual variables, (2*) is in accordance with (2). (It may be remarked that there are some controversies and unsolved problems concerning the properties of higher levels.)

2*. A sentence of the form 'for every . . . , - - -' is true if and only if all entities belonging to the range of the variable '. . .' have the property designated by '- - -' with respect to '. . .'. (To the range of an individual variable belong all individuals, to the range of a predicate variable of level r belong all properties of level r.)

To the definitions which we stated in the lower functional calculus, new ones can now be added which make use of predicates and variables of higher levels. We shall first give some rough explanations of the new expressions and later the definitions. First, identity can be defined; '$x=y$' is to say that x is the same object as y; this is defined by 'x and y have all properties in common' (Def. 8). Then we shall define the concept of a cardinal number of a property, restricting ourselves, for the sake of simplicity, to finite cardinal numbers. 'F is an m' is to say that the property F has the cardinal number m; i.e., that there are m objects with the property F. This concept is defined by a recursive definition (for finite cardinals only). 'F is a 0' is defined as saying that no object has the property F (Def. 9a). Then 'F is an m^+', where 'm^+' designates the next cardinal number greater than m, i.e., $m+1$, is defined in the following way in terms of 'm': there is a property G with the cardinal number m such that all objects which have the property G, and, in addition, some object x, but no other objects, have the property F (Def. 9b). A property K of numbers is called hereditary if, whenever a number m is a K, $m+1$ is also a K. Then 'm is a finite cardinal number' can be defined (as Frege has shown) in this way: m has all hereditary properties of 0 (Def. 10). The numerals '1', '2', etc., can easily be defined by '0^+', '1^+', etc. (Def. 11, etc.). The sum ('$m+n$') and the product ('$m \times n$') can be defined by recursive definitions, as is customary in arithmetic (Defs. 14 and 15).

Def. 8.   '$x=y$' for 'for every (property) F, if x is an F then y is an F'.
Analogously for any higher level.

Def. 9a. 'F is a 0' for 'not [for some x, x is an F]'.

  b. 'F is an m^+' for 'for some G, for some x, for every y [[y is an F if and only if [y is a G or $y=x$]] and G is an m and, not x is a G].

Def. 10.   'm is a finite cardinal number' for 'for every (property of numbers) K, if [0 is a K and, for every n [if n is a K then n^+ is a K]] then m is a K'.

Def. 11.   '1' for '0^+'.

Def. 12.   '2' for '1^+'.

Def. 13.   '3' for '2^+'.
Analogously for any further numeral.

Def. 14a. '$m+0$' for 'm'.

  b. '$m+n^+$' for '$[m+n]^+$'.

Def. 15a. '$m \times 0$' for '0'.

  b. '$m \times n^+$' for '$[m \times n]+m$'.

For the reasons mentioned before we have used, instead of arbitrary symbols, words whose ordinary use agrees approximately with the interpretation intended. It is, however, to be noticed that their exact interpretation in our language system is not to be derived from their ordinary use but from their definition in connection with the semantical rules (1) and (2*).

We see that it is possible to define within the logical calculus signs for numbers and arithmetical operations. It can further be shown that all theorems of ordinary arithmetic are provable in this calculus, if suitable rules of transformation are established.

The method of constructing a calculus of arithmetic within a logical calculus was first found by Frege (1884) and was then developed by Russell (1903) and Whitehead (1910). (Defs. 9–15 are, in their essential features, in accordance with Frege and Russell, but make use of some simplifications due to the recent development of symbolic logic.) We shall later outline another form of an arithmetical calculus (§ 17) and discuss the problem of mathematics more in detail (§ 20).

15. Application of Logical Calculi

The chief function of a logical calculus in its application to science is not to furnish logical theorems, i.e., L-true sentences, but to guide the deduction of factual conclusions from factual premisses. (In most presentations of logical systems the first point, the proofs, is overemphasized; the second, the derivations, neglected.)

For the following discussions we may make a rough distinction between *singular* and *universal* sentences among factual sentences. By a singular sentence of the language of science or of an interpreted calculus we mean a sentence concerning one or several things (or events or space-time-points), describing, e.g., a property of a thing or a relation between several things. By a universal sentence we mean a sentence concerning all objects of the field in question, e.g., all things or all space-time-points. A report about a certain event or a description of a certain landscape consists of singular sentences; on the other hand, the so-called laws of nature in any field (physics, biology, psychology, etc.) are universal. The simplest kind of an application of the logical calculus to factual sentences is the derivation of a singular sentence from other singular sentences (see, e.g., the second example of a derivation in B-C, end of § 9). Of greater practical importance is the deduction of a singular sentence from premisses which include both singular and universal sentences. We are involved in this kind of a deduction if we explain a known fact or if we predict an unknown fact. The form of the deduction is the same for these two cases. We have had this form in the first example of a derivation in B-C (§ 9); we find it again in the following example, which contains, besides signs of the logical calculus, some descriptive signs. In an application of the logical calculus, some descriptive signs have to be introduced as primitive; others may then be defined on their basis. SD-rules must then be laid down in order to establish the interpretation intended by the scientist. Premiss (3) is the law of thermic expansion in qualitative formulation. In later examples we shall apply the same law in quantitative formulation (D_1 in § 19; D_2 in § 23).

Premisses:
$\begin{cases} \text{1. } c \text{ is an iron rod.} \\ \text{2. } c \text{ is now heated.} \\ \text{3. for every } x, \text{ if } x \text{ is an iron rod and } x \text{ is heated, } x \text{ expands.} \end{cases}$

Conclusion: 4. c now expands.

A deduction of this form can occur in two practically quite different kinds of situations. In the first case we may have found (4) by observation and ask the physicist to explain the fact observed. He gives the *explanation* by referring to other facts (1) and (2) and a law (3). In the second case we may have found by observation the facts (1) and (2) but not (4). Here the deduction with the help of the law (3) supplies the prediction (4), which may then be tested by further observations.

The example given shows only a very short deduction, still more abbreviated by the omission of the intermediate steps between premisses and conclusion. But a less trivial deduction consisting of many steps of inference has fundamentally the same nature. In practice a deduction in science is usually made by a few jumps instead of many steps. It would, of course, be practically impossible to give each deduction which occurs the form of a complete derivation in the logical calculus, i.e., to dissolve it into single steps of such a kind that each step is the application of one of the rules of transformation of the calculus, including the definitions. An ordinary reasoning of a few seconds would then take days. But it is essential that this dissolution is theoretically possible and practically possible for any small part of the process. Any critical point can thus be put under the logical microscope and enlarged to the degree desired. In consequence of this, a scientific controversy can be split up into two fundamentally different components, a factual and a logical (including here the mathematical). With respect to the logical component the opponents can come to an agreement only by first agreeing upon the rules of the logical calculus to be applied and the L-semantical rules for its interpretation, and by then applying these rules, disregarding the interpretation of the descriptive signs. The discussion, of course, need not concern the whole calculus; it will be sufficient to expand the critical part of the controversial deduction to the degree required by the situation. The critical point will usually not be within the elementary part of the logical calculus (to which all examples of derivations discussed above belong), but to a more complex calculus, e.g., the higher, mathematical part of the logical calculus, or a specific mathematical calculus, or a physical calculus. This will be discussed later; then the advantage of the formal procedure will become more manifest.

16. General Remarks about Nonlogical Calculi (Axiom Systems)

In later sections we shall discuss certain other calculi which are applied in science. The logical calculus explained previously is distinguished from them by the fact that it serves as their basis. Each of the nonlogical calculi to be explained later consists, strictly speaking, of two parts: a logical *basic calculus* and a *specific calculus* added to it. The basic calculus could be approximately the same for all those calculi; it could consist of the sentential calculus and a smaller or greater part of the functional calculus as previously outlined. The specific partial calculus does not usually contain additional rules of inference but only additional primitive sentences, called *axioms*. As the basic calculus is essentially the same for all the different specific calculi, it is customary not to mention it at all but to describe only the specific part of the calculus. What usually is called an *axiom system* is thus the second part of a calculus whose character as a part is usually not noticed. For any of the mathematical and physical axiom systems in their ordinary form it is necessary to add a logical basic calculus. Without its help it would not be possible to prove any theorem of the system or to carry out any deduction by use of the system. Not only is a basic logical calculus tacitly presupposed in the customary formulation of an axiom system but so also is a special interpretation of the logical calculus, namely, that which we called the normal interpretation. An axiom system contains, besides the logical constants, other constants which we may call its specific or axiomatic constants. Some of them are taken as primitive; others may be defined. The definitions lead back to the primitive specific signs and logical signs. An interpretation of an axiom system is given by semantical rules for some of the specific signs, since for the logical signs the normal interpretation is presupposed. If semantical rules for the primitive specific signs are given, the interpretation of the defined specific signs is indirectly determined by these rules together with the definitions. But it is also possible—and sometimes convenient, as we shall see—to give the interpretation by laying down semantical rules for another suitable selection of specific signs, not including the primitive signs. If all specific signs are interpreted as logical signs, the interpretation is a logical and L-determinate one; otherwise it is a descriptive one. (Every logical interpretation is L-determinate; the converse does not always hold.)

17. An Elementary Mathematical Calculus

We take here as mathematical calculi those whose customary interpretation is mathematical, i.e., in terms of numbers and functions of numbers. As an example, we shall give the classical axiom system of Peano for (elementary) arithmetic. It is usually called an axiom system of arithmetic because in its customary interpretation it is interpreted as a theory of natural numbers, as we shall see. This interpretation is, however, by no means the only important one. The logical basic calculus presupposed has to include the lower functional calculus and some part of the higher, up to expressions 'for every F' for predicate variables of first level and Definition 8 for '$=$' (§ 14). The specific primitive signs are 'b', 'N', '$'$'. (The following axioms, of course, are, within the calculus, independent of any interpretation. Nevertheless, the reader who is not familiar with them will find it easier to conceive their form and function by looking at their interpretation given below.)

Axiom System of Peano:

P 1. b is an N.

P 2. For every x, if x is an N, then x' is an N.

P 3. For every x, y, if [x is an N and y is an N and $x'=y'$] then $x=y$.

P 4. For every x, if x is an N, then, not $b=x'$.

P 5. For every F, if [b is an F and, for every x [if x is an F then x' is an F]] then [for every y, if y is an N then y is an F].

   (Briefly: if F is any property of b which is hereditary [from x to x'] then all N are F.)

It is easy to see that any number of true *interpretations* of this calculus can be constructed. We have only to choose any infinite class, to select one of its elements as the beginning member of a sequence and to state a rule determining for any given member of the sequence its immediate successor. (An order of elements of this kind is called a progression.) Then we interpret in this way: 'b' designates the beginning member of the sequence; if '$\ldots$' designates a member of the sequence then '$\ldots'$' designates its immediate successor; 'N' designates the class of all members of the sequence that can be reached from the beginning member in a finite number of steps. It can easily be shown that in any interpretation of this kind the five axioms become true.

   Example: 'b' designates August 14, 1938; if '$\ldots$' designates a day, '$\ldots'$' designates the following day; 'N' designates the class (supposed to be infinite) of all days from August 14, 1938, on. This interpretation of the Peano system is descriptive, while the customary one is logical.

The *customary interpretation* of the Peano system may first be formulated in this way: 'b' designates the cardinal number 0; if '. . .' designates a cardinal number n, then '. . .' ' designates the next one, i.e., $n+1$; 'N' designates the class of finite cardinal numbers. Hence in this interpretation the system concerns the progression of finite cardinal numbers, ordered according to magnitude. Against the given semantical rule ' 'b' designates the cardinal number 0' perhaps the objection will be raised that the cardinal number 0 is not an object to which we could point, as to my desk. This remark is right; but it does not follow that the rule is incorrect. We shall give the interpretation in another way, with the help of a translation.

In the investigation of calculi the procedure of *translation* of one calculus into another is of great importance. A system of rules of translation of the calculus K_2 into the calculus K_1 determines for each primitive sign of K_2 an expression of K_1 called its correlated expression, and for each kind of variable in K_2 its correlated kind of variable in K_1. The rules must be such that the result of translating any sentence in K_2 is always a sentence in K_1. The translation is called C-true if the following three conditions are fulfilled: (1) every C-true sentence in K_2 becomes, if translated, C-true in K_1; (2) every C-false sentence in K_2 becomes C-false in K_1; (3) if the relation of C-implication in K_2 holds among some sentences, then the relation of C-implication in K_1 holds among those into which they are translated. If we have an interpretation I_1 for the calculus K_1, then the translation of K_2 into K_1 determines in connection with I_1 an interpretation I_2 for K_2. I_2 may be called a *secondary interpretation*. If the translation is C-true and the (primary) interpretation I_1 is true, I_2 is also true.

We shall now state rules of translation for the Peano system into the higher functional calculus and thereby give a secondary interpretation for that system. The logical basic calculus is translated into itself; thus we have to state the correlation only for the specific primitive signs. As correlates for 'b', '$'$', 'N', we take '0', '+', 'finite cardinal number'; for any variable a variable two levels higher. Accordingly, the five axioms are translated into the following sentences of the logical calculus.

P′ 1. 0 is a finite cardinal number.

P′ 2. For every m, if m is a finite cardinal number, then m^+ is a finite cardinal number.

P′ 3. For every m, n, if [m is a finite cardinal number and n is a finite cardinal number and $m^+ = n^+$] then $m = n$.

P′ 4. For every m, if m is a finite cardinal number, then, not $0 = m^+$.

P′ 5. For every K, if [0 is a K and, for every m [if m is a K then m^+ is a K]] then [for every n, if n is a finite cardinal number then n is a K].

The *customary interpretation* of the Peano system can now be formulated in another way. This interpretation consists of the given translation together with the normal interpretation of the higher functional calculus up to the third level. (P′ 5 contains a variable of this level.)

The whole interpretation is thus built up in the following way. We have two L-semantical rules for the primitive signs 'excludes' and 'for every' of the logical calculus, indicating truth conditions (rules [1] and [2*] in § 14). Then we have a chain of definitions leading to Definitions 9a and b and 11 for '0', '+', and 'finite cardinal number' (§ 14). Finally we have rules of translation which correlate these defined signs of the logical calculus to the primitive signs 'b', '′', and 'N' of the Peano system.

If we assume that the normal interpretation of the logical calculus is true, the given secondary interpretation for the Peano system is shown to be true by showing that the correlates of the axioms are C-true. And it can indeed be shown that the sentences P′ 1–5 are provable in the higher functional calculus, provided suitable rules of transformation are established. As the normal interpretation of the logical calculus is logical and L-true, the given interpretation of the Peano system is also logical and L-true.

We can now define signs within the Peano axiom system which correspond to the signs '0', '1', etc., '+', etc., of the logical calculus. For greater clarity we distinguish them by the subscript 'P'. (In an arithmetical calculus, however—whether in the form of Peano's or some other—one ordinarily does not use arbitrary symbols like '*b*' or '0_P', '*b*'' or '1_P', '$+_P$', etc., but, because of the customary interpretation, the corresponding signs of the ordinary language '0', '1', '+', etc.)

Def. P 1. '0_P' for '*b*'.

Def. P 2. '1_P' for '*b*''.

Def. P 3. '2_P' for '*b*'''.

  Etc.

Def. P 4a. '$x +_P 0_P$' for '*x*'.

  b. '$x +_P y$'' for '[$x +_P y$]''.

Def. P 5a. '$x \times_P 0_P$' for '0_P'.

  b. '$x \times_P y$'' for '[$x \times_P y$] $+_P x$'.

Thus the natural numbers and functions of them can be defined both in the logical calculus and in a specific arithmetical calculus, e.g., that of Peano. And the theorems of ordinary arithmetic are provable in both calculi. (Strictly speaking, they are not the same theorems in the different calculi, but corresponding theorems; if, however, the same signs are used—and, as mentioned before, this is convenient and usual—then corresponding theorems consist even of the same signs.)

18. Higher Mathematical Calculi

On the basis of a calculus of the arithmetic of natural numbers the whole edifice of classical mathematics can be erected without the use of new primitive signs. Whether a specific calculus of arithmetic or the logical calculus is taken as a basis does not make an essential difference, once the translation of the first into the second is established. It is not possible to outline here the construction of mathematics; we can make only a few remarks. There are many different possibilities for the introduction of further kinds of numbers. A simple method is the following one. The integers (positive and negative) are defined as pairs of natural numbers, the fractions as pairs of integers, the real numbers as classes either of integers or of fractions, the complex numbers as pairs of real numbers. Another way of introducing any one of these kinds of numbers consists in constructing a new specific calculus in which the numbers of that kind are taken as individuals, like the natural numbers in the Peano calculus.

This has been done especially for the real numbers. A specific calculus of this kind can be translated in one way or another into a more elementary specific calculus or into the logical calculus. (Example: The individual expressions of a specific calculus of real numbers may be translated into expressions for classes of integers or of fractions either in the Peano calculus or in the logical calculus.) For each of the kinds of numbers, functions (summation, multiplication, etc.) can be defined. Further, the concept of limit can be defined, and with its help the fundamental concepts of the infinitesimal calculus, the differential coefficient, and the integral.

If a mathematical calculus is based on the Peano calculus by the use of definitions, then its customary interpretation is determined by that of the latter. If, on the other hand, a mathematical calculus is constructed as an independent specific calculus, we can give an interpretation for it by translating it either into an enlarged Peano system or into an enlarged logical calculus (as indicated above for a calculus of real numbers.) Here we can scarcely speak of "the" customary interpretation, but only of the set of customary interpretations. Their forms may differ widely from one another; but they have in common the character of logical interpretations. If the interpretation is given by a translation either into the Peano system with reference to its customary interpretation or by a translation into the logical calculus with reference to its normal interpretation, this character is obvious. In a customary interpretation of a mathematical calculus every sign in it is interpreted as a logical sign, and hence every sentence consists only of logical signs and is therefore L-determinate (see § 7).

If we choose the form of the construction of mathematics within the logical calculus, we do not even need a translation; the interpretation is simply the normal interpretation of the logical calculus. In this case every mathematical sign is defined on the basis of the two primitive signs of the logical calculus, and hence every mathematical sentence is an abbreviation for a sentence containing, besides variables, only those two signs. In most cases, though, this sentence would be so long that it would not be possible to write it down within a lifetime. Therefore, the abbreviations introduced in the construction of mathematics are not only convenient but practically indispensable.

19. Application of Mathematical Calculi

The application of mathematical calculi in empirical science is not essentially different from that of logical calculi. Since mathematical sentences are, in the customary interpretation, L-determinate, they cannot have factual content; they do not convey information about facts which would have to be taken into consideration besides those described in empirical science. The function of mathematics for empirical science consists in providing, first, forms of expression shorter and more efficient than non-mathematical linguistic forms and, second, modes of logical deduction shorter and more efficient than those of elementary logic.

Mathematical calculi with their customary interpretation are distinguished from elementary logical calculi chiefly by the occurrence of numerical expressions. There are two procedures in empirical science which lead to the application of numerical expressions: counting and measurement (cf. Lenzen, Vol. I, No. 5, §§ 4 and 5). Counting is ascertaining the cardinal number of a class of single, separate things or of events. Measuring is ascertaining the value of a magnitude for a certain thing or place at a certain time. For each physical magnitude, e.g., length, weight, temperature, electric field, etc., there are one or several methods of measurement. The result of a measurement is a fraction or a real number. (Irrational real numbers can also occur, but only if, besides direct measurement, calculation is applied.) If a deduction has to do with results of counting, we may apply, besides an elementary logical calculus, a calculus of elementary arithmetic. If it has to do with results of measurements, we may apply a calculus of analysis, i.e., of real numbers.

Let us look at a very simple example of a logico-mathematical deduction. We apply a certain part of the higher functional calculus and an arithmetical calculus. We presuppose for the following derivation that in this arithmetical calculus the sentence

'3+6=9' (7) has been proved earlier. Whether we take the arithmetical calculus in the form of a part of the higher functional calculus (as in § 14) or in the form of a specific calculus (as in § 17) does not make any essential difference; in both cases sentence (7) is provable. In order to keep in closer contact with ordinary language, we use the following definition: 'there are m F's' for 'F is an m'; further, we write 'n.i.t.r.' for 'now in this room'.

<table>
<tr><td rowspan="4">Premisses</td><td>1.</td><td>There are 3 students n.i.t.r.</td></tr>
<tr><td>2.</td><td>There are 6 girls n.i.t.r.</td></tr>
<tr><td>3.</td><td>For every x [x is a person n.i.t.r. if and only if [x is a student n.i.t.r. or x is a girl n.i.t.r.]].</td></tr>
<tr><td>4.</td><td>For every x [if x is a girl n.i.t.r., then, not x is a student n.i.t.r.].</td></tr>
</table>

Defs. 1–9, 14   5. For every F, G, H, m, n [if [m and n are finite cardinal numbers and G is an m and H is an n and for every x [x is an F if and only if, x is a G or x is an H] and for every y [if y is a G then, not y is an H]] then F is an $m+n$].

[This says that, if a class F is divided into two parts, G and H, the cardinal number of F is the sum of the cardinal numbers of G and H.]

(1)(2)(3)(4)(5)   6. There are $3+6$ persons n.i.t.r.

Arithmet. theorem: 7. $3+6=9$.

(6)(7) *Conclusion:*   8. There are 9 persons n.i.t.r.

The premisses of this derivation describe some facts empirically established by observation (including counting). The conclusion is also a factual sentence; but its content, the amount of factual information it conveys, does not go beyond that of the premisses. We have discussed earlier (at the end of § 9) the application of proved theorems in a derivation; here (5) and (7) are examples of this method. These sentences do not contribute to the factual content of the conclusion; they merely help in transforming the premisses into the conclusion. To say that the result (8) is "calculated" from the data (1)–(4), means just this: it is obtained by a formal procedure involving a mathematical calculus. The effect of the application of a mathematical calculus is always, as in this example, the possibility of presenting in a shorter and more easily apprehensible way facts already known.

Here an objection will perhaps be raised. That the application of mathematics consists merely in a transformation of the premises without adding anything to what they say about the facts, may be true in trivial cases like the example given. If, however, we predict, with the help of mathematics, a future event, do we not come to a new factual content? Let us discuss an example of a derivation of this kind. The derivation—called D_1—leads to the prediction of a thermic expansion as in a former example (§ 15), but now with quantitative determinations. The premises of D_1 relate the results of measurements of the temperature of an iron rod at two time-points and its length at the first; further, the law of thermic expansion is one of the premisses, but now in quantitative formulation; and, finally, there is included a statement of the coefficient of thermic expansion. The conclusion states the amount of the expansion of the rod. We shall not represent D_1 here in detail because a similar derivation D_2 will be discussed later (§ 23); the premises of D_1 are not only the sentences (1)–(5) of D_2 but also (6) and (10); the conclusion in D_1 is the same as in D_2. In D_1 a calculus of real numbers (or at least of fractions) is applied. The conclusion describes a fact which has not yet been observed but could be tested by observations. Now, the question is whether the derivation D_1 does not lead, with the help of a mathematical calculus, to a factual content beyond that of the premises. This might seem so if we look only at the singular sentences among the premises. But two laws also belong to the premises of D_1 (the sentences [6] and [10] of D_2). They are universal; they say that certain regularities hold not only in the cases so far observed but at any place at any time. Thus, these sentences are very comprehensive. The conclusion merely restates what is already stated by the universal premises for all cases and hence also for the present case, but now explicitly for this case. Thus, the logico-mathematical derivation merely evolves what is implicitly involved in the premises. To be sure, if we state a new law on the basis of certain observations, the law says much more than the observation sentences known; but this is not a deduction. If, on the other hand, a law is used within a derivation with the help of a logico-mathematical calculus, then the law must be among the premisses, and hence the conclusion does not say more than the premisses. The situation is different in the application of a physical calculus, as we shall see later (§ 23).

On the basis of the presupposed interpretation, the premisses and the conclusion of the derivation D_1 are factual. But D_1 also contains sentences which are proved in a logico-mathematical calculus and hence, when interpreted, are L-true, e.g., the sentences which in D_2 occur as (7) and (13) (§ 23). As explained before, derivations are immensely simplified by the method of laying down for any future use certain partial sequences occurring in many derivations and containing only provable sentences. Each sequence of this kind is a proof of its last sentence; wherever it occurs in other proofs or derivations it may be represented by its last element, i.e., the theorem proved. Thus a logical or mathematical theorem is, regarded from the point of view of its application in empirical science, a device or tool enabling us to make a very complex and long chain of applications of the rules of the calculus by one stroke, so to speak. The theorem is itself, even when interpreted, not a factual statement but an instrument facilitating operations with factual statements, namely, the deduction of a factual conclusion from factual premisses. The service which mathematics renders to empirical science consists in furnishing these instruments; the mathematician not only produces them for any particular case of application but keeps them in store, so to speak, ready for any need that may arise.

It is important to notice the distinction between 'primitive sentence' and 'premiss'. A primitive sentence of a calculus C (no matter whether it belongs to the basic calculus or is one of the specific axioms, and no matter whether, in an interpretation, it becomes L-true or factual) is stated as C-true by the rules of the calculus C. Therefore, it has to become a true proposition in any adequate (i.e., true) interpretation of C. The premisses of a derivation D in C, on the other hand, need not be C-true in C or true in a true interpretation of C. It is merely shown by D that a certain other sentence (the conclusion of D) is derivable from the premises of D and must therefore, in a true interpretation, be true *if* the premises happen to be true; but whether this is the case is not determined by D.

20. The Controversies over "Foundations" of Mathematics

There have been many discussions in modern times about the nature of mathematics in general and of the various kinds of numbers, and, further, about the distinction and relationship between knowledge in mathematics and knowledge in empirical science. In the course of the last century, mathematicians found that all mathematical signs can be defined on the basis of the signs of the theory of natural numbers.

The fundamental concepts of the infinitesimal calculus (differential coefficient and integral) were defined by Cauchy and Weierstrass in terms of the calculus of real numbers, with the help of the concept 'limit (of a sequence of real numbers)'. Thereby they succeeded in entirely eliminating the dubious concept of "infinitely small magnitudes" and thus giving the infinitesimal calculus a rigorous basis in the theory of real numbers. The next step was made by Frege and Russell, who defined real numbers as classes of natural numbers or of fractions. (Fractions can easily be defined as pairs of natural numbers.)

The reduction mentioned was entirely inside of mathematics. Therefore, it left the more general and fundamental problems unanswered. These have been discussed especially during the last fifty years, usually under the heading "foundations of mathematics". Among the different doctrines developed in this field, three are outstanding and most often discussed; they are known as logicism, formalism, and intuitionism. We will indicate briefly some characteristic features of the three movements. *Logicism* was founded by Frege and developed by Russell and Whitehead. Its chief thesis is that mathematics is a branch of logic. This thesis was demonstrated by constructing a system for the whole of classical mathematics within a logical calculus (see § 14 and some remarks in § 18). Truth conditions for the primitive signs of the logical calculus were given; thereby an interpretation for the whole mathematical system was determined. In this interpretation all mathematical signs became logical signs, all mathematical theorems L-true propositions.

190

Formalism, founded by Hilbert and Bernays, proposed, in contradistinction to logicism, to construct the system of classical mathematics as a mere calculus without regard to interpretation. The theory developed is called metamathematics; it is, in our terminology, a syntax of the language system of mathematics, involving no semantics. Hilbert's system is a combination of a logical basic calculus with a specific mathematical calculus using as specific primitive signs '0' and '′' as did Peano's system (§ 17). The controversy between the two doctrines concerning the question whether first to construct logic and then mathematics within logic without new primitive signs, or both simultaneously, has at present lost much of its former appearance of importance. We see today that the logico-mathematical calculus can be constructed in either way and that it does not make much difference which one we choose. If the method of logicism is chosen, constructing the system of mathematics as a part of the logical calculus, then by the normal interpretation of the latter we get an interpretation, and moreover the customary one, of the former. The formalists have not concerned themselves much with the question how the mathematical calculus, if constructed according to their method, is to be interpreted and applied in empirical science. As already explained (§ 17), the interpretation can be given by rules of translation for the specific primitive signs into the logical calculus. Another way would be to lay down L-semantical rules for these signs, stating the truth conditions for the descriptive sentences in which they occur. Formalists do not give an interpretation for the mathematical calculus and even seem to regard it as impossible for the nonelementary parts of the calculus, but they emphasize very much the need for a proof of the consistency for the mathematical calculus and even regard it as the chief task of metamathematics. There is some relation between the two questions; if a proof of consistency for a calculus can be given, then a true interpretation and application of the calculus is logically possible. So far, a proof of consistency has been given only for a certain part of arithmetic; the most comprehensive one has been constructed by Gentzen (1936).

Gödel has shown (1931) that it is not possible to construct a proof for the consistency of a calculus C containing arithmetic, within a metalanguage possessing no other logical means (forms of expression and modes of deduction) than C. Hilbert's aim was to construct the proof of consistency in a "finitist" metalanguage (similar to an intuitionist system, see below). At the present, it is not yet known whether this aim can be reached in spite of Gödel's result. In any case, the concept of "finitist logic" is in need of further clarification.

The doctrine of *intuitionism* was originated by Brouwer (1912) and Weyl (1918) on the basis of earlier ideas of Kronecker and Poincaré. This doctrine rejects both the purely formal construction of mathematics as a calculus and the interpretation of mathematics as consisting of L-true sentences without factual content. Mathematics is rather regarded as a field of mental activities based upon "pure intuition". A definition, a sentence, or a deduction is only admitted if it is formulated in "constructive" terms; that is to say, a reference to a mere possibility is not allowed unless we know a method of actualizing it. Thus, for instance, the concept of provability (in the mathematical system) is rejected because there is no method which would lead, for any given sentence S, either to a proof for S or to a proof for the negation of S. It is only allowed to call a sentence proved after a proof has been constructed. For similar reasons, the principle of the excluded middle, the indirect proof of purely existential sentences, and other methods are rejected. In consequence, both elementary logic and classical mathematics are considerably curtailed and complicated. However, the boundary between the admissible and the nonadmissible is not stated clearly and varies with the different authors.

Concerning mathematics as a pure calculus there are no sharp controversies. These arise as soon as mathematics is dealt with as a system of "knowledge"; in our terminology, as an interpreted system. Now, if we regard interpreted mathematics as an instrument of deduction within the field of empirical knowledge rather than as a system of information, then many of the controversial problems are recognized as being questions not of truth but of technical expedience. The question is: Which form of the mathematical system is technically most suitable for the purpose mentioned? Which one provides the greatest safety?

If we compare, e.g., the systems of classical mathematics and of intuitionistic mathematics, we find that the first is much simpler and technically more efficient, while the second is more safe from surprising occurrences, e.g., contradictions. At the present time, any estimation of the degree of safety of the system of classical mathematics, in other words, the degree of plausibility of its principles, is rather subjective. The majority of mathematicians seem to regard this degree as sufficiently high for all practical purposes and therefore prefer the application of classical mathematics to that of intuitionistic mathematics. The latter has not, so far as I know, been seriously applied in physics by anybody.

The problems mentioned cannot here be discussed more in detail. Such discussion is planned for a later volume of this *Encyclopedia*. A more detailed discussion can be found in those of the books which deal with mathematics mentioned in the "Selected Bibliography" at the end of this monograph.

21. Geometrical Calculi and Their Interpretations

When we referred to mathematics in the previous sections, we did not mean to include geometry but only the mathematics of numbers and numerical functions. Geometry must be dealt with separately. To be sure, the geometrical calculi, aside from interpretation, are not fundamentally different in their character from the other calculi and, moreover, are closely related to the mathematical calculi. That is the reason why they too have been developed by mathematicians. But the customary interpretations of geometrical calculi are descriptive, while those of the mathematical calculi are logical.

A geometrical calculus is usually constructed as an axiom system, i.e., a specific calculus presupposing a logical calculus (with normal interpretation). Such a calculus describes a structure whose elements are left undetermined as long as we do not make an interpretation. The geometrical calculi describe many different structures. And for each structure, e.g., the Euclidean, there are many different possible forms of calculi describing it. As an example let us consider an axiom system of Euclidean geometry. We choose a form having six primitive signs; three for classes of individuals, 'P_1', 'P_2', 'P_3', and three for relations, 'I', 'B', 'K'. We write '$I(x,y)$' for 'the relation I holds between x and y', and '$B(x,y,z)$' for 'the (triadic) relation B holds for x,y,z'. We will give only a few examples out of the long series of axioms:

G 1. For every x, y [if [x is a P_1 and y is a P_1] then, for some z [z is a $P_{\llcorner}$ and $I(x,z)$ and $I(y,z)$]].

G 2. For every x [if x is a P_3 then, for some y [y is a P_1 and, not $I(y,x)$]].

G 3. For every x, y, z [if $B(x,y,z)$ then, not $B(y,x,z)$].

G 4. For every x, y, z $\Big[$ if [x is a P_1 and y is a P_2 and z is a P_3 and $I(x,z)$ and $I(y,z)$ and, not $I(x,y)$] then there is (exactly) 1 u such that [u is a P_2 and $I(x,u)$ and I (u,z) and, for every t [if $I(t,u)$ then, not $I(t,y)$]] $\Big]$. (Euclidean parallel axiom.)

For a geometrical calculus there are many interpretations, and even many quite different and interesting interpretations, some of them logical, some descriptive. The *customary interpretation* is descriptive. It consists of a translation into the physical calculus (to be dealt with in the next section) together with the customary interpretation of the physical calculus. Rules of translation: (1) 'P_1' is translated into 'point', (2) 'P_2' into 'straight line', (3) 'P_3' into 'plane', (4) '$I(x,y)$' into 'x is lying on y' (incidence), (5) '$B(x,y,z)$' into 'the point x is between the points y and z on a straight line', (6) '$K(x,y,u,v)$' into 'the segment x,y is congruent with the segment u,v (i.e., the distance between x and y is equal to the distance between u and v)'. It is to be noticed that the words 'point', etc., are here signs of the physical calculus in its customary interpretation. Hence we may think of a point as a place in the space of nature; straight lines may be characterized by reference to light rays in a vacuum or to stretched threads; congruence may be characterized by referring to a method of measuring length, etc. Thus the specific signs of a geometrical calculus are interpreted as descriptive signs. (On the other hand, the specific signs of a mathematical calculus are interpreted as logical signs, even if they occur in descriptive factual sentences stating the results of counting or measuring; see, e.g., the logical sign '3', defined by Def. 13, § 14, occurring in premiss [1], § 19.) The axioms and theorems of a geometrical calculus are translated into descriptive, factual propositions of interpreted physics; they form a theory which we may call *physical geometry*, because it is a branch of physics, in contradistinction to mathematical geometry i.e., the geometrical calculus. As an example, the four axioms stated above are translated into the following sentences of the physical calculus (formulated here, for simplicity, in the forms of ordinary language).

PG 1. For any two points there is a straight line on which they lie.

PG 2. For any plane there is a point not lying on it.

PG 3. If the points x, y, and z lie on a straight line and x is between y and z, then y is not between x and z.

PG 4. If the point x and the line y lie in the plane z, but x not on y, then there is one and only one line u in the plane z such that x lies on u and no point is both on u and y (hence u is the parallel to y through x).

22. The Distinction between Mathematical and Physical Geometry

The distinction between mathematical geometry, i.e., the calculus, and physical geometry is often overlooked because both are usually called geometry and both usually employ the same terminology. Instead of artificial symbols like 'P_1', etc., the words 'point', 'line', etc., are used in mathematical geometry as well. The axioms are then not formulated like G 1–4 but like PG 1–4, and hence there is no longer any difference in formulation between mathematical and physical geometry. This procedure is very convenient in practice—like the analagous procedure in the mathematical calculus, mentioned previously—because it saves the trouble of translating, and facilitates the understanding and manipulating of the calculus. But it is essential to keep in mind the fundamental difference between mathematical and physical geometry in spite of the identity of formulation. The difference becomes clear when we take into consideration other interpretations of the geometrical calculus.

Of especial importance for the development of geometry in the past few centuries has been a certain translation of the geometrical calculus into the mathematical calculus. This leads, in combination with the customary interpretation of the mathematical calculus, to a logical interpretation of the geometrical calculus. The translation was found by Descartes and is known as analytic geometry or geometry of coordinates. 'P_1' (or, in ordinary formulation, 'point') is translated into 'ordered triple of real numbers'; 'P_3' ('plane') into 'class of ordered triples of real numbers fulfilling a linear equation', etc. The axioms, translated in this way, become C-true sentences of the mathematical calculus; hence the translation is C-true. On the basis of the customary interpretation of the mathematical calculus, the axioms and theorems of geometry become L-true propositions.

The difference between mathematical and physical geometry became clear in the historical development by the discovery of non-Euclidean geometry, i.e., of axiom systems deviating from the Euclidean form by replacing the parallel axiom (G 4) by some other axiom incompatible with it. It has been shown that each of these systems, although they are incompatible with one another, does not contain a contradiction, provided the Euclidean system is free from contradictions. This was shown by giving a translation for each of the non-Euclidean systems into the Euclidean system. Mathematicians regarded all these systems on a par, investigating any one indifferently. Physicists, on the other hand, could not accept this plurality of geometries; they asked: "Which one is true? Has the space of nature the Euclidean or one of the non-Euclidean structures?" It became clear by an analysis of the discussions that the mathematician and the physicist were talking about different things, although they themselves were not aware of this in the beginning. Mathematicians have to do with the geometrical calculus, and with respect to a calculus there is no question of truth and falsity. Physicists, however, are concerned with a theory of space, i.e., of the system of possible configurations and movements of bodies, hence with the interpretation of a geometrical calculus. When an interpretation of the specific signs is established—and, to a certain extent, this is a matter of choice—then each of the calculi yields a physical geometry as a theory with factual content. Since they are incompatible, at most one can be true (truth of a class of sentences [see § 6]). The theories are factual.

The truth conditions, determined by the interpretation, refer to facts. Therefore, it is the task of the physicist, and not of the mathematician, to find out whether a certain one among the theories is true, i.e., whether a certain geometrical structure is that of the space of nature. (Of course, the truth of a system of physical geometry, like that of any other universal factual sentence or theory, can never be known with absolute certainty but at best with a high degree of confirmation.) For this purpose, the physicist has to carry out experiments and to see whether the predictions made with the help of the theory under investigation, in connection with other theories confirmed and accepted previously, are confirmed by the observed results of the experiments. The accuracy of the answer found by the physicist is, of course, dependent upon the accuracy of the instruments available. The answer given by classical physics was that the Euclidean system of geometry is in accordance with the results of measurements, within the limits of the accuracy of observations. Modern physics has modified this answer in the general theory of relativity by stating that the Euclidean geometry describes the structure of space, though not exactly, yet with a degree of approximation sufficient for almost all practical purposes; a more exact description is given by a certain non-Euclidean system of geometry. Physical geometry is in its methods not fundamentally different from the other parts of physics. This will become still more obvious when we shall see how other parts of physics can also take the form of calculi (§ 23).

The doctrine concerning geometry acknowledged by most philosophers in the past century was that of Kant, saying that geometry consists of "synthetic judgments a priori", i.e., of sentences which have factual content but which, nevertheless, are independent of experience and necessarily true. Kant attributed the same character also to the sentences of arithmetic. Modern logical analysis of language, however, does not find any sentences at all of this character. We may assume that the doctrine is not to be understood as applying to the formulas of a calculus; there is no question of truth with respect to them because they are not assertions; in any case they are not synthetic (i.e., factual). The doctrine was obviously meant to apply to arithmetic and geometry as theories, i.e., interpreted systems, with their customary interpretations. Then, however, the propositions of arithemetic are, to be sure, independent of experience, but only because they do not concern experience or facts at all; they are L-true (analytic), not factual (synthetic). For geometry there is also, as mentioned before, the possibility of a logico-mathematical interpretation; by it the sentences of geometry get the same character as those of mathematics. On the basis of the customary interpretation, however, the sentences of geometry, as propositions of physical geometry, are indeed factual (synthetic), but dependent upon experience, empirical. The Kantian doctrine is based on a failure to distinguish between mathematical and physical geometry. It is to this distinction that Einstein refers in his well-known dictum: "So far as the theorems of mathematics are about reality they are not certain; and so far as they are certain they are not about reality."

The question is frequently discussed whether arithmetic and geometry, looked at from the logical and methodological point of view, have the same nature or not. Now we see that the answer depends upon whether the calculi or the interpreted systems are meant. There is no fundamental difference between arithmetic and geometry as calculi, nor with respect to their *possible* interpretations; for either calculus there are both logical and descriptive interpretations. If, however, we take the systems with their *customary* interpretation—arithmetic as the theory of numbers and geometry as the theory of physical space—then we find an important difference: the propositions of arithmetic are logical, L-true, and without factual content; those of geometry are descriptive, factual, and empirical.

23. Physical Calculi and Their Interpretations

The method described with respect to geometry can be applied likewise to any other part of physics: we can first construct a calculus and then lay down the interpretation intended in the form of semantical rules, yielding a physical theory as an interpreted system with factual content. The customary formulation of a physical calculus is such that it presupposes a logico-mathematical calculus as its basis, e.g., a calculus of real numbers in any of the forms discussed above (§ 18). To this basic calculus are added the specific primitive signs and the axioms, i.e., specific primitive sentences, of the physical calculus in question.

Thus, for instance, a calculus of mechanics of mass points can be constructed. Some predicates and functors (i.e., signs for functions) are taken as specific primitive signs, and the fundamental laws of mechanics as axioms. Then semantical rules are laid down stating that the primitive signs designate, say, the class of material particles, the three spatial coordinates of a particle x at the time t, the mass of a particle x, the class of forces acting on a particle x or at a space point s at the time t. (As we shall see later [§ 24], the interpretation can also be given indirectly, i.e., by semantical rules, not for the primitive signs, but for certain defined signs of the calculus. This procedure must be chosen if the semantical rules are to refer only to observable properties.) By the interpretation, the theorems of the calculus of mechanics become physical laws, i.e., universal statements describing certain features of events; they constitute physical mechanics as a theory with factual content which can be tested by observations. The relation of this theory to the calculus of mechanics is entirely analogous to the relation of physical to mathematical geometry. The customary division into theoretical and experimental physics corresponds roughly to the distinction between calculus and interpreted system. The work in theoretical physics consists mainly in constructing calculi and carrying out deductions within them; this is essentially mathematical work. In experimental physics interpretations are made and theories are tested by experiments.

In order to show by an example how a deduction is carried out with the help of a physical calculus, we will discuss a calculus which can be interpreted as a theory of thermic expansion. To the primitive signs may belong the predicates 'Sol' and

'Fe', and the functors 'lg', 'te', and 'th'. Among the axioms may be A 1 and A 2. (Here, 'x', 'β' and the letters with subscripts are real number variables; the parentheses do not contain explanations as in former examples, but are used as in algebra and for the arguments of functors.)

A 1. For every $x, t_1, t_2, l_1, l_2, T_1, T_2, \beta$ [if [x is a Sol and $\lg(x,t_1) = l_1$ and $\lg(x,t_2) = l_2$ and $\mathrm{te}(x,t_1) = T_1$ and $\mathrm{te}(x,t_2) = T_2$ and $\mathrm{th}(x) = \beta$] then $l_2 = l_1 \times (1 + \beta \times (T_2 - T_1))$].

A 2. For every x, if [x is a Sol and x is a Fe] then $\mathrm{th}(x) = 0.000012$.

The *customary interpretation*, i.e., that for whose sake the calculus is constructed, is given by the following semantical rules. '$\lg(x,t)$' designates the length in centimeters of the body x at the time t (defined by the statement of a method of measurement); '$\mathrm{te}(x,t)$' designates the absolute temperature in centigrades of x at the time t (likewise defined by a method of measurement); '$\mathrm{th}(x)$' designates the coefficient of thermic expansion for the body x; 'Sol' designates the class of solid bodies; 'Fe' the class of iron bodies. By this interpretation, A 1 and A 2 become physical laws. A 1 is the law of thermic expansion in quantitative form, A 2 the statement of the coefficient of thermic expansion for iron. As A 2 shows, a statement of a physical constant for a certain substance is also a universal sentence. Further, we add semantical rules for two signs occuring in the subsequent example: the name 'c' designates the thing at such and such a place in our laboratory; the numerical variable 't' as time coordinate designates the time-point t seconds after August 17, 1938, 10:00 A.M.

Now we will analyze an example of a derivation within the calculus indicated. This derivation D_2 is, when interpreted by the rules mentioned, the deduction of a prediction from premisses giving the results of observations. The construction of the derivation D_2, however, is entirely independent of any interpretation. It makes use only of the rules of the calculus, namely, the physical calculus indicated together with a calculus of real numbers as basic calculus. We have discussed, but not written down, a similar derivation D_1 (§ 19), which, however, made use only of the mathematical calculus. Therefore the physical laws used had to be taken in D_1 as premisses. But here in D_2 they belong to the axioms of the calculus (A 1 and A 2, occurring as [6] and [10]). Any axiom or theorem proved in a physical calculus may be used within any derivation in that calculus without belonging to the premisses of the derivation, in exactly the same way in which a proved theorem is used within a derivation in a logical or mathematical calculus, e.g., in the first example of a derivation in § 19 sentence (7), and in D_1 (§ 19) the sentences which in D_2 are called (7) and (13). Therefore only singular sentences (not containing variables) occur as premisses in D_2. (For the distinction between premisses and axioms see the remark at the end of § 19.)

Derivation D_2:

Premisses	1. c is a Sol.
	2. c is a Fe.
	3. $\text{te}(c,0) = 300$.
	4. $\text{te}(c,600) = 350$.
	5. $\lg(c,0) = 1{,}000$.

Axiom A 1 6. For every x, t_1, t_2, l_1, l_2, T_1, T_2, β [if [x is a Sol and $\lg(x,t_1) = l_1$ and $\lg(x,t_2) = l_2$ and $\text{te}(x,t_1) = T_1$ and $\text{te}(x,t_2) = T_2$ and $\text{th}(x) = \beta$] then $l_2 = l_1 \times (1 + \beta \times (T_2 - T_1))$].

Proved mathem.
theorem: 7. For every l_1, l_2, T_1, T_2, β [$l_2 - l_1 = l_1 \times \beta \times (T_2 - T_1)$ if and only if $l_2 = l_1 \times (1 + \beta \times (T_2 - T_1))$].

(6)(7) 8. For every x, t_1, ... (as in [6]) ... [if [- - -] then $l_2 - l_1 = l_1 \times \beta \times (T_2 - T_1)$].

(1)(3)(4)(8) 9. For every l_1, l_2, β [if [$\text{th}(c) = \beta$ and $\lg(c, 0) = l_1$ and $\lg(c,600) = l_2$] then $l_2 - l_1 = l_1 \times \beta \times (350 - 300)$].

Axiom A 2 10. For every x, if [x is a Sol and x is a Fe] then $\text{th}(x) = 0.000012$.

(1)(2)(10) 11. $\text{th}(c) = 0.000012$.

(9)(11)(5) 12. For every l_1, l_2 [if [$\lg(c,0) = l_1$ and $\lg(c,600) = l_2$] then $l_2 - l_1 = 1{,}000 \times 0.000012 \times (350 - 300)$].

Proved mathem.
theorem: 13. $1{,}000 \times 0.000012 \times (350 - 300) = 0.6$.

(12)(13) *Conclusion:* 14. $\lg(c,600) - \lg(c,0) = 0.6$.

On the basis of the interpretation given before, the premises are singular sentences concerning the body c. They say that c is a solid body made of iron, that the temperature of c was at 10:00 A.M. 300° abs., and at 10:10 A.M. 350° abs., and that the length of c at 10:00 A.M. was 1,000 cm. The conclusion says that the increase in the length of c from 10:00 to 10:10 A.M. is 0.6 cm. Let us suppose that our measurements have confirmed the premisses. Then the derivation yields the conclusion as a prediction which may be tested by another measurement.

Any physical theory, and likewise the whole of physics, can in this way be presented in the form of an interpreted system, consisting of a specific calculus (axiom system) and a system of semantical rules for its interpretation; the axiom system is, tacitly or explicitly, based upon a logico-mathematical calculus with customary interpretation. It is, of course, logically possible to apply the same method to any other branch of science as well. But practically the situation is such that most of them seem at the present time to be not yet developed to a degree which would suggest this strict form of presentation. There is an interesting and successful attempt of an axiomatization of certain parts of biology, especially genetics, by Woodger (Vol. I, No. 10). Other scientific fields which we may expect to be soon accessible to this method are perhaps chemistry, economics, and some elementary parts of psychology and social science.

Within a physical calculus the mathematical and the physical theorems, i.e., C-true formulas, are treated on a par. But there is a fundamental difference between the corresponding *mathematical* and the *physical propositions* of the physical theory, i.e., the system with customary interpretation. This difference is often overlooked. That physical theorems are sometimes mistaken to be of the same nature as mathematical theorems is perhaps due to several factors, among them the fact that they contain mathematical symbols and numerical expressions and that they are often formulated incompletely in the form of a mathematical equation (e.g., A 1 simply in the form of the last equation occurring in it). A mathematical proposition may contain only logical signs, e.g., 'for every m, n, $m + n = n + m$', or descriptive signs also, if the mathematical calculus is applied in a descriptive system. In the latter case the proposition, although it contains signs not belonging to the mathematical calculus, may still be provable in this calculus, e.g., '$\lg(c) + \lg(d) = \lg(d) + \lg(c)$' ('lg' designates length as before). A physical proposition always contains descriptive signs, because otherwise it could not have factual content; in addition, it usually contains also logical signs. Thus the difference between mathematical theorems and physical theorems in the interpreted system does not depend upon the kinds of signs occurring but rather on the kind of truth of the theorems. The truth of a mathematical theorem, even if it contains descriptive signs, is not dependent upon any facts concerning the designata of these signs. We can determine its truth if we know only the semantical rules; hence it is L-true. (In the example of the theorem just mentioned, we need not know the length of the body c.) The truth of a physical theorem, on the other hand, depends upon the properties of the designata of the descriptive signs occuring. In order to determine its truth, we have to make observations concerning these designata; the knowledge of the semantical rules is not sufficient. (In the case of A 2, e.g., we have to carry out experiments with solid iron bodies.) Therefore, a physical theorem, in contradistinction to a mathematical theorem, has factual content.

24. Elementary and Abstract Terms

We find among the concepts of physics—and likewise among those of the whole of empirical science—differences of abstractness. Some are more elementary than others, in the sense that we can apply them in concrete cases on the basis of observations in a more direct way than others. The others are more abstract; in order to find out whether they hold in a certain case, we have to carry out a more complex procedure, which, however, also finally rests on observations. Between quite elementary concepts and those of high abstraction there are many intermediate levels. We shall not try to give an exact definition for 'degree of abstractness'; what is meant will become sufficiently clear by the following series of sets of concepts, proceeding from elementary to abstract concepts: bright, dark, red, blue, warm, cold, sour, sweet, hard, soft (all concepts of this first set are meant as properties of things, not as sense-data); coincidence; length; length of time; mass, velocity, acceleration, density, pressure; temperature, quantity of heat; electric charge, electric current, electric field; electric potential, electric resistance, coefficient of induction, frequency of oscillation; wave function.

Suppose that we intend to construct an interpreted system of physics—or of the whole of science. We shall first lay down a calculus. Then we have to state semantical rules of the kind SD for the specific signs, i.e., for the physical terms. (The SL-rules are presupposed as giving the customary interpretation of the logico-mathematical basic calculus.) Since the physical terms form a system, i.e., are connected with one another, obviously we need not state a semantical rule for each of them. For which terms, then, must we give rules, for the elementary or for the abstract ones? We can, of course, state a rule for any term, no matter what its degree of abstractness, in a form like this: 'the term 'te' designates temperature', provided the metalanguage used contains a corresponding expression (here the word 'temperature') to specify the designatum of the term in question. But suppose we have in mind the following purpose for our syntactical and semantical description of the system of physics: the description of the system shall teach a layman to understand it, i.e., to enable him to apply it to his observations in order to arrive at explanations and predictions. A layman is meant as one who does not know physics but has normal senses and understands a language in which observable properties of things can be described (e.g., a suitable part of everyday non-scientific English). A rule like 'the sign 'P' designates the property of being blue' will do for the purpose indicated; but a rule like 'the sign 'Q' designates the property of being electrically charged' will not do. In order to fulfil the purpose, we have to give semantical rules for elementary terms only, connecting them with observable properties of things. For our further discussion we suppose the system to consist of rules of this kind, as indicated in the following diagram.

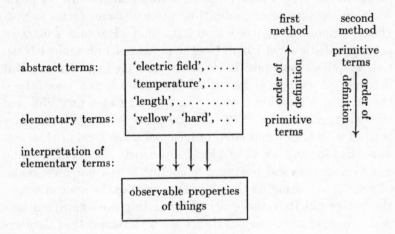

Now let us go back to the construction of the calculus. We have first to decide at which end of the series of terms to start the construction. Should we take elementary terms as primitive signs, or abstract terms? Our decision to lay down the semantical rules for the elementary terms does not decide this question. Either procedure is still possible and seems to have some reasons in its favor, depending on the point of view taken. The *first method* consists in taking elementary terms as primitive and then introducing on their basis further terms step by step, up to those of highest abstraction. In carrying out this procedure, we find that the introduction of further terms cannot always take the form of explicit definitions; conditional definitions must also be used (so-called reduction sentences [see Vol. I, No. 1, p. 50]). They describe a method of testing for a more abstract term, i.e., a procedure for finding out whether the term is applicable in particular cases, by referring to less abstract terms. The first method has the advantage of exhibiting clearly the connection between the system and observation and of making it easier to examine whether and how a given term is empirically founded. However, when we shift our attention from the terms of the system and the methods of empirical confirmation to the laws, i.e., the universal theorems, of the system, we get a different perspective. Would it be possible to formulate all laws of physics in elementary terms, admitting more abstract terms only as abbreviations? If so, we would have that ideal of a science in sensationalistic form which Goethe in his polemic against Newton, as well as some positivists, seems to have had in mind. But it turns out—this is an empirical fact, not a logical necessity—that it is not possible to arrive in this way at a powerful and efficacious system of laws. To be sure, historically, science started with laws formulated in terms of a low level of abstractness. But for any law of this kind, one nearly always later found some exceptions and thus had to confine it to a narrower realm of validity. The higher the physicists went in the scale of terms, the better did they succeed in formulating laws applying to a wide range of phenomena. Hence we understand that they are inclined to choose the *second method*. This method begins at the top of the system, so to speak, and then goes down to lower and lower levels. It consists in taking a few abstract terms as primitive signs and a few fundamental laws of great generality as axioms. Then further terms, less and less abstract, and finally elementary ones, are to be introduced by definitions; and here, so it seems at present, explicit definitions will do. More special laws, containing less abstract terms, are to be proved on the basis of the axioms. At least, this is the direction in which physicists have been striving with remarkable success, especially in the past few decades. But at the present time, the method cannot yet be carried through in the pure form indicated. For many less abstract terms no definition on the basis of abstract terms alone is as yet known; hence those terms must also be taken as primitive. And many more special laws, especially in biological fields, cannot yet be proved on the basis of laws in abstract terms only; hence those laws must also be taken as axioms.

Now let us examine the result of the interpretation if the first or the second method for the construction of the calculus is chosen. In both cases the semantical rules concern the elementary signs. In the first method these signs are taken as primitive. Hence, the semantical rules give a complete interpretation for these signs and those explicitly defined on their basis. There are, however, many signs, especially on the higher levels of abstraction, which can be introduced not by an explicit definition but only by a conditional one. The interpretation which the rules give for these signs is in a certain sense incomplete. This is due not to a defect in the semantical rules but to the method by which these signs are introduced; and this method is not arbitrary but corresponds to the way in which we really obtain knowledge about physical states by our observations.

If, on the other hand, abstract terms are taken as primitive—according to the second method, the one used in scientific physics—then the semantical rules have no direct relation to the primitive terms of the system but refer to terms introduced by long chains of definitions. The calculus is first constructed floating in the air, so to speak; the construction begins at the top and then adds lower and lower levels. Finally, by the semantical rules, the lowest level is anchored at the solid ground of the observable facts. The laws, whether general or special, are not directly interpreted, but only the singular sentences. For the more abstract terms, the rules determine only an *indirect interpretation*, which is—here as well as in the first method—incomplete in a certain sense. Suppose 'B' is defined on the basis of 'A'; then, if 'A' is directly interpreted, 'B' is, although indirectly, also interpreted completely; if, however, 'B' is directly interpreted, 'A' is not necessarily also interpreted completely (but only if 'A' is also definable by 'B').

To give an example, let us imagine a calculus of physics constructed, according to the second method, on the basis of primitive specific signs like 'electromagnetic field', 'gravitational field', 'electron', 'proton', etc. The system of definitions will then lead to elementary terms, e.g., to 'Fe', defined as a class of regions in which the configuration of particles fulfils certain conditions, and 'Na-yellow' as a class of space-time regions in which the temporal distribution of the electromagnetic field fulfils certain conditions. Then semantical rules are laid down stating that 'Fe' designates iron and 'Na-yellow' designates a specified yellow color. (If 'iron' is not accepted as sufficiently elementary, the rules can be stated for more elementary terms.) In this way the connection between the calculus and the realm of nature, to which it is to be applied, is made for terms of the calculus which are far remote from the primitive terms.

Let us examine, on the basis of these discussions, the example of a derivation D_2 (§ 23). The premises and the conclusion of D_2 are singular sentences, but most of the other sentences are not. Hence the premises and the conclusion of this as of all other derivations of the same type can be directly interpreted, understood, and confronted with the results of observations. More of an interpretation is not necessary for a practical application of a derivation. If, in confronting the interpreted premisses with our observations, we find them confirmed as true, then we accept the conclusion as a prediction and we may base a decision upon it. The sentences occurring in the derivation between premisses and conclusion are also interpreted, at least indirectly. But we need not make their interpretation explicit in order to be able to construct the derivation and to apply it. All that is necessary for its construction are the formal rules of the calculus. This is the advantage of the method of formalization, i.e., of the separation of the calculus as a formal system from the interpretation. If some persons want to come to an agreement about the formal correctness of a given derivation, they may leave aside all differences of opinion on material questions or questions of interpretation. They simply have to examine whether or not the given series of formulas fulfils the formal rules of the calculus. Here again, the function of calculi in empirical science becomes clear as instruments for transforming the expression of what we know or assume.

Against the view that for the application of a physical calculus we need an interpretation only for singular sentences, the following objection will perhaps be raised. Before we accept a derivation and believe its conclusion we must have accepted the physical calculus which furnishes the derivation; and how can we decide whether or not to accept a physical calculus for application without interpreting and understanding its axioms? To be sure, in order to pass judgment about the applicability of a given physical calculus we have to confront it in some way or other with observation, and for this purpose an interpretation is necessary. But we need no explicit interpretation of the axioms, nor even of any theorems. The empirical examination of a physical theory given in the form of a calculus with rules of interpretation is not made by interpreting and understanding the axioms and then considering whether they are true on the basis of our factual knowledge. Rather, the examination is carried out by the same procedure as that explained before for obtaining a prediction. We construct derivations in the calculus with premises which are singular sentences describing the results of our observations, and with singular sentences which we can test by observations as conclusions. The physical theory is indirectly confirmed to a higher and higher degree if more and more of these predictions are confirmed and none of them is disconfirmed by observations. Only singular sentences with elementary terms can be directly tested; therefore, we need an explicit interpretation only for these sentences.

25. "Understanding" in Physics

The development of physics in recent centuries, and especially in the past few decades, has more and more led to that method in the construction, testing, and application of physical theories which we call *formalization*, i.e., the construction of a calculus supplemented by an interpretation. It was the progress of knowledge and the particular structure of the subject matter that suggested and made practically possible this increasing formalization. In consequence it became more and more possible to forego an "intuitive understanding" of the abstract terms and axioms and theorems formulated with their help. The possibility and even necessity of abandoning the search for an understanding of that kind was not realized for a long time. When abstract, nonintuitive formulas, as, e.g., Maxwell's equations of electromagnetism, were proposed as new axioms, physicists endeavored to make them "intuitive" by constructing a "model", i.e., a way of representing electromagnetic microprocesses by an analogy to known macro-processes, e.g., movements of visible things. Many attempts have been made in this direction, but without satisfactory results. It is important to realize that the discovery of a model has no more than an aesthetic or didactic or at best a heuristic value, but is not at all essential for a successful application of the physical theory. The demand for an intuitive understanding of the axioms was less and less fulfilled when the development led to the general theory of relativity and then to quantum mechanics, involving the wave function. Many people, including physicists, have a feeling of regret and disappointment about this. Some, especially philosophers, go so far as even to contend that these modern theories, since they are not intuitively understandable, are not at all theories about nature but "mere formalistic constructions", "mere calculi". But this is a fundamental misunderstanding of the function of a physical theory. It is true a theory must not be a "mere calculus" but possess an interpretation, on the basis of which it can be applied to facts of nature. But it is sufficient, as we have seen, to make this interpretation explicit for elementary terms; the interpretation of the other terms is then indirectly determined by the formulas of the calculus, either definitions or laws, connecting them with the elementary terms. If we demand from the modern physicist an answer to the question what he means by the symbol 'ψ' of his calculus, and are astonished that he cannot give an answer, we ought to realize that the situation was already the same in classical physics. There the physicist could not tell us what he meant by the symbol 'E' in Maxwell's equations. Perhaps, in order not to refuse an answer, he would tell us that 'E' designates the electric field vector. To be sure, this statement has the form of a semantical rule, but it would not help us a bit to understand the theory. It simply refers from a symbol in a symbolic calculus to a corresponding word expression in a calculus of words. We are right in demanding an interpretation for 'E', but that will be given indirectly by semantical rules referring to elementary signs together with the formulas connecting them with 'E'. This interpretation enables us to use the laws containing 'E' for the derivation of predictions. Thus we understand 'E', if "understanding" of an expression, a sentence, or a theory means capability of its use for the description of known facts or the prediction of new facts. An "intuitive understanding" or a direct translation of '*E*' into terms referring to observable properties is neither necessary nor possible. The situation of the modern physicist is not essentially different. He knows how to use the symbol 'ψ' in the calculus in order to derive predictions which we can test by observations. (If they have the form of probability statements, they are tested by statistical results of observations.) Thus the physicist, although he cannot give us a translation into everyday language, understands the symbol 'ψ' and the laws of quantum mechanics. He possesses that kind of understanding which alone is essential in the field of knowledge and science.

Selected Bibliography

CARNAP, R. *Abriss der Logistik.* Wien, 1929.

———. "Die Mathematik als Zweig der Logik," *Blätter für deutsche Philosophie,* Vol. IV (1930).

———. *Logical Syntax of Language.* (Orig., Wien, 1934.) London and New York, 1937.

———. "Formalwissenschaft und Realwissenschaft," *Erkenntnis,* Vol. V (1935).

———. "Testability and Meaning," *Philosophy of Science,* Vols. III (1936) and IV (1937).

DEDEKIND, R. *Was sind und was sollen die Zahlen?* Braunschweig, 1888.

EINSTEIN, A. *Geometrie and Erfahrung.* Berlin, 1921.

FRAENKEL, A. *Einleitung in die Mengenlehre.* 3d ed. Berlin, 1928.

FRANK, P. *Interpretations and Misinterpretations of Modern Physics.* Paris, 1938.

FREGE, G. *Die Grundlagen der Arithmetik.* Breslau, 1884.

———. *Grundgesetze der Arithmetik,* Vols. I and II. Jena, 1893 and 1903.

HAHN, H. *Logik, Mathematik und Naturerkennen.* Wien, 1933.

HEYTING, A. *Mathematische Grundlagenforschung, Intuitionismus, Beweistheorie.* Berlin, 1934.

HILBERT, D. "Axiomatisches Denken," *Math. Annalen,* Vol. LXXVIII (1918).

HILBERT, D., and ACKERMANN, W. *Grundzüge der theoretischen Logik.* Berlin, 1928. 2d ed., 1938.

HILBERT, D., and BERNAYS, P. *Grundlagen der Mathematik,* Vol. I. Berlin, 1934.

Foundations of Logic and Mathematics

LEWIS, C. I., and LANGFORD, C. H. *Symbolic Logic*. New York and London, 1932.

MENGER, K. "The New Logic," *Philosophy of Science*, Vol. IV (1937).

MORRIS, C. W. *Logical Positivism, Pragmatism, and Scientific Empiricism*. Paris, 1937.

PEIRCE, C. S. *Collected Papers* (esp. Vol II). Cambridge, Mass., 1931 ff.

QUINE, W. V. "Truth by Convention," in *Philosophical Essays for A. N. Whitehead*. London and New York, 1936.

REICHENBACH, H. *Philosophie der Raum-Zeit-Lehre*. Berlin, 1928.

RUSSELL, B. *The Principles of Mathematics*. Cambridge, 1903. 2d ed., 1938.

———. *Introduction to Mathematical Philosophy*. London, 1919. 2d ed., 1920.

SCHOLZ, H. *Geschichte der Logik*. Berlin, 1931.

TARSKI, A. "Der Wahrheitsbegriff in den formalisierten Sprachen," *Studia philosophica*, Vol. I (1935).

———. "Grundlegung der wissenschaftlichen Semantik," in *Actes du congrès international de philosophie scientifique*. Paris, 1936.

———. *Einführung in die mathematische Logik*. Wien, 1937.

WAISMANN, F. *Einführung in das mathematische Denken*. Wien, 1936.

WHITEHEAD, A. N. and RUSSELL, B. *Principia mathematica*, Vols. I, II, and III. Cambridge, (1910) 1925, (1912) 1927, and (1913) 1927.

WITTGENSTEIN, L. *Tractatus logico-philosophicus*. London, 1922.

Index of Terms

[The numbers refer to the sections of this monograph.]

Linguistic Aspects of Science

Leonard Bloomfield

Linguistic Aspects of Science

Contents:

Contents:

217

Linguistic Aspects of Science
Leonard Bloomfield

I. Introduction
1. Language and Science

Language plays a very important part in science. A typical act of science might consist of the following steps: observation, report of observations, statement of hypotheses, calculation, prediction, testing of predictions by further observation. All but the first and last of these are acts of speech. Moreover, the accumulation of scientific results (the "body" of science) consists of records of speech utterance, such as tables of observed data, a repertoire of predictions, and formulas for convenient calculation.

The use of language in science is specialized and peculiar. In a brief speech the scientist manages to say things which in ordinary language would require a vast amount of talk. His hearers respond with great accuracy and uniformity. The range and exactitude of scientific prediction exceed any cleverness of everyday life: the scientist's use of language is strangely effective and powerful. Along with systematic observation, it is this peculiar use of language which distinguishes science from non-scientific behavior.

The present essay attempts to state briefly such general considerations of linguistics as may throw light upon the procedure of science.

2. The Present State of Linguistics

The ancient Greeks succeeded in describing the main syntactic and inflectional forms of their language. The description, to be sure, was incomplete and contained some serious misconceptions; especially the method of definition was unscientific.

With slight modifications, the ancient Greek doctrine has come down into our schools and constitutes today the equipment, as to linguistic knowledge, of the educated man. The ancient doctrine was able to persist because the principal modern languages of Europe are related to ancient Greek and have much the same structure.

Around the beginning of the nineteenth century the Sanskrit grammar of the ancient Hindus became known to European scholars. Hindu grammar described the Sanskrit language completely and in scientific terms, without prepossessions or philosophical intrusions. It was from this model that Western scholars learned, in the course of a few decades, to describe a language in terms of its own structure. The greatest progress in this respect occurred perhaps in connection with the native languages of America. The study of languages of diverse structure broke down parochial misconceptions according to which special features of Indo-European grammar were universal in human speech; it destroyed the pseudo-philosophical dogmas which were built up on these misconceptions. The Greek and medieval notions of linguistics, which still hold sway, it would seem ineradicably, in our schools, have thus been long out of date.

Acquaintance with the Sanskrit grammar and, at the same time, a new mastery of historical perspective brought about, at the beginning of the nineteenth century, the development of comparative and historical linguistics. The method of this study may fairly be called one of the triumphs of nineteenth-century science. In a survey of scientific method it should serve as a model of one type of investigation, since no other historical discipline has equaled it. Historical linguistics, like descriptive, has failed to influence our schools or to enter higher education, except for a haphazard and usually incorrect statement here and there in our schoolbooks. A confusion, strangely enough, of linguistic relationship with the breeding, in races, of domestic animals has found its way into popular sociology.

In the last half-century the study of variations within a language, especially of local dialects, has given us a new insight into the minute processes which make up linguistic change.

Unlike the science of chemistry, which is only a decade or so older, modern linguistics, perhaps for lack of immediate economic use, has failed to put its results into public possession. Not only the man in the street but also the educated public and even the practitioners of closely related branches of science are generally untouched by linguistic knowledge. Under the spell of the traditional dogma which is carried along in the schools the non-linguist responds often enough with incredulous surprise to well-established results that have long ago become commonplace among linguists.

3. Scope of This Essay

In this essay we are concerned only with such phases of linguistics as may throw light upon scientific procedure. Historical-comparative linguistics will not here concern us, since the use of language in science presupposes complete stability in the habits of speech. The linguistic changes which occur within a generation or two are relatively minute; such as they are, they disappear entirely under the agreements, explicit and other, which underlie the scientist's use of language.

As to descriptive linguistics, the vastly greater part of its data also can here be left aside, for we need not enter upon any examination of the widely differing types of structure that appear in different languages. It is enough for us to know that nearly all the structural features of our language which we are inclined to accept as universal—features such as the actor-action sentence, the elaborate part-of-speech system, or the special inflections of our nouns and verbs—are peculiarities of the Indo-European family of languages and are by no means universal in human speech. In part, moreover, the uniformity with which these features seem to appear in the languages that figure in our schooling is an illusion produced by the inaccuracy of the conventional description.

For our purpose we need scarcely touch upon the structural features of any one language; we shall be concerned only with the most general aspects of linguistic structure and with the function and effect of language. Beyond this, we shall need to consider the peculiarities of only one type of specialized dialect, for the language activity of scientists, in so far as it differs from other uses of language, constitutes the jargon or dialect of a craft, comparable to the dialects, say, of fishermen, miners, or carpenters.

This great restriction of our task does not remove the difficulties which are bound to arise. Even simple and well-established statements about language are likely to disturb or baffle the non-linguist, not because of any intrinsic difficulty but because of his prepossession with ancient doctrines that in the course of time have taken on the tenacity of popular superstitions. For the rest, our task demands that we go beyond such simple and well-established facts to matters which are subject to controversy. The writer can only do his utmost to speak plainly, in the hope that the reader will read attentively and, so far as may be, without injecting the prepossessions of our common-sense views about language.

4. Terminology

Linguists naturally have no respect for words. Engaged in describing structural systems of the widest diversity, they are accustomed, at need or at convenience, to invent and to discard all manner of technical terms. The varying terminologies of different linguists will concern only the reader who chooses to go farther afield: within this essay only one set of terms will appear.

On the other hand, the technical terms which are established among linguists often conflict or overlap with the meaning of these same terms as they occur in general scholastic usage and in philosophical discussion. It would be impractical in this essay to avoid them and to introduce the reader, instead, to fanciful innovations. At the time of definition technical terms will be given in italics, and an index will facilitate later reference to these definitions.

Since this essay, moreover, tries to make a specialized and hitherto neglected application of linguistics, we shall be compelled to use some temporary and unaccepted terms, and these, too, are likely to conflict with popular or scholastic usage.

Talking about the forms of speech is not easy. Perhaps only linguists are inured to this kind of discourse; others are likely to find it confusing. This difficulty is superficial and should be overcome without much trouble. Linguists are accustomed in printing to italicize the speech-forms which are under discussion or else to inclose them in square brackets; in this essay, however, conforming to more general usage, we shall place them between single quotation marks (for example: the word 'word').

5. Delimitation

Deep-seated inhibitions block the observation of language. To the unaccustomed observer language seems shapeless and fleeting. One does not talk about language. Among us an avenue of rationalization is provided in the traditional lore of the schoolroom. Where this does not suffice, we are accustomed to several lines of evasion: instead of observing language, one observes or, at any rate, discourses upon such matters as correctness of speech, literary values, or writing.

The notion that there is such a thing as "correct" and "incorrect" speech, that a speaker may "make mistakes" if he speaks "carelessly" in his native language, and that some kind of authoritative ruling may be sought, arose in the eighteenth century as an outgrowth of a peculiar social development. It has a realistic background (from which, however, it departs almost beyond recognition) in the existence, in large modern speech communities, of a standard dialect, spoken by the privileged and educated classes and employed in public speech (school, church, stage, court of law) and in nearly all writing; the standard dialect, common to all of a speech area (English) or to a large part of it (German, Dutch-Flemish), contrasts with local or regional dialects which enjoy a less favored position.

The discussion of literary values—that is, of the artistic use of language by specially gifted individuals—enjoys general favor as a substitute for the observation of language. This exercise, in spite of its prevalence in journalistic and academic spheres, need not here concern us.

6. Writing and Language

When the non-linguist sets out to talk about language, he very often lapses into discourse about writing. In order to avoid this confusion, we shall here use the term *'language'* only of the conventional use of vocal sound ("spoken" language), distinguishing this from *substitutes*, such as writing or drum signals, and from other actions, such as facial mimicry, which may serve in communication. In the present essay the term 'language' will therefore have a more restricted meaning than in other sections of this *Encyclopedia*. Similarly, phrases like 'a language' will here be used only of established ("natural") languages that prevail in communities, and not of restricted systems of symbolism, such as appear in mathematics and logic. For all linguistic study it is of primary importance to know that writing is not the same thing as language. Failure to make this distinction was one of the chief factors that prevented a beginning of linguistic science in the seventeenth and eighteenth centuries. The popular-scholastic contrast of "spoken language" and "written language" is entirely misleading.

In point of time language appears as a characteristic of the human species; men spoke as far back as we know anything about them; we must reckon here with biological reaches of time. To conjecture about the origin of language is to conjecture about the origin of the human species. Writing appears, by contrast, as a modern invention. At the earliest points of use (Mesopotamia, Egypt) it is only a few thousand years old.

Writing is a device for recording language by means of visual marks. By "recording" we mean that the beholder, if he knows the language of the writer and the system of writing, can repeat the speech which the writer uttered, audibly or internally, when he set down the marks.

Writing has been practiced in only few communities, and in these, until recently, almost always as a special skill of a few people. Anything like widespread literacy is a recent development covering only a small part of the world. Languages are quite the same whether their speakers practice writing or not; where there is widespread literacy, writing produces certain surface irregularities in the historical development of a language; these are not extensive, but their exact scope has not been determined. The best-known effects of this sort are the so-called spelling pronunciations, as when some people pronounce a *d* in 'Wednesday' or a *t* in 'often.'

A literate person finds it easy to talk about writing, because he acquired this skill under explicit verbal instruction, and because the permanent written markings record the movements of the writing hand. His acquisition of language, on the other hand, was unaccompanied, in the nature of the case, by any verbal accounting, and the sounds of language are fleeting and intangible. Hence the normal speaker finds it difficult to talk about language and cannot even describe the movements with which he produces speech. Some of these movements, in fact, though every child learns to make them, have so far baffled the physiologist's attempt at determination. The non-linguist, when he discusses linguistic matters, is likely to mistake writing for language.

A mathematical writer, for example, appreciating the advantages of a duodecimal system of numbers, invents two written symbols, say *t* for 'ten' and *e* for 'eleven' (so that *10* now represents 'twelve,' *84* represents 'one hundred,' *10e* 'one hundred and fifty-five,' etc.), and he is disappointed when people find this system too difficult to adopt. He has confused writing with language. Since the number-words of our language are decimal in structure, the proposed written forms are totally out of gear with our language and can be interpreted only by a cumbersome process of calculation.

All this concerns us here because the language of science tends to appear in written notation; in fact, its most characteristic and powerful form, mathematical discourse, can be transmitted only by means of a written record. The branching-out of written notation into forms which cannot be matched in actual speech represents a peculiar and highly specialized development of writing. This will concern us in the sequel; here we need say only that, in order to understand the specialized development, we must have a clear and correct picture of the underlying habit.

What applies to writing applies also to less elaborate communicative systems, such as gestures or signals. A period when such systems may have been independent of language, or co-ordinate with it, would, in any case, lie very far behind us. The conditions which might have prevailed in such a period are quite unknown. In times that are accessible to us and under human conditions as we know them, any system of gestures or signals that goes beyond vague beckoning appears simply as an outgrowth and substitutive reproduction of language.

The confusion, extremely common among literate but linguistically untrained persons, between language and its derivative substitutes often takes the form of inverting this relation or of ascribing some kind of "independence" to the substitutes. Alterations, no matter how fantastic, in a system of writing do not affect the language which is represented. If a new system of writing came into wide use in a community, it might in time produce some very modest linguistic modifications. This must not lead us to suppose that a change, say, from the Arabic to the Latin alphabet, such as has recently been effected for Turkish, has any immediate bearing on the language.

7. Language and Handling Activity

The difference between utterance of speech and all other events is naturally paramount in the study of language. The human acts which are observable under ordinary conditions are thus divided into *language*, the vocal utterance of the conventional type, and *handling activities*, a somewhat narrow name to cover all other normally observable acts, including not only manipulation but also mimicry, gesture, locomotion, acts of observation, etc. The linguist studies sequences in which language mediates between non-linguistic events.

Language creates and exemplifies a twofold value of some human actions. In its *biophysical* aspect language consists of sound-producing movements and of the resultant sound waves and of the vibration of the hearer's eardrums. The *biosocial* aspect of language consists in the fact that the persons in a community have been trained to produce these sounds in certain situations and to respond to them by appropriate actions. The biosocial function of language arises from a uniform, traditional, and arbitrary training of the persons in a certain group. They have been trained to utter conventional sounds as a secondary response to situations and to respond to these slight sounds, in a kind of trigger effect, with all sorts of actions.

In their turn, on a tertiary level of response, handling actions may be subjected biosocially to language: specific handling actions are conventionalized as a response to specific forms of speech, and these handling actions or their products serve as stimuli to call forth these same forms of speech. These substitutes for speech occur scantily in simple communities but play a great part in our civilization. Apart from speculations about a prehuman or semihuman antiquity, in man as we see him, all handling actions which bear elaborate communicative value owe this value to their biosocial subjection to language.

The most familiar example of this is the art of writing: permanent visible marks are produced conventionally as responses to speech and serve as stimuli for the production of speech. For this it is necessary, of course, that the marks be conventionally associated with features of language. These features may be of various kinds: Chinese characters and our numerical digits represent words; the letters of the alphabet represent single typical speech-sounds. The biophysical aspect of writing consists in the materials used for producing the marks, in the shape of the marks, and in the movements by which one makes them. Once we have established the communal habit or convention which attaches them biosocially to speech-forms, the biophysical features may vary within the convention. Thus, the variety of paper, pencil, or ink; the shape, always within our convention, of the letters—script, printed, Roman or italic, small or capital, etc.—and the movements of the writer's hand or the kind of printing press are all indifferent so far as the verbal message is concerned.

The biophysical features of substitutes for language are important enough on their own level. Systems of writing may differ as to the time and labor required for making the marks and as to their legibility. The permanence of the materials is sometimes important. Mechanical devices like the typewriter and the printing press may yield great advantages.

More important for our discussion are the conventions which associate the written marks with forms of language. The alphabet, which associates, in principle, each mark with a typical sound of speech, makes reading and writing relatively easy, since it requires only a few dozen different characters; for the same reason it lends itself easily to mechanical transmission and reproduction. The system of writing, best exemplified in Chinese, where a character is assigned to a word of the language, is much harder to use and to mechanize. On the other hand, a piece of writing can be read in various languages, provided that these agree in structure and that minor divergences are bridged by means of supplementary conventions. Moreover, word-writing has the value of compactness and easy survey. These advantages appear very clearly in the case of our numeral digits. Here, by confining a system of word-writing to a very limited domain of speech-forms, we make it readable, with the aid of supplementary conventions, in any language. Thus, a graph like *71* is read in English as 'seventy-one,' in German as 'one and seventy,' in French as 'sixty-eleven,' in Danish as 'one and half-four-times' (*sc.*, 'twenty'), etc.

Our numeral digits illustrate the advantage of a well-arranged written symbolism. Simple discourses which move entirely in this domain can be carried out by means of a calculating machine. Short of this extreme case, we may cite cable codes, where the written forms are revised in the direction of brevity; or, again, systems of notation such as are used in symbolic logic, where a stock of symbols is so devised as to yield extremely simple rules of discourse. The construction of a calculating machine or the rules of arrangement and substitution in a system of logistics require great care and present great interest: it is decidedly advantageous to study them for their own sake and without reference to the linguistic end points of the sequences in which they operate. Nevertheless, if they are to operate, they must be so planned that, starting with speech-forms, they yield speech-forms in the end. No serious use would be made of a calculating machine, or of a code, or of a system of logistics, which failed to deliver a linguistically significant end result. By way of contrast, the reader may find it not without value to consider such non-linguistic systems as musical notation, say for the piano, or, again, the moves of a game of chess. Persons unaccustomed to the consideration of language are prone to the error of overlooking the linguistic character of notational or mechanical subsidiaries of language and viewing them as "independent" systems; at the same time they may resort to the metaphor of calling these systems "languages." This metaphor is dangerous, since it may lead to the notion that such systems can liberate us from uncertainties or difficulties which inhere in the working of language.

Some students of language, among them the present writer, believe that widespread and deep-seated errors in supposedly scientific views of human behavior rest upon misconceptions of this sort—upon failure to distinguish between linguistic and non-linguistic events, upon confusion of the biophysical and the biosocial aspects of language and its subsidiaries, and, above all, upon a habit of ignoring the linguistic parts of a sequence and then calling upon metaphysical entities to bridge the gap. Several phases of this error will here demand our attention.

8. Apriorism

In the prescientific view of these matters, a term such as "reasoning" covers, on the one hand, observations which cost no great labor and, on the other hand, utterances of speech which are not recognized for what they are. Thus there arises the notion that knowledge may be obtained by a process of "reasoning a priori." Everyday observations, generally human or systematized by tribal tradition, are viewed as innate data of reason, and the ensuing deductions are clothed in a mystic validity. If the deductions are correctly made, the "a priori" procedure differs from an ordinary act of science only in that the basic observations are unsystematic and remain untested.

In scientific procedure we mean by *deduction* the purely verbal part of an act of science which leads from the report of observation and the hypotheses to a prediction. If we replace the report of observation by arbitrarily invented postulates, the discourse makes no pretense to validity in the sphere of handling actions. Deductive discourse of this kind is produced in logic, mathematics, or the methodology of science. It is made to fit some type of observational data, or else it exists for its own sake, in readiness for the emergence of observational data to which it may be applied. Until modern times, Euclidean geometry was viewed as an "a priori" system: the underlying everyday observations about the spatial character of objects were viewed as inborn and unquestionable truths. Today the same system, apart from the correction of flaws, is treated as a purely verbal discourse of deduction from postulates. It is especially useful because these postulates, by virtue of their historic origin, are such as to make the discourse applicable to the placing of objects, as this placing is observed in the first approximation that is customary in everyday handling. We have learned, however, that astronomical magnitudes make sensible the error in these postulates, and they accordingly demand a different discourse, based upon other postulates which, in turn, will be chosen so as to fit the new observations. One employs postulates which fit the observed data within the margin of error. The postulates are chosen so as to yield a simple calculation; the discrepancies are set aside to await more accurate measurements, which, in their turn, will make possible a more closely approximative discourse.

9. Mentalism

In the common sense of many peoples, perhaps of all, language is largely ignored, and its effects are explained as owing to non-physical factors, the action of a "mind," "will," or the like. These terms, as well as the many others connected with them,

yield service in daily life, in art, and in religion; that they have
no place in science is the contention of many scientists. Mentalistic terms do not figure in the procedure of physics, biology,
or linguistics, but many students of these subjects employ them
in the theoretical parts of their discourse.

An individual may base himself upon a purely practical, an
artistic, a religious, or a scientific acceptance of the universe,
and that aspect which he takes as basic will transcend and include the others. The choice, at the present state of our knowledge, can be made only by an act of faith, and with this the issue
of mentalism should not be confounded.

It is the belief of the present writer that the scientific description of the universe, whatever this description may be worth, requires none of the mentalistic terms, because the gaps which
these terms are intended to bridge exist only so long as language
is left out of account. If language is taken into account, then
we can distinguish science from other phases of human activity
by agreeing that science shall deal only with events that are accessible in their time and place to any and all observers (strict
behaviorism) or only with events that are placed in co-ordinates
of time and space (*mechanism*), or that science shall employ only
such initial statements and predictions as lead to definite handling operations (*operationalism*), or only terms such as are derivable by rigid definition from a set of everyday terms concerning physical happenings (*physicalism*). These several formulations, independently reached by different scientists, all lead to
the same delimitation, and this delimitation does not restrict
the subject matter of science but rather characterizes its method. It is clear even now, with science still in a very elementary
stage, that, under the method thus characterized, science can
account in its own way for human behavior—provided, always,
that language be considered as a factor and not replaced by the
extra-scientific terms of mentalism.

10. Solipsism

Much of the procedure of science and particularly the end
result of each act of science consists of speech in a somewhat

specialized form. In order to give an account of science, we must know something of language. Linguistics, however, in any feasible arrangement, occupies a rather late place among the divisions of science, since it comes after biology and all studies of the animal (and not specifically human) circumstances of man.

The fact that we are thus inevitably caught in a circle should not be exploited in favor of a naïve solipsism which is surprisingly prevalent even among otherwise competent men of science. It is true, of course, that science can deal with only such events as have called forth a verbal response on the part of some person—at any rate, of the scientist who undertakes to deal with a given event. More generally, the solipsist says that the universe consists, of necessity, only of his "experiences" or "perceptions." The truth of this axiom cannot be affected by the study of language or of "experiences" or "perceptions," since these studies occupy a late place in science and deal with only a small part of the universe.

If it were strictly applied, the solipsist's axiom would remain irrelevant and harmless. Any predicate that is applied to everything in the world will play no part in science, for science deals only with correlations of events within the universe. The solipsist, having tagged everything, indifferently and without exception, as his "percept" or "experience," goes on to study things exactly as other scientists study them. He does not allow his solipsism to interfere with work in his own field of science. In more general discussion, however, the solipsist commits the fallacy of using his meaningless axiom as a bludgeon to knock over special points of discourse. He is most likely to do this in the face of any attempt at scientific study of human behavior, and especially in the face of any linguistic considerations. It is as though in practical life the solipsist should suddenly recall that an oncoming railway train was only a creature of his perceptions.

II. The Function of Language

11. The Speech Community

Language makes human behavior extremely different from that of animals because it establishes a minute and accurate interaction between individuals. Among animals such interaction, where it exists, concerns only a few gross situations or else is rigidly set in an unvarying pattern. Apart from this, each individual's response to stimuli is limited by the powers of this individual's body. In man these ordinary responses, to which we give the name of 'handling actions,' are paralleled by a second set of responses—the utterance of speech. The speech sounds act as a stimulus upon other persons who may then perform a handling response such as to give a biologically favorable outcome to the speaker's situation. Thus a person who is in need of food but unable by his own bodily power to get it may, by speech, prompt others to get it for him.

Thus, in addition to the normal biological series $S \to R$, man has also the series

$$S \to r \text{\textemdash} s \to R.$$

Here r——s denotes the act of language; the biologically effective stimulus S and response R are no longer confined to occurrence within one body. Language bridges the gap between the individual nervous systems. It makes possible a minute division of labor and high specialization of individual abilities.

Much as single cells are combined in a many-celled animal, separate persons are combined in a speech community—a higher and more effective type of organization. If the word 'organism' be not confined to denote an individual animal, we may speak here, without metaphor, of a social organism. Primarily, the social organism is the speech community—the community of persons speaking one language—but bilingual or multilingual persons mediate everywhere between these communities: culture areas, such as Europe with her daughter-nations, approach the coherence of a single-speech community; some degree of communication now subsists between all persons on earth.

12. Relayed Speech

The simplest case of speech utterance is that in which the hearer performs a handling action in response to a non-linguistic stimulus which impinges on the speaker. Very often, however, the hearer responds by addressing speech to the first speaker or to other persons. Many relays of speech may intervene between a non-linguistic stimulus and a handling response. The stimuli of various individuals may contribute to the sequence of speech; the sequence itself may be multiple, carried on simultaneously by many chains or a network of speaker-hearer connections; and the handling response may be performed by many persons, co-operatively or in independent actions. The intermediate utterances in such a chain or net exemplify the case where speech is prompted by no immediate non-verbal stimulus and calls forth no immediate handling response but figures merely as a part of a sequence of linguistic and other events in a community. The word 'sumach,' for instance, in its primary and simple use will be uttered in the presence (under the visual stimulus) of a certain kind of tree, but a speaker hitherto ignorant of the word, once this is pointed out to him, will be able, without further explanation, to take part in sequences of action and discourse in which the word 'sumach' occurs in absence of the primary stimulus. Other speech-forms, such as most of those used in this monograph, adhere to no simple stimulus of that sort but occur entirely in complex situations of discourse.

Speech utterance itself, on a different level, may serve as a relatively final response, as in instruction in a foreign language or mathematics, or in a discussion leading to agreement as to the use of some technical term. If we follow a sequence far enough, we expect, of course, to find some modification of non-verbal activity: even poetry or fiction will in the end lead to a more than verbal result.

13. Verbal Self-stimulation

The normal human being, totally uncritical as to language, sees himself not only as a separate body but also as a source of effect upon other persons. However pervasive and at times pow-

234

erful this effect may be, it is nearly always uncertain. In contrast with this, he is able, with rare exceptions, to co-ordinate his earlier speech ("intention") with later handling actions of his own. This contributes toward the view of the "self" or "ego" as a more than bodily entity.

What here interests us is not merely the relative sureness but also the usefulness of verbal self-stimulation. The utterance of a speech-form is not only a response but serves also as a stimulus to the speaker himself. The utterance can be easily repeated and replaces conveniently an evanescent or remote stimulus. The varied situations of counting (as, say, a flock of sheep before and after a storm) can be adduced to illustrate this.

A child talks to himself at first out loud; then he learns to mumble or whisper; finally, he suppresses all audible and even all visible movements of speech. In the popular view no movement at all is supposed to remain. This is a view which we could adopt only by abandoning the basic assumptions of physics. We must suppose rather that the movements of speech —which, as we shall see, consist of a small number of contrasting units—are replaced by internal movements, at first presumably as mere reductions of the normal movements of speech, but capable, in the course of time, of any degree of substitution. This *inner speech* accounts for the main body of the vaguely bounded system of actions that in everyday parlance goes by the name of "thinking."

14. Meaning

In the sequence $S \to r\text{---}s \to R$ and its complex derivatives, the speech or sequence of speeches has no immediate gross biological effect and serves merely as a "sign" mediating between the more practically important stimuli and responses, which are here represented by the large letters S and R. These, to be sure, may themselves consist of speech, but, in the intention of the formula, this speech will then be on a lower level than the speech represented by the small $r\text{---}s$; an example of this would be discourse about the validity of an earlier speech, or, with another difference of level, discourse about the forms of some language. These special cases need not here concern us: we may speak of the end points S and R as speaker's stimulus and hearer's response, without regard to their verbal or non-verbal character. The two together constitute, in linguistic terminology, the *meaning* of the speech utterance r——s. This holds good even under a mentalistic view: in this view it is merely supposed that the speaker's stimulus and the hearer's response are "ideas," "concepts," or the like, which may be postulated in more or less exact accommodation to the uttered speech-forms and serve to link these to the actually observable stimulus and response.

The term 'meaning,' which is used by all linguists, is necessarily inclusive, since it must embrace all aspects of semiosis that may be distinguished by a philosophical or logical analysis: relation, on various levels, of speech-forms to other speech-forms, relation of speech-forms to non-verbal situations (objects, events, etc.), and relations, again on various levels, to the persons who are participating in the act of communication.

When the correlations of speech-forms with meanings are known, some utterances turn out to be conditioned more immediately by the speaker's stimulus, and others by the hearer's response. Contrast, for example, a report, such as 'It's raining,' with a command, such as 'Come here!' In earlier stages of an infant's language-learning, speaker's meaning and hearer's meaning may be imperfectly correlated, but in the normal use of language both these aspects of meaning are so firmly knit to the speech-form that no distinction is possible. In the description of a language we need not define each form twice over, determining first the situations in which it is uttered and then the responses to which it leads. In general, we define in terms of stimulus because the earlier step in the sequence exhibits less variation. The speaker has been trained, as part of his acquisition of language, to play indifferently either part in the interchange of speech. To be sure, each speaker understands a wider range of speech-forms than he utters, but this does not bring about any discrepancy between the two aspects of meaning: in the adult speaker they are entirely merged in a firm correlation which is guaranteed by the evident working of language.

15. Acquisition of Meaning

Hearing a speech in a language of which we are entirely ignorant, we must include in our first estimate of the meaning the total situation of the speaker and all the ensuing actions of the hearer. To consider meaning from any less inclusive position would lay us open to prepossessions which lurk close by. The more striking features of gesture, situation, and immediate response will often lead us to a hypothesis, to be removed or confirmed by further experience and by the correlations that will be gradually built up. After we have thus acquired the use of a small supply of speech-forms, becoming, to this extent, members of the community, we may induce full-fledged speakers to talk about their language: we ask them the names of things and lead them to define speech-forms in terms of other speech-forms. In the history of travel and adventure all this has many times occurred; the student of language naturally prefers to seek the mediation of a bilingual speaker. For the infant's acquisition of language, however—though little is known of it—we must postulate exactly this process. The elders, of course, facilitate the process by uttering simple speech-forms with strikingly apparent and much repeated practical emphasis upon the relevant features of situation and response. This elementary process has been called *demonstration;* this use of the word is distinct, of course, from its use in logic and mathematics as a synonym of 'proof.' A speech-form has been acquired by demonstration when the learner utters it in the conventionally appropriate situations and responds to it by the conventionally appropriate actions.

Teacher and learner may develop an agreement under which the demonstration of meaning, for certain types of speech-forms, is shortened to a single act, such as holding up an object or unmistakably pointing at it while speaking its name.

Another factor of learning is the occurrence of a speech-form in contexts whose other components are familiar. Certain types of forms, such as the words 'and,' 'or,' 'because,' 'the,' are presumably acquired in this way.

Finally, there is the process of *definition*. For the most part, definition is informal: a speech-form is equated with roughly synonymous forms. Thus we may tell a child that 'rapid' means 'quick' or 'fast,' and we expect the statistical effect of future demonstration and context to train him to use the new word in its more exact conventional setting. Bilingual statements of meaning, such as 'cheval:horse' are in general of this rough type; even apart from differences of structure and function, the meanings in two languages almost never coincide.

We call a definition *formal* when, for some sphere of discourse, the new form and the old one by which it is defined are freely and completely interchangeable. Formal definition occurs in ordinary life only in the case of a very few of the simplest and most abstract speech-forms. The notable instance is furnished by the number words: 'eight' means 'seven and one.' Other instances doubtless occur: 'down' could be defined as 'in the direction in which heavy things fall when we drop them.' The chief place of formal definition, however, is in explicit agreement. This is familiar to us from scientific practice: for a certain discourse, and perhaps for whole types of discourse, participants in some technical procedure agree to use a new term as the exact equivalent of some older speech-form. Thereafter they initiate learners into this agreement. Formal definitions may be bilingual (as 'Kraft:force'), provided abstraction is made from structural and functional differences (for instance, gender of a noun in French or German, as opposed to English).

It will be seen that, even in the case of formal definition, the degree of uniformity among the speakers and even the consistency of any one speaker will be subject to any uncertainty as to the meaning of the defining speech-forms. These may in turn have been formally defined, but in the end we must come to forms which have been only roughly defined and, for each speaker, to forms which he got in infancy from context or, at the very beginning, from demonstration. The meaning of a speech-form in the habit of any one speaker contains factors and fringes of

238

variation; these may be greatly reduced, but probably never entirely eliminated, for the observer by consideration of many speakers, and for the speakers themselves by copious and consistent interchange of speech upon some topic that demands accurate agreement.

III. The Structure of Language

16. Phonemic Structure

In ordinary discussion human situations and responses appear perhaps less flowing and vague than we have here described them in the guise of meanings, for there we are free (as we are not here, in our linguistic discussion) to endow them with some of the permanence and neat outline which they obtain by virtue of their correlation with the forms of language. In language we order and classify the flowing phenomena of our universe; our habit of doing this is so pervasive that we cannot describe things as they may appear to an infant or a speechless animal. The price we pay is a sensible inadequacy of our speech, offset by the privilege of any degree of approximation such as may be seen in some microscopic investigation of science or in the work of the poet. It is the entire task of the linguist to study the ordering and formalization which is language; he thus obtains the privilege of imagining it removed and catching a distant glimpse of the kind of universe which then remains.

The ordering and formalizing effect of language appears, first of all, in the fact that its meaningful forms are all composed of a small number of meaningless elements. We should obtain, in this respect, a parallel to language if, with a dozen or so of different flags, we devised a code in which the exhibition of several flags (in the limiting case, of one flag) in a fixed position and arrangement would constitute a meaningful sign.

The forms of every language are made up out of a small number—ranging perhaps between fifteen and seventy-five—of typical unit sounds which have no meaning but, in certain fixed arrangements, make up the meaningful forms that are uttered. These signals are the *phonemes* of the language. The speakers have the habit of responding to the characteristic features of sound which in their language mark off the various phonemes and of ignoring all other acoustic features of a speech. Thus, a German who has not been specially trained will hear no difference between such English forms as 'bag' and 'back,' because the difference in his language is not phonemic; it is one of the acoustic differences which he has been trained to ignore. In the same way, a speaker of English will hear no difference, until he is trained to do so, between two Chinese words which sound to him, say, like 'man,' and differ as to their scheme of pitch; we fail to hear the difference because in our language such a difference is not connected with a difference of meaning and is consistently ignored whenever it chances to occur. The acoustic features which set off a phoneme from all other phonemes in its language, and from "inarticulate" sound, exhibit some range of variation. It is not required that this range be continuous: acoustically diverse features may be united, by the habit of the speakers, in one phoneme.

The number of phonemes which will be stated as existing in any one language depends in part upon the method of counting. For instance, we shall recognize an English phoneme [j] which appears initially in forms like 'yes,' 'year,' 'young,' and another phoneme [e] in the vowel sound of words like 'egg,' 'ebb,' 'bet.' The longer vowel sound in words like 'aim,' 'say,' and 'bait' may then be counted as another phoneme, or else one may describe it as a combination of the phonemes [e] and [j]. This option would not exist if our language contained a succession of [e] plus [j] which differed in sound, and as to significant forms in which it occurred, from the vowel sound of 'aim,' 'say,' 'bait.' Thus, the English sound [č], which appears in words like 'chin,' 'rich,' 'church,' must be counted as a single phoneme and not as a combination of [t] as in 'ten' and [š] as in 'she,' because in forms like 'it shall' or 'courtship' we have a combination of [t] plus [š] which differs in sound and as to significant forms from [č] in 'itch Al' or 'core-chip.' The fact that these last two forms are unusual or nonsensical does not affect the distinction. The count of phonemes in Standard English will vary, according to economy, from forty-odd to around sixty.

For the most part, the phonemes appear in utterance in a linear order. Where this is not the case, the arrangement is so simple that we can easily put our description into linear order. For instance, the noun 'convict' has a phoneme of stress (loudness) which starts with the beginning of the word and covers the first vowel phoneme; the verb 'convict' differs in that the same stress phoneme is similarly placed upon the beginning of the partial form '-vict.' If we wish to put our description of these forms into linear order, we need only agree upon a convention of aligning a symbol for the stress phonemes, e.g., *'convict* and *con'vict*.

Thus, every speech in a given dialect can be represented by a linear arrangement of a few dozen symbols. The traditional system of writing English, with its twenty-six letters and half-dozen marks of punctuation, does this very imperfectly but sufficiently well for most practical needs.

This rigid simplicity of language contrasts with the continuous variability of non-linguistic stimulation and response. For this reason linguists employ the word *'form'* for any meaningful segment of speech, in contrast with their use of 'meaning' for stimulus and response.

The sound produced in a speech is to all ordinary purposes a continuum. To determine which features are phonemic, we must have some indication of meaning. A German observer, say, who, studying English as a totally unknown language, noticed in a few utterances the acoustic difference between 'bag' and 'back,' could decide that this is a phonemic difference only when he learned that it goes steadily hand in hand with a difference of meaning.

Two utterances, say of the form 'Give me an apple,' no matter how much they may differ in non-phonemic features of sound, are said to consist of the *same* speech-form; utterances which are not same are *different*. The decision of the speakers is practically always absolute and unanimous. This fact is of primary concern to us, since by virtue of it the speakers are able to adhere to strict agreements about speech-forms and to establish all manner of correspondences, orderings, and operations in this realm. To take an everyday instance: anyone can look up a word in a dictionary or a name in a directory.

It would not do to overlook the fact that the phonemes of a language are identifiable only by differences of meaning. For this, however, a relatively small number of gross differences will suffice: once the phonemes are established, any form of the language is completely and rigidly definable (apart from its meaning) as a linear or quasi-linear sequence of phonemes. We do not possess a workable classification of everything in the universe, and, apart from language, we cannot even envisage anything of the sort; the forms of language, on the other hand, thanks to their phonemic structure, can be classified and ordered in all manner of ways and can be subjected to strict agreements of correspondence and operation. For this reason, linguistics classifies speech-forms by form and not by meaning. When a speech-form has been identified, we state, as well as may be, its meaning: our success depends upon the perfection of sciences other than linguistics. The reverse of this would be impossible. For instance, we shall usually seek a given word in a thesaurus of synonyms by looking it up in the alphabetical index. We could not use a telephone directory which arranged the names of the subscribers not in their alphabetical order, but according to some non-verbal characteristic, such as weight, height, or generosity.

17. Grammatical Structure

Some utterances are partly alike in form and meaning; for instance:

> Poor John ran away.
> Our horses ran away.
> Poor John got tired.
> Our horses got tired.

This forces us to recognize meaningful constituent parts, such as 'poor John,' 'our horses,' 'ran away,' 'got tired.'

A form which can be uttered alone with meaning is a *free*

form; all our examples so far are free forms. A form ('form' always means 'meaningful form') which cannot be uttered alone with meaning is a *bound* form. Examples of bound forms are the suffix '-ish' in 'boyish,' 'girlish,' 'childish,' or the suffix '-s' in 'hats,' 'caps,' 'books.'

A free form which does not consist entirely of lesser free forms is a *word*. Thus, 'boy,' which admits of no further analysis into meaningful parts, is a word; 'boyish,' although capable of such analysis, is a word, because one of the constituents, the suffix '-ish,' is a bound form; other words, such as 'receive,' 'perceive,' 'remit,' 'permit,' consist entirely of bound forms.

A free form which consists entirely of lesser free forms is a *phrase;* examples are 'poor John' or 'poor John ran away.'

Sets of words, such as 'perceive: receive: remit' or 'perceive: permit: remit,' establish a parallelism between the extremes, 'perceive' and 'remit.' The habit which is thus revealed is a *morphologic construction*. In the same way, sets of phrases, such as 'John ran: John fell: Bill fell' or 'John ran: Bill ran: Bill fell,' establish a parallelism between the extremes 'John ran' and 'Bill fell,' and illustrate a *syntactic construction*. The parts of a form which exhibits a construction are the *constituents* of the form: the form itself is a *resultant* form.

In the study of an unknown language we proceed as above: partial similarities between forms reveal their complexity, and we progressively recognize constituents and determine, often with some difficulty, whether they are free or bound. In presenting the description of a language, however, we begin with the constituents and describe the constructions in which they appear.

A construction, morphologic or syntactic, consists in the arrangement of the constituents. In addition to the meaning of the constituents, the resultant form bears a constructional meaning, which is common to all forms that exhibit the same construction. Even more than other elements of meaning, constructional meanings are likely to present difficulties of definition, for they are often remote from simple non-linguistic events.

The features of arrangement differ in different languages.

Modulation is the use of certain special phonemes, *secondary* phonemes, which mark certain forms in construction. In English, features of stress play a large part as secondary phonemes. We have seen this in the contrast between the verb 'convict' and the noun 'convict.' In syntax it appears in the absence of word-stress on certain forms. Thus, in a phrase like 'the house,' the word 'the' is unstressed; on the other hand, it may receive a sentence stress when it is an important feature of the utterance.

Phonetic modification is the substitution of phonemes in a constituent. For instance, 'duke,' when combined with the suffix '-ess' or '-y' is replaced by 'duch-'; in syntax the words 'do not' are optionally replaced, with a slight difference of meaning, by 'don't.' Neither modulation nor phonetic modification plays any part in the specialized scientific uses of language; it is otherwise with the features of arrangement which we now have to consider.

The *selection* of the constituent forms plays a part apparently in all languages. If we combine the word 'milk' with words like 'fresh,' 'cold,' 'good,' we get designations of special kinds of milk: 'fresh milk,' 'cold milk,' 'good milk'; if we combine it with words like 'drink,' 'fetch,' 'use,' we get designations of acts: 'drink milk,' 'fetch milk,' 'use milk.' The difference in constructional meaning goes hand in hand with the selection of the forms. We describe these habits by saying that the construction has two (or more) *positions* which are *filled* by the constituents. A *function* of a form is its privilege of appearing in a certain position of a certain construction. *The function*, collectively, of a form is the sum total of its functions. Forms which have a function in common constitute a *form-class*. Thus, the forms 'milk,' 'fresh milk,' 'cold water,' 'some fine sand,' etc., are in a common form-class, since all of them combine with forms of the form-class 'drink,' 'don't drink,' 'carefully sift,' etc., in the construction of action-on-object. In syntax, as these examples indicate, words and phrases appear in common form-classes. If words alone are considered, their largest inclusive form-classes are known as *parts of speech*. In many languages, and very strikingly in English, the form-classes of syntax over-

lap in so complex a fashion that various part-of-speech classifications are possible, according to the functions which one
chooses primarily to take into account.

The forms of a form-class contain a common feature of meaning, the *class meaning*. The traditional grammar of our schools
gets into hopeless difficulties because it tries to define form-
classes by their class meaning and not by the formal features
which constitute their function.

The use of *order* as a feature of arrangement is by no means as
widespread as the use of selection, but, on account of its simplicity and economy, it plays a great part in the scientific
specializations of language. In English the order of the constituents is a feature of nearly all constructions; thus, in 'fresh milk'
or 'drink milk' the constituents appear only in this order. In
some instances, features of order alone distinguish the positions:
contrast, for example, 'John hit Bill' with 'Bill hit John.'

18. The Sentence

In any one utterance a form which, in this utterance, is not a
constituent of any larger form is a *sentence*. By definition, any
free form and no bound form can occur as a sentence. Various
supplementary features are used in different languages to mark
the sentence, especially its end. In English, secondary phonemes of pitch are used in this way. In much the same manner
as constructions, *sentence types* are distinguished by features of
arrangement. The meanings of these types have to do largely
with the relation of speaker and hearer ("pragmatic" features of
meaning). Thus, pitch and, in part, selection and order determine in English such types as statement ('at four o'clock'),
yes-or-no question ('at four o'clock?'), and supplement question
('at what time?').

In many languages, perhaps in all, certain free forms are
marked off as especially suited to sentence use. A sentence
which consists of such a form is a *full* sentence. In English the
favorite sentence forms are phrases which exhibit certain constructions. The most important is the actor-action construction in which a nominative substantive expression is joined

with a finite-verb expression: 'Poor John ran away.' 'John ran.' 'I'm coming at four o'clock.' 'Can you hear me?' A sentence which does not consist of a favorite sentence form is a *minor* sentence: 'Yes.' 'Fire!' 'At four o'clock.' 'If you can hear me.'

English and many other languages distinguish clearly a type of sentence whose type-meaning can perhaps be described by the term 'report.' In English the report sentences are full-sentence statements exhibiting the actor-action construction or a co-ordination of several actor-action phrases. A great deal of labor has been spent upon attempts at giving a precise definition of this type-meaning, in disregard of the likelihood of its differing in different languages and in oblivion of the danger that our sociology may not be far enough advanced to yield such a definition. For our purpose, at least a rough outline of this meaning will be needed. In the normal response to a report the hearer behaves henceforth as if his sense organs had been stimulated by the impingement of the reported situation upon the sense organs of the speaker. Since the meaningful speech-forms of the report, however, constitute at bottom a discrete arrangement, the hearer's responses can correspond to the speaker's situation to the extent only that is made possible by the approximative character of the report. Thus, when a speaker has said, 'There are some apples in the pantry,' the hearer behaves as though his sense organs had been stimulated by the impingement of the apples upon the speaker's sense organs—as though the speaker's adventure with the apples, to the extent that it is represented by the meanings of the speech-forms, had been witnessed by the hearer, not visually, but through some sense organ capable of a certain discontinuous range of stimulation.

Irony, jest, mendacity, and the like represent derived types of speech and response; they need not here concern us.

19. Constructional Level and Scope

Constructions are classified, first of all, by the form-class of the resultant form.

If the resultant form differs, as to the big distinctions of form-class, from the constituents, the construction is said to be *exocentric*. For instance, actor-action phrases like 'John ran away' or 'He ran away' differ in form-class from nominative substantive expressions like 'John' or 'he' and from finite-verb expressions like 'ran away.' Similarly, the functions of prepositional phrases, such as 'in the house' or 'with him,' differ from those of a preposition ('in,' 'with') and from those of an objective substantive expression ('the house,' 'him').

If the resultant form agrees as to the major distinctions of form-class with one or more of the constituents, then the construction is said to be *endocentric*. For instance, the phrase 'bread and butter' has much the same function as the words 'bread,' 'butter.'

If, as in this example, two or more of the constituents have the same function as the resultant form, the construction is *coordinative* and these constituents are the *members* of the coordination. If only one constituent agrees in form-class with the resultant form, the construction is *subordinative;* this constituent is the *head* of the subordination, and any other constituent is an *attribute* of this head. Thus, in 'fresh milk,' the head is 'milk' and the attribute is 'fresh'; in 'this fresh milk,' the head is 'fresh milk' and the attribute 'this'; in 'very fresh,' the head is 'fresh' and the attribute 'very'; in 'very fresh milk,' the head is 'milk' and the attribute is 'very fresh.'

The difference of analysis in these two cases is worth observing:

> this / fresh milk
> very fresh / milk

Although we are unable to give precise definitions of meaning, especially of such ethnically created ranges as constructional meanings and class meanings, yet the mere subsistence of like and unlike sets determines schemes of construction. Only in rare cases does the structure of a language leave us a choice between different orders of description. At each step of analysis we must discover the *immediate* constituents of the form; if we fail in this, our scheme will be contradicted by the constructional meanings of the language.

If a form contains repeated levels of endocentric construction, there will be a word or co-ordinated set of words which serves as the *center* of the entire phrase. Thus, in the phrase 'this very fresh milk,' the word 'milk' is the center.

The formal features of construction—selection of constituent forms, order, phonetic modification, and modulation by means of secondary phonemes—differ greatly in various languages and sometimes lead to very complex structures of word or phrase, but they seem nowhere to permit of an unlimited box-within-box cumulation. Even simple formations may lead to ambiguity because the *scope*—that is, the accompanying constituents on the proper level—of a form may not be marked. For instance, 'an apple and a pear or a peach' may mean exactly two pieces of fruit: then the immediate constituents are 'an apple / and / a pear or a peach,' and the phrase 'a pear or a peach' and the phrase 'an apple' constitute the scope of the form 'and.' On the other hand, the phrase may mean either two pieces of fruit or one piece: then the immediate constituents are 'an apple and a pear / or / a peach,' and the scope of 'and' now consists, on its level, of the phrases 'an apple,' 'a pear.' Similarly, 'three times five less two times two' may mean 26, 18, 11, or 3. These uncertainties are not tolerable in the scientific use of language; it is a striking peculiarity of this use that they are removed only in written notation—as especially by the parentheses and brackets that are used in algebra. The result is a system of writing which cannot be paralleled in actual speech.

20. Varieties of Reference

A thoroughgoing comparison of speech-forms, say in some one language, with features of the non-linguistic world is impossible at the present state of our knowledge. Our system of responses, with its neat discrimination of objects, classes, positions, qualities, movements, etc., results very largely from our use of language. We cannot return to the animal's or the infant's state of speechless response.

In order to find out how much of our world is independent of any one language, we might try to compare the grammars and lexicons of different languages. At present we have reasonably complete data for a few languages only; at some future time, when this task can be undertaken, the results will be of great interest. The forms of any one language could scarcely serve as a frame of reference: we should need, instead, a non-linguistic scale by which to measure.

It is the task of science to provide a system of responses which are independent of the habits of any person or community. These responses are twofold, in accordance with the universal scheme of human behavior: science provides relevant handling responses and clarified speech-forms. In the nature of the case, however, the entire result is transmitted and preserved in a verbal record. If science had completed its task, we could accurately define the meanings of speech-forms.

Even the most favorable type of meanings will show the difficulty of definition. Clusters of stimuli which produce roughly the same elementary responses in all people and, in accordance with this, are not necessarily tied up with communal habits, have been successfully studied: this is the domain of so-called external phenomena, the domain of physical and biological science. Here some of the simpler lexical classifications of language correspond in the main to the classifications of science, as, for instance, in the names of familiar species of plants and animals. However, there is often some gross divergence, as when several species are called by the same name, or one species by several names, and there is a great deal of less manageable vagueness at the borders—species which sometimes are and sometimes are not included in a designation. Even in this simplest sphere, the meaning of many speech-forms involves ethnological features. Here, too, we encounter, on the simplest level, speech-forms which have no extra-linguistic validity, unless it be in the designation of secondarily created artifacts: dragons, griffins, unicorns, etc.

Where science reveals a continuous scale of phenomena, such as color, the segments included under linguistic terms vary greatly in different languages; they overlap and grow vague at the edges; and they are subject to extraneous limitations ('bay,' 'roan').

When we come to meanings which are involved in the habit of communities and individuals, we fall even farther short of accurate definition, since the branches of science which deal with these things are quite undeveloped. In practice we resort here to artistic, practical and ethical, or religious terminologies of definition, and these, however valuable for our subsequent conduct, fail to satisfy the peculiar requirements of science.

In all spheres the structure of languages reveals elements of meaning which are quite remote from the shape of any one situation and are attached rather to constellations which include, often enough, personal or ethnical features. Relatively simple instances are words like 'if,' 'concerning,' 'because,' or the subtle difference, so important in English, between the types 'he ran' : 'he was running' : 'he has run' : 'he has been running.' The difficulty is even greater in the case of bound forms, which cannot be isolated in their language; consider, for instance, the deprecative feature in some of the uses of '-ish' ('mannish').

Constructional meanings and class meanings pervade a language, in part as universally present *categories;* they generally defy our powers of definition. The singular and plural categories of nouns in English are relatively manageable, but include some troublesome features, such as 'wheat' versus 'oats.' Gender-classes, as in French or German, are almost entirely ethnological in character. The normal speaker, without special training, is incapable of talking about these features; they are not reflected in any habits beyond their mere presence in the structure of the language. The major form-classes are remote from any extra-linguistic phenomena. If we assign to the English class of substantives some such meaning as "object," then words like 'fire,' 'wind,' and 'stream' require an ethnologic commentary. The mechanics of a language often require that otherwise similar designations occur in more than one grammatical class. Thus, in English, as a center for the actor in the actor-action construction, we require a noun: hence we have forms like 'height' beside 'high' or 'movement' beside '(it) moves.' Duplications of this kind are not symptoms of any special level of culture but result merely from a rather common grammatical condition.

21. Substitution and Determination

Apparently, all languages save labor by providing *substitute* forms whose meaning rests wholly upon the situation of speaker and hearer, especially upon earlier speech. Since these occur more frequently than specific forms, they are easily uttered and understood; moreover, they are nearly always short and, often enough, bound forms. Thus 'I' and 'you' replace names, and 'this' and 'that' the naming of a thing which may be identified by gesture. The most important type of substitution, for our subject, is *anaphora:* the substitute replaces repetition of a speech-form which has just been uttered or is soon to be uttered. Thus, the set 'he, she, it, they' replaces noun expressions, and the set 'do, does, did' replaces finite-verb expressions ('I'll go by train if John does'). A form competent to fill one position of a construction may suffice for anaphora of a phrase embodying the whole construction: 'Mary dances better than Jane'; here 'Jane' serves as the anaphoric substitute for 'Jane dances.'

Akin to the substitute forms, and very often identical with them, are *determiners*, which indicate a range within the class of phenomena that is designated by an ordinary speech-form: 'this apple,' 'the apple' (anaphora), 'every apple,' 'all apples,' etc. We shall be interested in determiners which leave the specimen entirely unrestricted: 'an apple,' 'some apple,' 'any apple.' If only one specimen is involved, anaphora is easily made ('it,' 'the apple,' 'this apple'); but, where several specimens are involved, English, like other languages, provides very poor means for distinguishing them. To provide for the identification of more than one variable, we must look to other phases of language which contain the germs of a more accurate system of speech.

IV. Precision in Natural Language

22. Reporting Statements

To discuss the meaning of all the varieties of utterance would be equivalent to outlining a complete sociology. We need deal only with a single type, the report (§ 18), since it alone is required for science.

The welfare of a community depends, so far as the actions of people are concerned, most directly upon simple handling activities whose occasion and performance are plainly observable—activities such as the gathering of food, hunting, fishing, construction of dwellings, boats, and containers, manufacture of clothing and tools, etc. These are manipulations of non-human objects, satisfactory in their biophysical aspect. Even where human bodies figure as objects, as in surgery or conflict, these actions suffice in themselves, with a minimum of biosocial significance. The situation in which an act of this sort will succeed does not always present itself in full to the performer; another person may mediate by speech: 'There are berries beyond the cliff'; 'The fish are biting today'; 'My moccasins need patching'; etc. Reports like these concern matters where behavior is uniform: in general, people will agree on the outcome of a test. This is the sphere of ordinary life out of which science grows forth. Natural science grows forth directly; the scientific study of man is hampered by the difficulty of subjecting biosocially conditioned behavior to such simple and testable reports.

If we try for a moment, and with full recognition of inadequacy, to ignore the forms of language, we may perhaps say that a report of this kind conveys, in the first place, the verbal substitute of a stimulus: 'It's raining.' Here the 'it' is an empty and merely formal indication of a point of reference, for which there is in this case no practical need. In most instances, however, some other stimulus, which has already affected the hearer or has been verbally represented to him, serves as a point of reference for the placing of the new stimulus which the hearer has not experienced: 'There are some apples in the pantry'—the last three words may represent nothing new, a familiar complex of stimuli to which the apples are now added. This adherence of a new stimulus to an old one is perhaps the practical background that is formalized in the actor-and-action or subject-and-predicate constructions which appear in the favorite sentence types of many languages: 'The fish | are biting |

today'; Russian 'Iván dóma,' literally 'John | at home.' However, there is no rigid agreement between the structure of the practical stimuli and the formal structure of the utterance.

The behavior of the speakers distinguishes very well between the features of the report which convey the relevant handling stimulus and the features of purely social and personal significance, such as especially the formal structure. Two reports of different structure ('There are berries beyond the cliff' and 'Behind the steep cliff over there you can find some berries') may mediate the same simple handling sequence; it is only the accompanying personal and social adjustments which differ. It is a well-tried hypothesis of linguistics that formally different utterances always differ in meaning; they may be *equivalent*, however, as to some one partial phase of meaning. Of this, the best example is the practical phase of the simple report; out of it there grows forth the equivalence of variously worded statements in scientific discourse. Here, as in the simple reporting of ordinary language, the equivalence covers the phase of meaning which is observable indifferently by all persons.

23. Negation

Every language, apparently, contains inhibitory forms, such as 'Don't!' The report may be thrown into reverse by utterance in a *negative* form: 'There aren't any apples in the pantry.' As this English example shows, the negative version may differ formally in complicated ways from the positive. The human voyage in space and time is linear: response cannot be made simultaneously to a report and its negative. If both are received as sentences, without comment as to biosocial values, the hearer is no better able to act than before; he has heard a *contradiction*.

It is very important, but not always easy, to distinguish, in this matter, between formal grammatical features and features of meaning. Contradiction is a feature of meanings, not of grammatical forms. In the normal case, where the contradictory phrases appear as separate sentences, there is, by definition, no grammatical nexus between them. In the more difficult case, where they appear in the same sentence ('It is green because it is not green'), there is no grammatical incongruity. It is the meaning of the negating speech-forms which is here involved.

If we wished, using the full extent of a language (like English) in its ordinary form, to guard ourselves against contradiction in every discourse, no matter how long, we should have to master the universe in what would amount to omniscience.

One is likely to be deceived about this because in simple cases the rules for non-contradiction may take on a formal character. For instance, in Old English and in most dialects of modern English, a negated sentence often contains more than one negative unit ('I ain't got none'); in Latin and in present-day Standard English two negatives are separately superadded so as to cancel each other ('I did not have nothing'). What is here involved is the meaning of the negative words. The contradiction in a phrase like 'a round square' rests upon the meaning of the terms 'round' and 'square' or upon that of the basic terms which underlie successive definitions.

In miniature linguistic systems, such as are produced in logic and mathematics, the conventions for avoiding contradiction are rules of meaning (semantic rules). Thus, in a system of logistic, it may be agreed that a statement and the same statement preceded by the symbol '$\sim$' may not, upon pain of contradiction, appear as sentences in any one discourse. This agreement defines the meaning of '$\sim$.'

The dichotomy of contradictory sentences inheres in the nature of human speech: a sentence in a discourse excludes its contrary. Thus we obtain *implication*. The sentences 'Socrates is a man' and 'All men are mortal' exclude the sentence 'Socrates is not mortal,' and this is the same as saying that they imply the sentence 'Socrates is mortal.' These effects are due to the meanings of the words 'all,' 'is,' 'a,' and 'not,' and to the meanings of the grammatical forms.

24. Abstraction and Approximation

A report concerning a simple handling activity covers, in a rough way, only so much of the situation as is useful. If the speaker is prompted, say by an additional question ('What color are the apples?'), he is usually able to extend his report. Moreover, he can often subject himself, in the way of continued observation, to further stimuli of the complex in question ('I'll look and see how many apples there are'). Every apple has a color, and every set of apples a number, but these features are not communicated in the report, 'There are some apples in the pantry.' It is a trick of pseudo-philosophy to postulate a metaphysical "concept" of an apple to account for the imperfect reporting function of the word 'apple.' The obvious fact is simply that a speech does not mention every feature of stimulus. Since the ranges of stimulation and of predisposition are to all practical purposes continuous, and language can provide only a discrete set of forms, this *abstract* character of language is inevitable: not all the features of a situation appear in the report. If we do not consider the extension of an object, we may speak of it as a 'point'; if we speak of one dimension only, we may call it a 'line'; if of two only, we call it a 'surface'; terms like 'straight line,' 'plane,' 'triangle,' etc., add further characteristics, but still leave unmentioned certain simple features which are present in every object. This does not create a world of "concepts."

By lengthening his report, the speaker may tell more: we distinguish degrees of *approximation*. So far as the speaker has observed, or else perhaps only under reservation of irrelevant detail, the linear object if turned in a certain way would occupy the same position as before; hence the speaker says that the 'line' is a 'straight' one. It may be true that no object has been found to fulfill this condition to such an extent as to appear 'straight' under our best observation with mechanical aids. This means merely that the speaker did not employ these aids or else that his report was incomplete in this respect.

Although the meanings of language are discrete, there is no limit to their cumulation. By extending his utterance, the speaker may come closer and closer to a full picture of the situation. This is familiar, for one thing, from the art of fiction. In the realm of handling operation one rarely approximates beyond the features that are useful. In the scientific expansion of this domain, however, one often dwells upon features which have no immediate use in practical life—such features, for instance, as appear in the botanist's systematic classification of families, genera, and species. Accordingly, scientists and specialists in practical operation invent *technical terms*, either by redefining everyday expressions or by borrowing or creating new words. A technical term, then, replaces long phrases, or even a complicated discourse, and its meaning is fixed by an agreement of definition, which, in science, receives explicit formulation and strict adherence.

The useful approximation, in a simple society, will be a rough one; as civilization progresses, usefulness is discovered in closer approximations. Utterances and responses become more variable. This *variability* of response in individuals, and, thanks to manifold specialization of individuals, in the community, may yield a basis for a scientific definition of what we mean in everyday life by such words as 'welfare' or 'happiness.'

25. Counting

The part of ordinary language which most immediately opens into the language-forms of science is the number complex. The equality and inequality of sets of discrete objects are defined in terms of the result of placing the objects of the sets in one-to-one correspondence. Actual placing together of the objects is often inconvenient or impossible. The fingers (and, in suitable climate and surroundings, the toes) serve as an intermediate set. Speech-forms are more convenient. The quinary, decimal, and vigesimal groupings of these forms reflect the habit of counting on the fingers. Some languages provide only a few number-words; many, however, have an indefinitely extensible system. If any number-words are otherwise meaningful, this does not affect their use in counting: all that is needed, and, in most instances, all that is provided, is a set of otherwise meaningless free forms which every child learns to recite in a fixed order.

The set is more easily remembered, and can become indefinitely extensible, if it consists of a short sequence repeated over and over again, with an auxiliary counting of the repetitions. Thus, in the decadic system we have:

one, two, ... , nine, ten;
ten one, ten two, ... , ten nine, two tens;
two tens one, two tens two, ... , two tens nine, three tens;

    .   .   .   .

ten tens one, ten tens two, ... , ten tens nine, ten tens ten;
ten tens ten one, ...

The longer forms may be replaced by shorter substitutes, as 'ten tens' by 'one hundred,' 'ten hundreds' by 'one thousand,' etc. Later in the sequence such abbreviative forms may be agreed upon by specialists, as 'billion,' which in England means 'a million millions,' but in the United States 'a thousand millions.'

The system thus outlined appears plainly in Chinese; in most languages it is encumbered, but not changed, by irregularities, such as our 'eleven' for 'ten one,' 'twenty' for 'two tens,' etc.

Evidently there is no point at which the recitation has to end. No matter what number expression be given, one can always cap it by one which belongs later in the sequence. This is what we mean, of course, when we say that the system is indefinitely extensible.

Of all the features of ordinary language, the number expressions enter most directly into the scientific use of language, and they continue there to occupy the principal place. Putting discrete objects in one-to-one correspondence is perhaps as uniform, from person to person, as any operation. Scientists try to reduce their tasks to this shape. Our uniformity in the use of number expressions becomes the basis of complex systems of discourse which confine themselves largely to these expressions and enable us to perform long calculations without leaving this safe ground.

26. Infinite Classes of Speech-Forms

The indefinite extensibility of the system of number expressions of ordinary language leads to the *infinite classes* of mathematics. This linguistic background is worth examining, if only to save mystical aberrations.

Given any set of number expressions, every speaker is able to utter, without doubt or dispute, a number expression that is not in the set. This is what we mean by an *infinite class* of speech-forms.

In mathematics a less direct definition is useful: to say that a class is *infinite* means that it can be put in one-to-one correspondence with a genuine part of itself. Thus, we can put the set of all (positive integer) numbers in one-to-one correspondence with the set of all even (positive integer) numbers by simply assigning to each number its double.

This mathematical definition demands something more than the linguistic definition which we have given above, since we can define a one-to-one correspondence only if there is some order or system in the class. This condition is fulfilled, of course, in the case of the number expressions of ordinary language, and it will be fulfilled in any infinite class of speech-forms that is at all useful in discourse. In practice mathematicians sometimes employ the linguistic version, as, for instance, in Euclid's proof of the theorem that the class of prime numbers is infinite.

The popular or religious use of the word 'infinite' has no place in science, for in this use the word means something which cannot be dealt with, even verbally—something which cannot be grasped or understood—by the powers of a human being. In the sense with which we are concerned, the only infinite classes are classes of speech-forms. One might perhaps devise an indefinitely extensible system of other actions, such as gestures or graphic markings, but our saturation in language would from the very outset force us to assign verbal substitutes to the forms of such a system. Persons not accustomed to the observation of language are likely, in this matter, to see objects where only speech-forms are present. To name or define an infinite class of hypothetical objects or events is merely to adduce a class of speech-forms. Archimedes showed that one may name a number greater than the possible number of grains of sand in the solar system.

Any infinite class of speech-forms can be put into linear order, for each form consists of a linear (or quasi-linear, § 16) sequence of phonemes, and the forms may be alphabetized according to an arbitrary rank assigned to the phonemes. Apart from the imperfections of our traditional system of writing, which do not affect the matter, this is what we do in our everyday alphabetizing. No matter what new word may come into English, or what strange name into a list of telephone subscribers, there is no difficulty as to its place in the alphabetical sequence.

If we make the additional demand that the order be like that of the number expressions in counting, such that every form has an immediate successor (with no intervening forms), then we must call in the number expressions: the speech-forms must be grouped first according to the number of phonemes (or, in traditional writing, of letters) in each one and, then, within each of these groups, alphabetically.

Mathematicians, to be sure, set themselves a much harder task, since they deal with infinite classes each of whose members is an infinite class of speech-forms, as, for instance, with classes of unending decimal expressions. One begins with such forms as 'one-third' or 'the square root of two' or 'pi' (this last defined as the limit sum of a simply constructed infinite series). Then one may demand some special form of expression (such as that of a decimal) whose constituents (such as the digits of the decimal) may require laborious calculation, one by one. Then, further, one may define new classes whose members depend upon these singly calculated forms, as, for example, an unending decimal whose digits depend, according to some stated formula, upon the corresponding digits of the decimal expression of pi. Various types of discourse can be agreed upon, according to the kind of infinite classes that may be admissible. The actually uttered speech-forms, no matter how elaborate, which define or name any class, can always be alphabetized.

The utterance of all members of an infinite class can be required neither in mathematics nor anywhere else.

V. Scientific Language

27. Development of Scientific Language

Persons who carry on a specialized activity develop technical terms and locutions; these shorten speech and make response more accurate. Such are the special vocabularies of fishermen, carpenters, miners, and other craftsmen. These terminologies contribute to the dialectal differentiation which exists in all fair-sized speech communities. The special vocabularies and turns of speech which are used in the various branches of science belong in this same general type; only, as scientific observation reaches beyond the interests of ordinary life, the vocabulary of science becomes very large. From timid neologisms it grows to a state where some scheme of word creation stands at the service of every member of the guild. In this way European and American scientists freely coin words by derivation and composition of Latin and ancient Greek stems; such words, with adaptations of grammar and phonetics, are accepted as loan-words in the scientific dialects of the several languages.

The exact responses, and the careful and often complex calculations of science, enforce an unusually meticulous style of speech. The syntactic scope of forms and the domain of substitutes have to be clearly indicated. This, with the elimination of personal factors, produces a general scientific style of utterance. The sentences may extend to great length and may evoke an immediate response only in hearers or readers who are favorably predisposed by training; on the other hand, the message, once grasped, is unmistakable. In pseudo-science the difficulties but not the advantages are imitated; the clinical symptoms are locutions which do not lead to handling response, appeals to personal or ethical connotation, and, above all, an obscurity which remains even under analysis by a trained recipient.

At an advanced stage the demands for exhibition of data and for complex but unerring calculation lead to speech-forms and

260

especially to written discourses which move outside the sphere of ordinary language. The ancient Greeks carried on mathematical demonstrations largely in ordinary language; it was the development, in the early modern period, of arithmetic and algebra, with its box-within-box markings of scope, that divorced scientific calculation not only from ordinary language but, to all practical purposes, from vocal utterance. People learned to calculate rapidly and accurately by visual reception and graphic manipulation of a small stock of characters in simple arrangements. Thus there arose the plan of conducting, or at least outlining and testing, scientific discourse by means of simple and rigidly manipulated graphic systems.

Without an entirely sharp boundary, we have, then, linguistically, two types of scientific discourse which we shall here distinguish by the names *informal* and *formal*. (We are here using the term 'formal' in its everyday sense and not with the technical meaning which it has in logic.) *Informal* scientific discourse uses ordinary language with the addition of technical words and turns of phrase and with syntactic and stylistic restrictions in favor of uniform response. It is generally capable of reception by a qualified listener. *Formal* scientific discourse uses a rigidly limited vocabulary and syntax and moves from sentence to sentence only within the range of conventional rules. In general, it can be carried on only in writing, mainly because no vocal equivalents have been devised or practiced for the elaborate markings of scope.

Within formal scientific discourse it is customary to distinguish, again without a sharp boundary, between mathematical discourse in general and a special type, symbolic logic, which is devised to establish and test the basic rules of scientific discourse.

Within mathematical discourse there is probably no linguistic difference between applied mathematics—that is, calculations which form part of a scientific discourse—and pure mathematics, where calculation is made for its own interest, with arbitrary axioms replacing the observational data and hypotheses of scientific procedure. Linguistic variety consists primarily in the use or non-use of the number vocabulary. The term 'mathematics' is ordinarily applied only to formal discourse whose basic vocabulary is numerical, and to geometry even when numbers are absent or play a subsidiary part. Other examples of non-numerical mathematical discourse appear, however, in such symbolisms and calculations as those of chemistry and of linguistics. One tries, wherever it is possible, to employ numerical discourse, because of the favorable character of the number-words and because of the stock of ready-made devices and calculations which has been accumulated in the pursuit of pure mathematics.

In all this development we have not left the domain of language. We reach its outskirts in the use of written discourses which will fail of effect if given in vocal form (§ 19). In general, to be sure, the separate written characters have been agreed upon as substitutes for specific words or phrases. In many cases, however, we manage best by ignoring these values and confining ourselves to the manipulation of the written symbols; systems of symbolic logic, especially, may be viewed, in a formal way, as systems of marks and conventions for the arrangement of these marks. The transition to non-linguistic activity could be made if we devised such marks and conventions without any initial or final linguistic interpretation, quite as in children's games that are played with paper and pencil. The marks could then no longer be qualified as writing. Actually, our formal systems serve merely as written or mechanical mediations between utterances of language. On the other hand, important linguistic conditions may be obscured when we speak of a formal system, like a system of symbolic logic, as a "language." The interpretation, initial and final, of the procedure is made in terms of some natural language (such as English), and the system as a whole is meaningless to a reader to whom it has not been interpreted in these terms. It differs even from an "artificial language," such as Esperanto, since the latter supplies a complete set of speech responses for ordinary use, while a mathematical system or a system of symbolic logic supplies only a limited set of responses that mediate between acts of speech.

By way of parenthesis it may be well to add that no artificial language, so far, has reached the function of a natural language. The artificial language is devised by speakers of a natural language, inevitably in terms of this and with little semantic deviation, and it is acquired, in similar terms, by persons who already speak a natural language. It would attain the status of such a language if a group of infants acquired it, by the usual process of demonstration, as their native speech. The only actual event even approaching this has been the implanting of Hebrew upon infants in Palestine: preserved only in written records, Hebrew had for some two thousand years been no person's native language.

Even such a thing as a tabulation of numbers is linguistic; apart from the verbal character of the elements, the arrangement leads to a linguistic interpretation. We leave the domain of language only when we come to a drawing, a geometrical diagram, or a map: here, indeed, we employ a non-verbal object directly as a representation of another non-verbal object.

A formal dialect, such as a system of symbolic logic, may very well be used to state the rules which govern its use. This means simply that the formal dialect suffices for statements about word-order, selection, and substitution. It neither, on the one hand, removes the system from its linguistic status nor, on the other hand, gives it the standing of an independent "language."

28. General Character of Scientific Language

An act of speech is a happening in the world and, as such, an object of science; the branch of science which studies it is linguistics. Scientists, however, are speakers and may agree to utter speech in certain ways; thanks to the simplicity of phonetic structure, they are able quite accurately and uniformly to adhere to these agreements. Accordingly, they treat their own utterances not as an object of science but as a part of scientific procedure. In this sense, and to the extent that social agreements about speech can be maintained, scientists may be said to "control" the forms of their technical dialect, in contrast with the world of meanings—that is, the world of events, including the utterance of speech other than that which forms part of the scientist's own activity. This outside world is reportable and predictable only to the extent that earlier acts of science have mastered it—at best imperfectly.

The scientist may construct a discourse, as in pure mathematics, in which the speech-forms have no meaning beyond that which is created by the scientific agreements governing their use—a type of discourse anticipated by the natural numbers of ordinary speech and, in most instances, based upon them. Such a discourse produces a calculation, made for its own interest, or as a model, or with a view to eventual use; about the outside world it tells nothing. We may be sure of its correctness because it moves only within the verbal agreements upon which it is based.

On the other hand, as soon as we admit meanings of the outside world, we risk error, and our certainty is then only such as may result from earlier acts of science. In a priori reasoning we see a sleight of hand which introduces observations or beliefs of everyday life into a seemingly pure calculation.

It is our task to discover which of our terms are undefined or partially defined or draggled with fringes of connotation, and to catch our hypotheses and exhibit them by clear statements, instead of letting them haunt us in the dark. The mentalist fails to list his undefined terms or to state his hypotheses; he wonders at the obtuseness with which we refuse to accept certain "concepts" which are necessary in the vocabulary of everyday life.

29. Publicity and Translatability

Science deals with the phases of response that are alike for all normal persons. Its observations and predictions can be tested by anyone. Where a temporal feature is present (as in the passage of a meteor), the question concerns the acceptability of a report and is usually settled by agreement of qualified independent observers. Unique personal or communal behavior figures in science as an object, which may be observed like any other; but it does not figure as a part of scientific procedure. This exclusion demands a redefinition of speech-forms; even number words like 'seven' or 'thirteen' have to be stripped of superstitious connotation. In the terminology of physics, the most advanced branch of science, one can see how far this stripping has been carried and surmise how much farther it still must go. Linguistically, as well as in handling, science is a *public* activity. In scientific colloquy recognition is granted neither to the private predispositions of the participants nor to the private connotations which they attach to forms of language; each participant burns his own smoke.

This does not mean that such predispositions, private adventures, or connotations are excluded from the object range of science: as objects they will be studied in psychology, biography, history, aesthetics, etc.

As, by convention and training, the participants in scientific discourse learn consistently to ignore all private factors of meaning, the lexical, grammatical, and stylistic features of their informal discourse become indifferent: each scientist responds to each discourse only with the relevant operations or their linguistic substitutes. Thus, half-a-dozen differently worded treatises, say on elementary mechanics, will produce the same result, so far as science is concerned. In this uniformity the differences between languages (as English, French, German), far-reaching and deep-seated as they are, constitute merely a part of the communicative dross. We say that scientific discourse is *translatable,* and mean by this that not only the difference between languages but, within each language, the difference between operationally equivalent wordings has no scientific effect.

30. Postulational Form

This stripping-down of meanings and exclusion of silent hypotheses has cost mankind much labor and many heartaches, and will cost more. Twists of meaning and of belief that prevail in our community may deceive us all; whoever has detected one or another finds himself misunderstood, since his fellows often relapse into attaching the traditional meaning to his words or inserting the traditional hypothesis into their reading of his calculations.

In order to unmask blind connotations and beliefs and to bring disagreements into the light of operation, where they may be subject to test, scientists resort—not often enough, to be sure—to the method of *postulates*, an explicit statement of what is taken for granted. One lists the undefined terms which one takes from everyday language or, more often, from other branches of science where they have been defined. Physicalism, as we have seen (§ 9), is the hypothesis which supposes that, in the unified vocabulary of science which is thus laid out, the ultimately undefined words will be simple terms in the domain of elementary physics—which, in turn, of course, rest upon physical terms of everyday life. In the same way, alongside the observed data, and on a par with them as starting-points for calculation, one states the hypotheses—the suppositions, generally results of other branches of science, which one accepts as prior to the work in hand. All new terms, after that, are rigidly defined: the new term is to be fully and freely interchangeable with the defining phrase. Only predictions, reached by acceptable calculation, may be added, by way of testing, to the list of hypotheses. If the terms are few enough and the structure of hypothesis and observation is simple enough, a mathematical system may be found or devised for the calculations. A dramatic instance of this was the invention of co-ordinate geometry. At best, of course, the uncertainties of all human response will play into the choice and character of our observation and, indirectly, through the failings of other sciences, into our structure of hypothesis. In the sciences that deal with man there is little enough that we have even learned to observe. It is all the more desirable that we lay bare our situation and our doubts by the frank survey of the postulational method.

It is the task of logic to examine the consistency of our calculations, mathematical or informal. If calculation can be performed in terms of numerical mathematics, its validity stands or falls with the validity of this discipline, and this, so far, has been the main concern of modern logic. If we cannot translate our discourse into an accepted dialect of mathematics, we had better travel with care. Formal rules of calculation would be equivalent to the meaning of our terms and to the content of our hypotheses, but these are often too vague or complex for formal discourse. Most scientific investigations are born with the makeshift help of informal methodology rather than with the professional guidance of formal logic.

31. Sentence-Forms of Scientific Language

The translatability of scientific discourse allows informal discourse to maintain a wide range of variation in vocabulary, grammar, and style; but, by the same token, this variation plays no serious part in the work of science. In principle we could agree upon any number of formal dialects, each capable of a uniform version of the results of science. The character of such a dialect is limited only by the fundamental linguistic type of scientific discourse. However, we have seen that certain speech-forms, most strikingly the number expressions, offer advantages great enough to make our discourse tend always in their direction. Apart from the special vocabularies of the several branches of science—or rather, apart from the great vocabulary of science—our discourse tends always toward the shape that is provided by mathematics and formal logic. Accordingly, we need here outline only the features which seem necessary in a formal dialect that is to serve for the use of science, and we may ignore the possibilities of expansion and variation.

Of sentence types, only the full-sentence statement comes into consideration. Every sentence will consist either of a statement-phrase (§ 18) or of several such in co-ordination. Statements, of course, will figure also as subordinate parts of large sentences.

This restriction would make bound forms of all parts of utterance other than the favored type of phrase: the structure of our statements would be a matter of morphology. In fact, it is possible to devise systems of discourse in which, for example, every phoneme (or, graphically, every letter) will have a meaning.

Such a system will be very compact but inconveniently remote from ordinary language.

It is customary, instead, even in formal systems, to use words and phrases of ordinary language as the smallest meaningful units. This is done because, on the one hand, the morphology of most languages is whimsical and complicated, and, on the other hand, we wish in explanatory discourse, in definition, and in logical discussion to isolate every meaningful form. Hence we speak of forms like 'not,' 'and,' 'plus,' etc., as "words," even though within the system of formal speech they dare not appear as sentences.

Calculation may be viewed as a process of exclusion. A set of initial sentences (report of observation and hypotheses) excludes certain other sentences, including the negatives of certain other sentences; a sentence whose negative is excluded is thereby included (implied) in our discourse. All other sentences are irrelevant. Accordingly, a scientific dialect will contain such forms as 'not,' 'excludes,' 'implies' ('therefore,' 'if . . . ., then . . . .'). One or several such must be undefined; the rest can be defined. The dichotomy of including and excluding statements inheres in the nature of language. A system which contained intermediate values (as, say, of probability) would still have to provide this dichotomy for statements in its discourse.

A report transmits either the mere existence of a stimulus or the accompaniment of a known stimulus by a new one. In either case, the report may give some analysis of the stimuli. Hence we may expect statements of such types as 'There exists . . . .' and '. . . . is. . . . .' Formally, if we make the necessary agreements, the mere presentation of a speech-form or of a sequence of speech-forms in a fixed order might be made to suffice; we approximate ordinary language by using words or phrases of *existence* and of *predication*.

In most languages the constituents of a predication (two-part statement) belong to different form-classes: 'John | ran'; 'This apple | is red.' Senseless locutions like 'Ran | ran' or 'Is red | is red' are grammatically impossible. However, the provision of duplicate forms, such as 'red' and 'redness'—lexically similar expressions in more than one form-class—makes it grammatically possible to say 'Redness | is red.' If this is not apprehended as nonsense, contradictions may arise. Thus, if a class of three members is a "triad," and in our discussion there appear exactly three such classes, A, B, C, then we may be tempted to say that the "class" of triads (T) "is a member of itself"; then, however, there are four such classes—A, B, C, T—and the "class" of triads is not "a member of itself"; but, remove T, and there are again three—a hopeless contradiction. Accordingly, if one wishes to use locutions of the type 'Red is a color,' one must distinguish different levels among the forms which enter into predication.

If the stimuli are broken into parts, more than one speech-form may appear in statements of existence, and more than two in predicative statements: 'There exists (a pair of men in the relation of) father-son'; and, George and Edward being known, 'George (and) Edward are father-son.' Here 'father-son' figures as a unit combining with the two units 'George' and 'Edward.'

A third type of sentence will be *equational*, of a form like '. . . . equals . . . .' or '. . . . means. . . . .' It is this type which makes definition possible; accordingly, it must remain undefined. We have seen that, in scientific speech, definition implies complete interchangeability of the new term with the old: if this is not agreed upon, we cannot develop the kind of dialect that serves in scientific use.

Finally, we shall have a form for the exclusion of statements, such as 'not. . . . .' From this most strikingly, but actually not more than from our other fundamental expressions, there arise the rules of calculation. These rules embody such meaning as is granted to the undefined forms of a system. They govern the sequence of sentences: they are not grammatical (morphologic or syntactic) but lexical.

32. Syntactic Features

The type of statement which says that (the known) George is the father of (the known) Edward will present a formal shape something like 'FS (George, Edward).' Here the two names are syntactically co-ordinate but not interchangeable, since the order (father first) has been agreed upon. A commutative construction would appear if we said that Edward and George were brothers, as 'BB (Edward, George).' We require a construction which co-ordinates any number of terms, to begin with, in a linear sequence, with order fixed or free. Such sequences, familiar from Cartesian geometry and from physics, are *vectors*. The definitions of this term which appear in elementary treatises put the cart before the horse, since by appealing to "direction" or specifying conditions for a "change of co-ordinates," they very improperly use an application or a special eventuality of reckoning to define a form of speech. It is only after we have defined a numerical vector as a sequence of numbers in fixed order that it devolves upon the geometer or physicist to show that the vector can be used to state a direction or to discuss how its terms will be altered by a new frame of reference. Otherwise we are exposed to mysticism: the vector may become in the end a "creation of our thoughts" ("ein Gedankending").

A more complex constellation may require a higher ordering: *matrices* are syntactically of two dimensions, as when we name someone's grandparents, say paternal first and men first:

John	Edna
Thomas	Lilian

The written form allows of two syntactic dimensions; if we used a model in space, say of wires and significant beads, we could construct super-matrices of three syntactic dimensions. It would be easy to formulate problems which required more than three syntactic dimensions, but difficult to devise an appropriate symbolism.

Scientific speech inevitably follows ordinary language in designating sets of similar phenomena by one term, but it then requires a far more systematic determination (§ 21). If several phenomena of the set play different parts in the discourse, the term itself is a *variable*, and some unmistakable identification distinguishes the separate specimens (as, in algebra, 'x_1,' 'x_2,' 'x_3,' etc.). This allows us to dispense with the 'a,' 'any,' 'the' of ordinary language. By means of existence statements one can then define precise terms in the sphere of our 'some,' 'all,' 'no.'

33. Special Features

We can bind ourselves to no limit upon the number of occurrences of any one type of phenomenon which will be studied or upon the minuteness of subdivision to which a phenomenon may be subjected. This is equivalent to a demand that our dialect contain infinite classes of speech-forms. In this matter philosophers and mathematicians have often failed to recognize fundamental linguistic facts. So far as concerns anything accessible to science, the only infinite classes are classes of speech-forms; such situations as are referred to by terms like 'limit,' 'dense,' and 'continuous' arise only from our agreements as to the use of speech-forms and will be sought in vain in that outer world which is studied by science.

In the class of all English sentences that may be uttered, without limit upon length, we have an infinite class of the lowest type, and, if we imagine ourselves incapable of phonetics and ignorant of writing, this class lacks anything like order. By selecting from it and agreeing upon types of order, we define the infinite classes which serve us in scientific discourse. Our ordinary speech furnishes the simplest of these in the shape of the number-words, linearly and discretely ordered, with a first member 'one.'

Linguistic devices like these are entirely the creation of society; their usefulness, but never their operation, depends upon our handling activity. Viewed from the strictly linguistic level, it is an accident that the divisibility of matter goes beyond the power of our finest instruments, and an accident, no less, that our physics postulates molecular structure. Regardless of the latter circumstance, the former brings to us an engineering demand for a densely and linearly ordered infinite class: in the order there shall be a form between any two forms that may be named. This demand is met by means of number-pairs (two-place vectors) in the shape of the rational numbers, with the familiar agreement that, if ad precedes bc, then among the rational numbers (a, b) shall precede (c, d). However, one could also agree upon an ordering of the natural numbers that would make them dense. From this it follows, that, leaving the decadic syntax of the natural numbers, we could devise a densely ordered class out of repetitions of a single speech-form and, in greater variety, out of phrases built, say, of two speech-forms—witness the decimal expressions consisting of 0's and 1's.

A "continuous" object, such as a piece of wire, presents itself between any two of its points, no matter how we swing the knife. A straight line, in geometry, is met by lines at points which are not designated by rational co-ordinates. Given a linearly and densely ordered class of speech-forms, we require, therefore, that any expression (within the vocabulary and syntax of our dialect) which divides ("cuts") the class in the familiar manner of Dedekind's postulate shall be a member of a new class. This class is then "continuous"; it contains a member to match every member of the old class, since these members make the required division, and it contains, further, any other phrases (within our dialect) which define a cut. Mathematicians sometimes ignore the obvious fact that the possibility of defining the "cuts" depends entirely upon the vocabulary and syntax of our discourse and by no means upon our "perception of time" or upon any mystical realm of "ideas." In the discourse of numbers the agreements of multiplication ('square,' etc.) make possible one kind of cut, and those of limits another. It is for the speakers to decide what expressions they will admit into their discourse.

VI. Summary

34. The Place of Linguistics in the Scheme of Science

The subject matter of linguistics, of course, is human speech. Other activities, such as writing, which serve as substitutes for speech, concern linguistics only in their semiotic aspect, as representations of phonemes or speech-forms. Since the meanings of speech cover everything (designata, including denotata; syntactic relations; pragmatic slants), linguistics, even more than other branches of science, depends for its range and accuracy upon the success of science as a whole. For the most part, our statements of meaning are makeshift. Even if this were not the case, linguistics would still study forms first and then look into their meanings, since language consists in the human response to the flow and variety of the world by simple sequences of a very few typical speech-sounds.

Linguistics is the chief contributor to semiotic. Among the special branches of science, it intervenes between biology, on the one hand, and ethnology, sociology, and psychology, on the other: it stands between physical and cultural anthropology.

Language establishes, by means of sound waves and on the basis of a communal habit, an ever ready connection between the bodies of individuals—a connection between their nervous systems which enables each person to respond to the stimuli that act upon other persons. The division of labor, civilization, and culture arise from this interaction. Popularly and even, to a large extent, academically, we are not accustomed to observing language and its effects: these effects are generally explained instead by the postulation of "mental" factors. In the cosmos, language produces human society, a structure more complex than the individual, related to him somewhat as the many-celled organism is related to the single cell.

35. Relation of Linguistics to Logic and Mathematics

Specialized uses of language involve no great alterations of structure; the specialization consists rather in the way that language is applied. Thus, the study of literature requires that we investigate the institutions and traditions of the community and the psychology (physiology, social status, biography) of the creative individual. In connection with science, language is specialized in the direction of forms which successfully communicate handling responses and lend themselves to elaborate re-shaping (calculation). To invent and to employ these forms is to carry on mathematics. The critique and theory of scientific speech is the task of logic. Logic is a branch of science closely related to linguistics, since it observes how people conduct a certain type of discourse. In contrast with this, the invention and skilful manipulation of speech-forms is not a science but a skill, craft, or art; it is as such that we class mathematics. Mathematics appears as a science only so long as we believe that the mathematician is not creating speech-forms and discourses but exploring an unknown realm of "concepts" or "ideas."

Since mathematics is a verbal activity and logic a study of verbal activities, both of these disciplines presuppose linguistics. However, the forms of language which enter into mathematics, and are to be examined by logic, are simple and fairly normal: in principle, neither pursuit requires any technical knowledge of linguistics. In practice, since we labor under a load of traditional and popular misconception about language, a great deal of doubt, error, and dispute will be avoided if mathematicians and logicians acquire enough linguistics to remove these misconceptions. The principal sources of difficulty are twofold. Our popular belief distorts the relation of writing to language, placing the two on a par ("written" and "spoken" language) or even reversing the dependence, so as to suppose that a change in writing equals or prompts a change in language. Our popular belief replaces the function and effects of language by "mental" factors, which, whatever their place in literature or religion, are excluded, as non-physical, from the subject matter and procedure of science.

Selected Bibliography

§ 2. On the doctrine of the ancient Greeks: B. Delbrück, *Einleitung in das Studium der indogermanischen Sprachen* ("Bibliothek indogermanischer Grammatiken," Vol. IV [6th ed.; Leipzig, 1919]).

For the Sanskrit grammar: *Language*, V (1929), 267. The comparative method: A. Meillet, *La Méthode comparative en linguistique historique* ("Instituttet for sammenlignende kulturforskning," Ser. A, No. 2 [Oslo, 1925]). History of modern linguistics: H. Pedersen, *Linguistic Science in the Nineteenth Century* (Cambridge, Mass., 1931). Elementary outline of the subject: L. Bloomfield, *Language* (New York, 1933; London, 1935). Dialect geography: E. C. Roedder in *Germanic Review*, I (1926), 281.

§ 4. Distinction between speech-forms of discourse and speech-forms under discussion: R. Carnap, *Logical Syntax of Language* (Vienna, 1934; London and New York, 1937), sec. 42.

§ 5. On "correctness" in language: C. C. Fries, *The Teaching of the English Language* (New York, 1927); S. A. Leonard, *The Doctrine of Correctness in English Usage, 1700–1800* ("University of Wisconsin Studies in Language and Literature," Vol. XXV [Madison, 1929]); see also *American Speech*, II (1927), 432.

§ 6. Writing: Pedersen, *op. cit.;* E. H. Sturtevant, *Linguistic Change* (Chicago, 1917). Duodecimal notation confused with speech-form: *Atlantic Monthly*, CLIV (1934), 459. Gesture: W. Wundt, *Völkerpsychologie*, Vol. I: *Die Sprache* (3d ed.; Leipzig, 1911), p. 143.

§ 7. Biophysical and biosocial: A. P. Weiss, *A Theoretical Basis of Human Behavior* (2d ed.; Columbus, 1929), p. 84.

§ 9. Mentalistic doctrines of various types: A. P. Weiss in *Psychological Review*, XXIV (1917), 301, 353; in *Journal of Psychology*, XVI (1919), 626. See also *Psychological Review*, XXVI (1919), 327; *ibid.*, XXIX (1922), 329. Behaviorism: Weiss, *Theoretical Basis of Human Behavior;* operationalism: P. W. Bridgman, *The Logic of Modern Physics* (New York, 1927); physicalism: R. Carnap, *The Unity of Science* ("Psyche Miniatures: General Series," No. 63 [London, 1934]); *Philosophy and Logical Syntax* ("Psyche Miniatures: General Series," No. 70 [London, 1935]); O. Neurath in *The Monist*, XLI (1931), 618; see also *Language* XII (1936), 89.

§ 10. A. P. Weiss in *Psychological Review*, XXXVIII (1931), 474.

§ 14. Meaning is discussed with bibliography, on a mentalistic basis, to be sure, by G. Stern, *Meaning and Change of Meaning* ("Göteborg högskolas årsskrift," Vol. XXXVIII, No. 1 [Gothenburg, 1932]). See also C. W. Morris' monograph, *Foundations of the Theory of Signs* ("International Encyclopedia of Unified Science," Vol. I, No. 2 [Chicago, 1938]).

§ 16. The phoneme as a signal: E. Sapir, *Language* (New York, 1921).

§ 18. The sentence: in *Language*, VII (1931), 204. On "pragmatic" features of meaning: Morris, *op. cit.*

§ 19. Levels and ranks of construction: O. Jespersen, *The Philosophy of Grammar* (London and New York, 1924).

§ 20. Categories: F. Boas, "Introduction" in *Handbook of American Indian Languages* (Smithsonian Institution, Bureau of American Ethnology, Bull. 40 [Washington, 1911]), Vol. I.

275

§ 24. See in *Philosophy of Science*, II (1935), 499; *Language*, XII (1936), 94. On variability: Weiss, *Theoretical Basis of Human Behavior*, p. 134.

§ 26. Euclid's proof, conveniently given in L. E. Dickson, *Introduction to the Theory of Numbers* (Chicago, 1929), p. 4. *Archimedes*, ed. J. L. Heilig (Leipzig, 1913), II, 219.

§ 31. Calculation: K. Menger in *Philosophy of Science*, IV (1937), 299.

§ 33. Elementary outline: F. Waismann, *Einführung in das mathematische Denken* (Vienna, 1936).

Index of Technical Terms

[Numbers refer to pages of this monograph.]

Procedures of Empirical Science

Victor F. Lenzen

Procedures of Empirical Science

Contents:

Procedures of Empirical Science

Victor F. Lenzen

I. Introduction

1. The Problem of Empirical Science

The problem of empirical science is the acquisition and systematization of knowledge concerning the things and phenomena experienced in observation.

The basic procedures of empirical science occur in daily life. Prior to his cultivation of science an individual perceives relatively stable things in space and time, describes them with the aid of symbols which record and communicate the results of observation, and explains perceptible phenomena in terms of causes. Simple experimental techniques are also used in the ordinary conduct of life. The child learns the operations of counting, of measuring length and time, of weighing with a balance. The builder uses tools, the housewife applies heat to produce the chemical reactions of cookery, the farmer cultivates crops. Such procedures are based upon prehistoric discoveries and inventions which have become the heritage of the race. In our historic era empirical science criticizes, augments, and systematizes practical experience. The science of one generation becomes incorporated in the technology of the succeeding one. Science and practice co-operate in the adjustment of man to his environment.

The preceding description of the interdependence of science and practice may be illustrated by a sketch of the origin of science in ancient Greece. It is traditional that the Greeks created European science, but their achievement was founded on knowledge and procedures which had been inherited from earlier Babylonian and Egyptian civilizations. The observations of correlations between the apparent positions of the heavenly bodies by the Babylonians provided a basis for the measurement of time and furnished data for a geometrical picture of celestial motions. The procedures used by the Egyptians in their surveys of land were formulated in propositions whose deductive relations were set forth in Euclidean geometry, which has been the classic model for systems of science. The Egyptians practiced medicine and surgery, and the Greeks under the leadership of Hippocrates developed this field by observation and experiment. Out of elements derived from practice was created the science of biology, which was especially developed by Aristotle, who made observations on animals and invented a system of classification. Machines were employed prior to the creative Greek period; on Egyptian temples the god Osiris is depicted weighing the soul with a balance. The principles implied in such machines are formulated in the science of statics which was founded by Archimedes. Thus the Greeks built upon the particular knowledge and techniques of the Babylonians and Egyptians. They organized the observations and procedures of their predecessors into theories founded upon principles.

The Greek interest in systematization also led to the creation of constructive hypotheses which reduced the diversity of perceptible things to a unitary basis. The theories concerning the nature of things initiated by Thales and his successors eventually led to the creation of the atomic theory, which in the modern era has provided a unified interpretation of physical and chemical phenomena. The Greeks emphasized the rational factor in science at the expense of observation. They were fertile in the creation of theories, but failed to develop adequately the technique of experiment. Greek science lost its creative power as ancient civilization decayed, but with the revival of science during the dawn of the modern era the method of controlled experimentation came to be adequately appreciated. Vesalius' insistence upon dissection for anatomy, Galileo's experiments on falling bodies, and Bacon's attempt to formulate the method of induction recognized the need for observation and experiment in empirical science. The experimental point of view was clearly stated by Newton in his assertion that physical properties are to be derived from experiments. The properties of things are modes of reaction to conditions that are subject to experimental control. Significant experimentation requires the guidance of hypotheses which serve to predict the results of observation. Accordingly, in the well-developed empirical sciences a theory which applies to a selected universe of discourse assumes the form of a hypothetico-deductive system, and scientific procedure consists in deriving predictions which are tested by the results of experiments. This union of the Greek conception of theory with experimental procedure has resulted in the modern development of science, which through technology created the industrial revolution and today is even more radically transforming the practice of daily life. Refinements in technique are providing the instruments for future developments in the theories which systematize the results of observation.

2. The Subject Matter of Empirical Science

In preparation for the analysis of procedures I shall sketch the general character of the subject matter of empirical science. The initial objects of science are the things experienced in perception, and their most general characters are position in space and time. The systematic and ultimately quantitative investigation of space-time order may be called generalized physics. Thus one arrives at the doctrine of physicalism, which asserts that the concepts of empirical science are reducible to those which express the properties of spatio-temporal things.

Carnap has shown that by a method of reduction, of which definition is a special case, the terms of a science are introduced by statements which involve terms designating perceptible things and properties. An outline of physicalist analysis, with especial reference to biology, is given in Volume I, Number 1. I present an analysis, adapted from Carnap,[1] of some biological terms. An organism is a special type of space-time structure, and hence the designation of terms such as 'species,' 'genus,' 'events in organisms,' is always determined on the basis of perceptible criteria. Thus " 'fertilization' is defined as the union of spermatazoon and egg; 'spermatazoon' and 'egg' are defined as cells of specified origin and specified perceptible properties; 'union' as an event consisting of a specified spatial redistribution of parts." Such biological terms as 'metabolism,' 'growth,' 'regeneration,' 'cell division,' etc., are also introduced in terms of perceptible criteria.

In behavioristics the responses of organisms to their environment are investigated, and in sociology the relations of human beings to one another and to the environment. As Neurath has emphasized, sociology deals with space-time structures. The essential difference between mechanics and sociology is that the relative simplicity of mechanical phenomena renders possible the repetition of experiments, whereas the complexity of social processes makes controlled experimentation difficult.

The formation of precise and quantitative concepts for the properties of spatio-temporal things is the first problem of physics, which plays a fundamental role in empirical science. The analysis of physical procedure is therefore basic in this monograph.

II. Observation

3. Perception

The basic procedure of empirical science is observation. Scientific description starts with observation; confirmation of the hypotheses of a theory is attained when phenomena predicted on the theory are observed. The term 'observation' has a meaning which is relative to a scientific situation. In daily life observation consists of perception with the unaided senses, in astronomy observation of the heavenly bodies is mediated by telescopes, in biology observation is through a microscope, in atomic physics observation is theoretical interpretation of experimentally controlled phenomena. The observation of microphysical entities requires the explicit use of physical principles as instruments of interpretation, but all observation involves more or less explicitly the element of hypothesis. In the present part of this monograph I shall describe the different types of observation in the order of increasing explicitness of the hypothetical factor. Let us begin with perception.

The defining characteristic of perception is the occurrence of a sense datum and its interpretation as the aspect of an objective thing. Perception thus involves the hypothesis that there exists an object to which given aspects are referred. The hypothesis that various common things exist is continually being confirmed by the reproduction of perceptions of them. I repeatedly have perceptions which are described as responses to a desk with relatively stable properties. Different types of perception are found to be correlated; thus, upon sight of my desk I expect to touch it. The truth of a perception is confirmed or disconfirmed by testing the predictions derivable from it. The development of the concept of an object is completed by the hypothesis of the identity of the perceptible objects of a society of observers. Thus the concept of objective thing is social; science is tested by social procedure.[2] The scientific criterion of objectivity ultimately rests upon the possibility of occurrence of predicted perceptions to a society of observers.

In daily life perception usually passes unreflectively into action. As I walk along the street, I perceive someone coming toward me and automatically step out of the way. I reach the curb and start to cross the street, but I perceive an automobile and hesitate. Nevertheless, even in the almost unreflective practice of common experience there are flashes of discrimination of qualities and comparisons between them. I notice that the approaching automobile is red; I judge that one man is taller than his companion. A phase of perception, accordingly, is discrimination and comparison of given qualities and relations. The results of such procedure can be recorded and communicated only if the experienced qualities and relations are symbolized. When things are perceived to have aspects that are similar in a specific respect, they are assigned a common quality or relation which is designated by a general name. The designation of the name of a simple quality such as redness can be understood only if one has immediately experienced the quality. General names are instruments of analysis. A qualitative analysis of the data of perception provides the basis for the description of a thing in terms of predicates. For example, an apple may be described as red, round, smooth, sweet, etc. Thus perception is completed by analysis of perceptible properties and the expression of the results of observation in descriptions. This procedure is a first step in the systematization of knowledge. Description of things is a mode of classification which in turn furnishes material for a more general classification. In its descriptive stage, which is based upon perception, empirical science introduces order into cognitions by classification.

On the perceptual level of knowledge the properties of a thing are commonly discovered by manipulation. An object which visually appears to be at hand may be denied reality and called a hallucination because it cannot be grasped.

But things may also be investigated by sight; indeed, for the study of microscopic objects the procedure is to observe them with the aid of optical instruments. In virtue of the capacity of glass to refract light, it is possible to make microscopes and telescopes, so that on looking at an object through an optical instrument its visual aspect is magnified. The phenomenon of magnification renders it possible to infer the existence of objects which do not appreciably affect the unaided senses. Observation with instruments is an extension of perception in which the hypothetical element is more explicit than in the ordinary perceptions of daily life. Yet the hypotheses have been so often confirmed that practical certainty is achieved.

In the development of empirical science qualitative description of things and phenomena is supplemented by quantitative representation. In addition to characterizing a group of objects as many, one may assign to it a number; one may not rest with the description of a rod as long or short, but record that it is so many meters long. Quantitative representation requires procedures for assigning numbers to measurable properties. I shall sketch the methods for the assignment of numbers to collections and to continuous manifolds such as space and time.

4. Counting

The fundamental quantitative procedure of science is counting a set of objects in order to characterize it by a number. A collection may consist of similar things such as the sheep in a flock; or the members of a collection may be as dissimilar as the books, papers, and other things on my desk. For the purpose of counting, differences in characteristics of the members of a collection are ignored, but their distinguishability must be preserved.

The basic operation in counting is illustrated in the following quotation from Conant's *The Number Concept*.[3] "The savage can form no mental concept of what civilized man means by such a word as soul; nor would his idea of the abstract number 5 be much clearer. When he says five, he uses, in many cases at least, the same word that serves him when he wishes to say hand, ... and his only comprehension of the number is, 'these objects are as many as the fingers on my hand.' " This example suggests that counting is an operation of determining similarity between collections. Two collections are defined to be similar if they can be put into one to one correspondence, so that to every member of one collection is correlated a member of the other collection. Similar collections, or classes, are assigned the same number. The null class is characterized by the number zero, unit classes by one, couples by two, trios by three, etc. Indeed, Whitehead and Russell define a cardinal number as the class of all similar classes. Thus we may define the natural numbers which serve to describe collections of objects.

The number of a collection is determined by counting. As one counts, the members are put into one to one correspondence with the natural numbers. If one has used the natural numbers from 1 to n, it is established that the number of objects in the collection is the same as the number of natural numbers from 1 to n, and, since this number is n, the collection counted has n objects. The number of a collection is independent of the order in which the counting occurs.

Given two collections we may combine them to form a new collection. For example, the addition of a collection of three objects to a collection of two objects yields a collection of five objects, and the result is the same if the collection of two is added to the collection of three. The formation of the new collection by addition may be represented by the addition of the numbers of the collections added, thus $3 + 2 = 2 + 3 = 5$. A similar relation holds for all instances of addition, and hence we may infer a general law, $a + b = b + a$, the commutative law for addition.

Laws for multiplication are also derived from observation. If one combines two collections each containing three objects, the resultant collection contains six objects. The combination of three collections each containing two objects also yields six objects. The formation of collections by multiplication may be represented by the numerical expression '$2 \times 3 = 3 \times 2 = 6$.' A similar relation holds for every multiplication of collections, and, hence, one infers the general commutative law for multiplication, $a \times b = b \times a$.

The preceding discussion of the commutative laws of addition and multiplication demonstrates that the fundamental propositions of ordinary algebra are initially derived from observation. Numbers are first discovered as characters of collections; but, once principles expressing their relations are set up, the numbers acquire properties defined in terms of their relations to one another. They become the subject matter of an abstract theory which defines their properties independently of any empirical application. As the number system is extended from the natural numbers to include negative, rational, irrational, and complex numbers, the original connection between numbers and collections is lost. The real numbers find a geometrical representation in the points of a line, and complex numbers in vectors.

The operation of counting is performed by pointing or otherwise indicating the members of a collection to which one assigns the numbers 1, 2, etc., respectively. The physicist, however, has invented mechanical counters so that, for example, the number of revolutions of a wheel is recorded. In contemporary physics the number of microphysical events, such as the passages of cosmic-ray particles through a Geiger counter, can be registered by a mechanical device. In order to determine the number of molecules in a specific volume of gas, however, it is necessary to employ indirect methods based upon theories.

Statistical surveys are important for many problems, and counting is their initial procedure. I have indicated the importance of statistics in physics, but the social sciences are even more dependent upon counting for their materials. Counts are taken of the number of inhabitants in defined areas, of the number of births per year, and similarly of deaths, marriages, homicides, etc. From such statistical data there are calculated birthrates, death-rates, and other results which give useful information about a given society.

5. Measurement of Length

Measurement is the general procedure of assigning numbers to the properties of objects. A measurable property is usually called a magnitude, but the term 'quantity' is also used. A basic measurement is that of length or distance by a procedure which was invented in remote antiquity. In order to measure the length of a rod, one selects a standard of length and counts the number of times that it can be laid off on the rod. I shall explain the general procedure of measurement by analyzing that of length.

The basic principle of measurement is that the space-time coincidence of objective events is perceptible to a community of observers. The most direct exemplification of this principle is offered by the measurement of length, which depends upon the determination of contact of two things from the contact of their aspects in perception. The empirical concept of contact is only approximately precise, but for theory one sets up the postulate that two coincident points are perceived to be coincident. Brunswik has explained how coincidence is the basis of objectivity. Two coincident points are perceived under exactly the same conditions; hence identical spatial perceptions are stimulated by the objects. If, for example, perception is mediated by light which is scattered by the coincident points, light from both points will travel over the same path to the same point on the retina and produce the same perceptual reactions. The objectivity of measurement is based upon the fundamental function of the perception of coincidence.

The physical concept of length is empirically derivable from solid bodies, which in view of the properties to be described may be called practically rigid bodies. Two points on a rigid body determine a stretch which is defined to include its end points. Let us place two bodies adjacent to each other so that two points on the one coincide with two points on the other. Assuming constancy in external conditions, the coincidence of the two sets of end points of the stretches remains constant in time. It is also independent of position in space, for, if the two bodies are displaced together, coincidence is preserved. Accordingly, one characterizes the two stretches as congruent. Congruence is observed to be a symmetrical relation, that is, if A is congruent to B, B is congruent to A; it is also transitive, that is, if A is congruent to B, and B is congruent to C, then A is congruent to C. To the congruent stretches one assigns the same number, the length of each stretch or the distance between its end points.

Thus far I have described the test for congruence of adjacent stretches. The test breaks down if the two stretches are separated in space. Observation shows, however, that, if separated stretches are again brought together, the coincidence of end points is restored. Furthermore, stretches that may successively be exhibited as congruent to a standard stretch may be demonstrated to be congruent when brought together at a distance from the standard. In view of such experimental results, one is led to postulate that stretches are congruent at a distance if they prove themselves to be congruent when adjacent. In effect, we postulate that the distance between two points on a solid body is unchanged in a displacement. In the present context it is meaningless to ask if this convention is really true. Such a question would be significant only if there were a more fundamental definition of length or distance. Accordingly, we may adopt as a standard of length the distance between two marks on some solid body. The international legal standard of length is the meter. It was originally defined as 1/10,000,000 of the distance from either pole to the equator and was approximately exemplified by the distance between two scratches on a bar, the *Mètre des Archives*, at the temperature of melting ice under atmospheric pressure. Later the distance between the two scratches was arbitrarily chosen as the standard. The wave-length of a red spectral line emitted by cadmium has been measured in terms of the standard meter, thus preparing the way for the adoption of this wave-length as the standard of length.

Thus far we have considered congruence of stretches and identity of length of congruent stretches. I have not yet explained the procedure for measuring the length of any stretch in terms of a standard. Let us suppose we are given a line. In nature a line may be realized by a ray of light, by a stretched cord, or by the edge of some solid. One may measure the length of a line by the following procedure: Beginning at one end, place stretches, congruent to the standard stretch, end to end until the other end of the line is reached. The number of stretches is the numerical measure of the length of the line relative to the adopted standard. In practice the congruent stretches are constructed by placing a standard alongside the line and making points on it which coincide with the end points of the stretch. The accuracy of a measurement of length can be indefinitely increased by decreasing the standard of length.

Our description of procedure in measuring length has presupposed constancy of the external environment and of the standard. In practice, however, corrections must be made for a change in conditions. Suppose that we have measured the dimensions of various bodies with a standard rod. If the measurements are repeated with a heated rod, it will be found that the numerical measures are smaller. As Carnap has shown, we have in principle a choice between two methods of explaining the change. We may postulate that the standard rod retains the same length but that the heating of the rod has produced, by an action at a distance, changes in the dimensions of the bodies in the environment. Or we may infer a change in the standard rod. If the standard rod is heated by a flame in contact with it, the second explanation is in accordance with a principle of contiguous causality which states that a physical change is to be attributed to an agency in the neighborhood of the body undergoing the change. This universally accepted kind of explanation allows the standard of length to vary with temperature. Accordingly, the definition of the standard of length requires specification of its temperature. But the definition of temperature presupposes the concept of length; for example, temperature may be defined in terms of the length of a thread of mercury in a glass tube. Thus we seem to have become involved in a vicious circle. In order to measure length, we must correct for the temperature of the rod, but, in order to measure temperature, we need to measure length.

The circle is avoided by the method of successive approximation. Let the standard of length be the distance between two scratches on a particular rod; this constitutes a definition to the first approximation. With the aid of our standard we can construct a thermometer with which we may discover the law for the dependence of length on temperature. Thus the definition of a standard to the first approximation provides a basis for a definition of temperature in terms of which the standard can then be defined to a second approximation. The possibility of this procedure is based upon the fact that a change in temperature produces a relatively small change in length. An error in the measurement of temperature resulting from a small error in the standard of length used to construct the scale of the thermometer gives rise only to errors of the second order of small quantities in the standard of length that is specified in terms of the temperature. The method of successive approximation is also used in controlling the constancy of other physical properties of the rod. The procedure of measuring length thus involves the performance of certain operations under controlled conditions. Our description of the measurement of length illustrates the experimental basis and operational nature of scientific concepts.

The results of measurement need to be appropriately symbolized in order to enter as elements in a mathematical development. The result of a measurement of length is stated by a proposition such as, 'The length of this rod is 2 meters.' Carnap has shown that the foregoing proposition expresses a relation between the number 2 and the object to which it is assigned. The proposition may then be written

2 (length in meters) this rod.

The last proposition is of the form xRy, where the relation R is one-many; there are many rods to which the number has the relation designated by 'length in meters.' Whitehead and Russell have shown that a one-many relation gives rise to a descriptive function; thus from xRy one obtains

$$x = \text{the } R \text{ of } y,$$

or, in symbols,

$$x = R\,{}^{\prime}y.$$

Applying this analysis to the present problem one obtains

2 = the length in meters of this rod ,

2 = the length in meters 'this rod .

Relations between measurable properties are represented by functional relations between their numerical measures. This may be illustrated by the law of addition which characterizes length as an extensive quantity. Two stretches A and B on a straight line may be adjoined to form a stretch C. If the lengths of the stretches are measured in terms of a standard, L, the results of measurement may be recorded by 'a = the length relative to L of A,' etc. The adjunction of the stretches is then represented by the proposition which expresses a relation between measures, '$a + b = c$.' The goal of exact empirical science is the expression of natural laws as functional relations between numerical values.

The quantitative concept of length is the basis of metrical geometry which expresses the spatial properties of figures. The geometer initially studies the spatial relations of practically rigid bodies, but he also makes figures by stretching cords and by drawing with a ruler and compass. Since the paths of light rays are usually straight, triangles and other figures may be formed of light rays. Indeed, the rectilinear propagation of light furnishes a practical test of straightness; the carpenter tests the straightness of an edge by sighting along it.

The properties of triangles may be used to measure distances by calculation from observations. In the method of triangulation one side of a triangle is the straight line between two stakes, and the other two sides are rays of light from a distant object to the stakes. The surveyor measures the length of the straight line between the stakes with a tape; from measures of the angles that the other two sides make with the base line and the general laws for triangles he calculates the distances of the object from the stakes.

Geometry deals initially with fixed structures at rest in a frame of reference such as the surface of the earth. If geometrical figures are changing, one may specify their instantaneous properties. The motion of figures relative to a given frame of reference introduces new problems. In classical kinematics it was assumed that geometrical figures are independent of their state of motion. Analysis of the operation of measuring the length of a body in motion reveals that the concept of simultaneity is presupposed. Suppose, for example, that a straight rod is moving with uniform velocity with respect to a given frame of reference. The procedure for measuring its length that may be adopted by an observer at rest in that frame is to mark on the frame the simultaneous positions of the end points of the rod. The length of the moving rod relative to the given frame is the distance between the two points marked on the frame. The special theory of relativity determines simultaneity to be relative to the frame of reference, so that the length of a rod relative to a frame in which the rod is moving is different from its length relative to a frame in which the rod is at rest.

The geometrical study of the spatial relations of bodies yields a concept of physical space. In order to increase definiteness, use is made of relatively small bodies or small portions of bodies which are called points. Examples of points are dots, pinholes, knots in cords. For maximum definiteness there is formed the limiting concept of a point which has a definite position. Space may then be described as the system of relative positions of points. The metrical structure of space is defined in terms of the properties of configurations of rigid bodies. In view of relativity, space is defined for a selected frame of reference. The surface of the earth was used by the Greeks as the frame for physical space, but in the modern era the preferred frame has been one with its origin at the center of mass of the solar system, with the axes oriented with respect to the fixed stars. In this frame physical space is Euclidean to at least the first approximation. This means, for example, that it is possible to construct a cubical lattice out of equal rods, that is, a Cartesian coordinate system. The general theory of relativity, however, involves the view that matter determines physical space to be non-Euclidean.

The propositions of geometry are to be viewed as initially generalizations from observations on the spatial properties of structures of practically rigid bodies. In Euclidean geometry the science is based upon a small number of axioms from which the propositions can be deduced as theorems. In abstract geometry the original axioms have been transformed into postulates which define implicitly the fundamental concepts of geometry. From this point of view the postulates of Euclidean geometry are descriptions of the formal spatial properties of rigid bodies. That the concepts of these forms are applicable to the objects of perception is a hypothesis to be confirmed and limited by observation.

6. Measurement of Time

The problem of the measurement of time is to invent a procedure for assigning to events numbers, called the times or dates of events. An event is a process of relatively short duration, the shortness depending on the precision with which one intends to describe phenomena. In theory one forms the concept of instantaneous event as a theoretical construct. The basic temporal relations are simultaneity and succession of events. Two events are objectively simultaneous if they are simultaneously perceptible to a community of observers. A similar criterion may be given for succession. We must distinguish between local time, the time system at a specific place, and extended time, the time system throughout a space.

The procedure of measuring local time is based upon some concrete temporal process, usually a periodic motion. The behavior of a standard clock defines the scale of time. Now, various physical processes can be used for the definition of metrical time: the rotation of the earth about its axis, the revolution of the earth around the sun, the vibration of a pendulum, the revolution of the moon around the earth, etc.

The procedure for measuring time may be illustrated by adopting as the fundamental temporal process the vibration of a pendulum. The fundamental principle is that successive vibrations of the pendulum take equal times. This principle has an empirical basis. We have a qualitative estimate of the duration of processes and can judge, for example, that the time of one vibration of a pendulum is less than the time between sunrise and sunset. Hence we may estimate that two successive vibrations of a pendulum take the same time. Again, all pendulums which are similar in structure vibrate in synchronism, that is, if two pendulums of equal length are released simultaneously, they vibrate together, passing through corresponding points at the same time. But the principle that successive vibrations take the same time, although suggested by experience, is a definition of equal intervals of time. It is a convention concerning which it is meaningless to ask whether it is true or false. The question of truth or falsity would presuppose another standard, for which one would have to assume that each performance of a periodic process requires the same time.

Let us then suppose that we have chosen the vibration of a pendulum as the basis of a metrical structure for time. We may select the beginning of a particular vibration as the origin of time; to the ends of successive vibrations are assigned the numbers 1, 2, 3, etc. The time of any event is expressed by assigning to it the number which is correlated with the vibration, the end of which is simultaneous with the event. If the end of the vibration and the event are not simultaneous, we may imagine clocks with shorter and shorter periods and thus, by interpolation, approximate as accurately as we please to a precise assignment of time to the event. The duration of a process is, then, expressed numerically by the difference of the times of its beginning and end.

The physical process that serves for the definition of a time scale must be subject to constant conditions. The period of a pendulum, for example, is constant only if the conditions of the environment are invariable. For example, the earth's gravitational field must remain constant, the action of electric and magnetic fields must be negligible, the temperature must not change, etc. The control of conditions is accomplished by the method of successive approximation. We have initially a qualitative estimate of constancy of conditions, and therefore we may apply the principle that a specific pendulum keeps the same time on various occasions. For daily life such a definition may be adequate, but for scientific observation the conditions must be quantitatively defined. The definition of time to the first approximation enables one to define 'acceleration,' 'force,' 'electric field,' etc., quantitatively. We may then specify quantitatively the constant conditions for the clock, and thus the time scale can be defined to a second approximation.

In practice it may not be possible to control the conditions to which clocks are subject. If one has a quantitative description of the actual conditions, however, it may be possible to correct the times assigned in terms of the actual clock, and thereby find the times which would be indicated by an undisturbed clock. The earth is the standard clock for astronomical measurements; the definition of time is given by the convention that the angular velocity of the earth about its axis is constant. Now, certain anomalies in the moon's motion can be explained on the hypothesis that the earth is slowing down on account of tidal friction. This explanation presupposes the laws of mechanics, which have been confirmed by experiments in which time was measured by the rotation of the earth. The explanation implies that the earth-clock indicates only an approximate time. One may say, however, that time is to be defined by the rotation of the earth—assuming that there are no frictional forces. The empirically indicated time would then have to be corrected in order to find the time that would be indicated by a frictionless earth. The astronomer does not actually compute the correction from the friction and the laws of mechanics but obtains the correction by comparison with the moon. This illustration, however, shows that corrections may be made for disturbing conditions.

In the historical development different processes have been employed for the measurement of time. The ancients measured time by the motions of the heavenly bodies, but they also measured time by the amount of sand that ran out of an hourglass. The two methods agree approximately on account of the empirically observed correlation between the flow of sand out of the hourglass and celestial motions. We choose the astronomical method as the standard and ascribe the inaccuracy of hourglass time to variable conditions such as differences in the size of grains, smoothness of surfaces, etc. That is, the disagreement between hourglass time and astronomical time is explained by the hypothesis that differences in the grains affect their motions and not the motion of the heavenly bodies. The use of accepted physical principles in the definition of physical quantities is here exemplified.

I supplement the description of procedure by a discussion of the considerations which determine the choice of a standard clock. In the first place, one seeks a process that is as permanent as possible; the rotation of the earth and the motion of the moon especially satisfy this requirement. Furthermore, the clock is to be as free as possible from disturbing influences. The clocks on the earth are subject to disturbances, hence the astronomical clocks are preferable. A pendulum, however, is readily reproducible and is useful as a secondary clock when it has been standardized. Most desirable of all for a definition of time is independence of special properties of matter. A pendulum requires the earth's gravitational field; the mainspring of a watch is dependent on the elastic properties of a particular substance; the heavenly bodies are subject to destruction. The preferred definition is in terms of functional relations between physical quantities. For example, we may define time as the independent variable in the equations of dynamics. The equations which express physical laws then constitute an implicit definition of time. In particular, time may be thought of as defined by the first law of motion which states that a body acted upon by no forces persists in a state of uniform rectilinear motion. By this definition, equal intervals of time are indicated by equal distances passed over by a body under no forces. This definition of time in terms of the first law achieves the dissociation of the time scale from special processes or bodies. The change in definition exemplifies again the method of successive definition. Initially, physical quantities are defined in terms of special operations and provide the basis for the empirical discovery of general laws, which may then be transformed into implicit definitions of the physical quantities involved in them. But it then becomes an experimental fact that the measure of a quantity which is obtained by special operations approximately satisfies the definition of the quantity in terms of the general laws. For example, the measure of time by a pendulum approximately satisfies the definition of time in terms of the first law of motion.

So far, the discussion has been restricted to local time; I now turn to the problem of the time system throughout a space. If P_1 and P_2 are two separated points in space, how are we to define a time scale at P_2 which is the same as that at P_1? We must postulate a law of connection between local times.

In this discussion the points of space will be referred to a definite frame of reference. It is assumed that similar clocks at rest may be placed at any point in the given space. Similar clocks have the property that, if at rest at the same place, they keep the same time. The problem is: Given the time scale at P_1, how shall we extend it to P_2? Suppose that at P_1 there is a set of similar clocks. If one of the clocks is moved slowly to P_2, we may transport its time scale by the postulate that the clock at P_2 is synchronous with the clocks at P_1. Since no immediate perception of the synchronism is possible when the clocks are separated, the postulate is a definition by which the time system at P_1 is extended to the point P_2. There is some empirical foundation for this definition. If two clocks which are synchronous at P_1 are transported to P_2, they will be synchronous at P_2. This experimental result is found even if the two clocks are transported along different paths. Again, if a clock which is synchronous with the clocks at P_1 is transported and then returned to P_1, it will again be synchronous with the clocks at the starting-point. All these experimental results support the convention that a time system is extended throughout space by the slow transport of a clock. This method of extending a scale of time is employed in daily life. Thus, the locomotive engineer extends along the track the time system of the place at which he sets his watch. If a ship carries a chronometer, it extends a time system along its course. In transporting a clock, we must not unduly accelerate and disturb it; but the accelerations to which ordinary clocks are subject do not affect them appreciably.

The preferred method of extending a time system employs light signals. At time t_1 as indicated by the clock at P_1 a signal is sent and arrives at P_2 at the time t_2 as indicated by the clock there. The clocks at the separated points keep the same time if $t_2 = t_1 + l/c$, where l is the distance between the two points and c is the speed of the signal. In effect, the principle of the constancy of the speed of light in a vacuum is postulated as a definition by which a time system is extended throughout space. Recognition of this procedure occurs in the special theory of relativity.

Thus far I have described procedures developed by astronomers and physicists for the exact measurement of time. Estimates of time are also made by the geologist, who investigates the history of the earth. A fundamental problem of geology is the temporal order of strata. If it is possible to assume that strata have not been appreciably displaced from the positions in which they were created, the following principle is applied: The order of superposition is the order in time, the oldest stratum being at the bottom and the newest at the top. This application of the principle is restricted by the circumstance that strata may disappear underground or be continued by a different series. William Smith, however, discovered a method of correlating strata in different regions. From observations upon exposed sections of strata in England, he found that each group of strata contained characteristic fossils, so that the order of superposition of the strata indicated the order of succession of the fossils. This discovery furnished the empirical basis for the procedure of correlating the strata in different regions by means of their characteristic fossils. The hypothesis implied by this procedure is that strata which have been laid down in widely separated periods of time will contain quite different fossils, while those which were formed approximately contemporaneously will contain similar fossils.

The preceding discussion explains the procedure of determining simultaneity and succession of strata. The geologist also seeks to make quantitative estimates of time. In order to determine the age of a sedimentary deposit, he may make an estimate of the present rate of deposition and, from the thickness of the deposit, calculate the time required to produce it. The same procedure is used in estimating the age of the earth from the mass of salt in the ocean and the rate at which it is entering from the rivers. The most accurate method of estimating geologic time is based upon radioactive phenomena. Radioactive elements like uranium and thorium spontaneously disintegrate at a definite rate and give rise to elements of lower atomic weight. The final products are metallic lead, of atomic weight 206 if derived from uranium, and of atomic weight 208 if the final product is of the thorium series. If a rock is rich in uranium, one may measure the masses of uranium and lead which it contains and, from the rate of transformation of uranium into lead, calculate the age of the rock. Since helium is a product of radioactive disintegration, it may also be used to estimate the age of rocks. Chemical analyses of rocks from all parts of the world show that radioactive elements are widely distributed; these radioactive clocks in rocks indicate their ages.

Lecomte du Noüy has defined biological time by the dependence of the rate of reparation of cells upon the age of organisms. He found that the rate of cicatrization of wounds decreases with age as ordinarily determined; in a man of sixty the rate is one-fifth that of a child of ten. Processes that are uniform when measured in terms of astronomical time become nonuniform on the biological time scale.

7. Measurement of Weight

The measurements of length and time are observations in which the results of operations are perceived and interpreted with the aid of principles. In fundamental measurements of length the basic operation consists of laying off the standard on a line. Since a measuring rod is operated by the observer and its state is experimentally controlled, the procedure of measuring length is experimental. Now, it may be contended that there is direct perception of length and time, and hence measurements of them are frequently called direct. The term 'direct' contrasts length and time with properties that are known only as they manifest themselves in experiments which are constructively interpreted. A discussion of some of these experimentally exhibited properties will reveal further the method of experiment and will illustrate Newton's dictum that the properties of things are derived from experiments.

The first example is the physical property, weight. In a sense we perceive length and experience duration, but observation of weight requires constructive interpretation. In order to observe that a material body has weight, I may support the body with my hand. The muscles attached to the hand exert a force which is experienced through kinesthetic sensations. Now, a fundamental principle of statics states that, if a body is at rest, the forces on it must be in equilibrium. This principle of equilibrium accordingly requires that I conceive of the body as having a weight, directed downward, which is balanced by the upward force exerted through the hand. This simple experiment therefore exhibits weight as a force that balances some other force. The weight is assumed to continue in existence when the upward force is removed, so that, if the body is released and

falls freely to the earth, the weight of the body is interpreted
to be the cause of its acceleration.

The measurement of weight may be based upon a lever such
as is used in a beam balance. The empirical foundation for the
procedure is the fact that two bodies may be found such that if
they are attached respectively to the ends of a level with equal
arms, the lever remains horizontal. It is also an empirical fact
that if two bodies maintain one lever horizontal, they will maintain all others horizontal, regardless of position, length, material, color, etc. The two bodies behave similarly in different contexts, and hence it is convenient to define them to be equal in
weight. If two bodies of equal weight are attached to one end
of the lever, a body at the other end which maintains the lever
horizontal may be assigned a weight twice that of the first. By
this procedure one may build up a set of bodies with weights
that are integral multiples of a standard weight. One may also
define fractional weights: If two standard weights are balanced
by three equal weights, each of the latter is two-thirds of the
standard. The scale of weights is constructed so that it satisfies
the law of addition for extensive quantities. The present discussion interprets the principle that equal weights maintain an
equal arm lever horizontal, which was selected by Archimedes
to be a fundamental principle of statics, as an empirically founded definition of equality of weight. Of course, one could use another definition of equality of weight, and then the principle of
the lever would be an experimental law. But the alternative
definition would presuppose the selection of some other principle
of mechanics as a definition.

After weight has been ascribed to a body, it is possible to use
this force to discover other forces. If a body is attached to a
spring balance, the spring is stretched before equilibrium is attained; it is assumed that the end of the spring is acted upon by
two forces in equilibrium, the weight of the body and the tension
in the spring which is equal in magnitude but upward in direction. If one attaches bodies of different weight to the spring and
measures its extension, one can discover Hooke's law that the
stress in a spring is proportional to its extension. Hooke's law

may be used as an alternative definition of force in statics. To conclude: Given a single type of force, weight, it is possible to interpret statical experiments as exhibiting weight to be balanced by other forces such as tensions in springs and electric and magnetic forces. Observation of forces consists in constructive interpretation of mechanical experiments in the light of principles which play the role of definitions. The physical concept of force expresses the assignment of numbers in order to describe the conditions of motion. The procedure involves the element of hypothesis. The physical quantities which are assigned by constructive interpretation of experiments must be instrumental in predicting the results of other observations.

8. Observation through Causality

I have thus far analyzed observation of perceptible things and properties. Nonperceptible entities are also inferred to exist as the hypothetical causes of perceptible phenomena. Such inference through causality eventually becomes observation. I use here a crude concept of efficient causality, but in the pages on systematization I analyze it as expressing functional relationship.

The transformation of explanation by constructive hypotheses expressing causation into observation may be illustrated by an analysis of vision. Let us suppose that one may touch a thing but cannot see it. Under appropriate conditions the thing becomes visible, that is, it becomes possible to experience visual aspects which are correlated with the data of tactual perception. For example, if I introduce a lighted candle into a dark room, things become visible; with my eyes open I may see a table. Hence we must think of the visual aspect as produced, at least in part, by the candle. If explanation is to be expressed in terms of the perceptible, one must conceive of this production as an action at a distance, since the candle and the thing perceived are separated in space. The physicist, however, interprets the process as an action by contiguous causality; he defines radiation through the principle that the visual aspect of a thing is functionally dependent on radiation which travels from a source to the thing and is scattered toward the observer.

Thus a principle of contiguous causality yields a definition of radiation, which is assumed as a construct. The definition is justified, since the assumed radiation is instrumental in predicting new phenomena. The definition accordingly plays the role of a hypothesis which is tested by its predictions.

Again, if we keep the illuminated thing constant, as estimated by touch, and change the source of radiation, the visual aspect changes—in color, for example. The color of an aspect is the basis of assigning a specific property of radiation, the wavelength as measured in Young's double-slit experiment. The properties of radiation are thus defined in terms of the visual aspects which it makes possible. Radiation not only produces visual aspects but also affects a photographic plate. On allowing radiation to pass through a prism or grating, it is spread into a spectrum; radiation of a specific wave-length produces a line having a specific position on the plate. To the spectroscopist the perception of a spectral line constitutes an observation of the radiation which produced the line. Experiments on the pressure of light have shown that it exerts a pressure; radiation may therefore be observed through the momentum which it communicates to some directly perceptible object.

A visual aspect is partly produced by radiation, but the aspect also depends upon the thing perceived. If the source of radiation is kept constant and the thing illuminated is varied, the visual aspect changes; for example, the visual aspect of a chair differs from that of a desk in the same light. Hence we must think of the visual aspect as functionally dependent on the radiation and thing conjointly. The visual aspect manifests the reaction of the thing to radiation; in physical language, the visual aspect depends upon the reflection of radiation by the thing. The preceding statement expresses a law which may be viewed as a generalization from observation based upon the definition of a thing in terms of tactual aspects and the principle of contiguous causality. In the development of physics, however, the principle that a thing reflects radiation becomes an essential element in the definition of physical reality. This is the basis of observation by photography. An object reflects radiation which is focused by a system of lenses so that an image is produced on a plate. Perception of the image is the basis of inference to the structure of the object.

9. Observation of Microphysical Entities

Observation through causality, which is exemplified by the assumption of radiation, is the procedure for the study of microphysical entities such as electrons, protons, neutrons, etc. Observation of such entities consists in the perception of macrophysical phenomena that may be interpreted as effects of microphysical objects. In this field, principles become constructive instruments of interpretation, and so observation is more subject to the uncertainties of hypotheses than is perception of common things.

I present some examples of the observation of electrified particles through their effects. If a high-speed alpha particle strikes an appropriate screen, it produces a scintillation which consists of light assumed to be emitted by countless atoms and molecules that have been excited by the particle. Thus, a single particle can be detected by visual perception of the macrophysical scintillation that it produces. If an electrified particle with sufficient energy passes through a cloud chamber, it ionizes the molecules that it strikes, producing ions on which water vapor condenses. Perception of the track of waterdrops completes the observation of the ionizing particle. Again, a Geiger counter is a tube in which a momentary current flows when a particle of sufficient energy passes through and produces ionization. The momentary current is amplified and actuates a mechanical counter which registers the number of particles that pass through the tube. Hence the production of scintillations and condensation tracks, and the actuation of Geiger counters, enable the physicist to detect individual microphysical entities. If many particles impinge on an appropriate plate, a perceptible pattern may be produced. The ultimate elements of physical theory are observed through perceptible macrophysical phenomena.

The physicist determines the properties of elementary particles by investigating their behavior under experimentally controlled conditions. For example, an electron may be subjected to magnetic or electric fields, and from the curvature of the path, observed in a cloud chamber by the condensation track and in a cathode-ray tube by the deflection of the effect on a screen, it is possible to determine the ratio of electric charge to mass as defined by assumed physical principles. In Millikan's measurement of electronic charge, electrons were captured by perceptible oil drops the behavior of which was observed under specified physical conditions. The measurement was completed by a calculation of the charge from the data of the experiment and the assumed physical principles.

An observation in which the element of hypothesis is quite explicit is that of the energy levels of the atom. According to contemporary theory, an atom consists of a positively electrified nucleus to which are bound electrons distributed among concentric shells. The electronic shells are defined by quantum conditions and constitute the basis for a discrete set of stationary states of constant energy of the atom. As electrons jump from one shell to another, the stationary state of the atom changes discontinuously with the absorption or emission of radiation, the frequency of which is determined by the difference between the energies in the initial and final states. Radiation emitted or absorbed produces spectral lines upon a photographic plate, and from the serial order of the lines it is possible to determine the energy levels of the atom. These levels, or quantum states, are the object of a constructive hypothesis which serves to correlate and predict spectral data, but the theory has been so often confirmed that an observation of spectral lines now seems practically a direct observation of the energy levels of the atom. In the development of physical theory during the last two decades there has been a transition from the active construction of hypotheses for atomic theory to the almost unreflective acknowledgment of its objects as real. Indirect observation, consisting of measurements on spectral lines plus the theory from which calculations are made, has achieved the practical certainty of direct observation.

10. Partition between Object and Observer

As one traces the development of observation from perception through measurements of length, time, and weight to the detection of radiation and the electrified particles of microphysics, it is evident that the function of apparatus becomes more and more important. Bohr has emphasized the fact that the observer and his instruments must be presupposed in any investigation, so that the instruments are not part of the phenomenon described but are used. The problem accordingly arises of defining the partition between object and the observer and his apparatus.

I present some examples of the partition between object and observer. Tactual perception is an interaction between a body and end organs such as those in the tip of a finger. If one touches a desk with a finger, the partition is between them. An observer, however, may be extended by mechanical devices. Bohr has cited the following example: If one firmly grasps a long stick in one's hand and touches it to a body, the body touched is the object of observation, and the stick is an apparatus that may be viewed as part of the observer. It is a psychological fact that one locates the tactual aspect at the end of the stick, so that the partition is between the body and the end of the stick. If, however, the stick is held loosely in the hand, the stick becomes the perceived object, and the partition is between stick and hand.

In vision perception is mediated by radiation which travels from the object to the observer. On account of the finite speed of propagation of radiation, the state of the object is prior to, and distant from, the perception of that state. The position of the object is of primary biological significance, and so the perceiver habitually places the partition at the object and unreflectively accepts the radiation which the object emits or reflects as part of the observer. For example, the visual perception of a stick is dependent on the sunlight which is reflected from the stick to the eye. In daily life the object of interest is the stick, and hence the light is treated as an instrument of observation which is an integral part of the observer. But, if the stick is in water and appears to be bent, the explanation of this illusion of vision in terms of the refraction of light by the water presupposes that the partition be placed between the eye and the light.

In perception the partition is determined by the biological needs of the observer and is ordinarily difficult to displace. Brunswik, however, has shown that a change in perceptual attitude is possible; for example, we can compare objects with respect to the size of the pattern on the retina produced by the light from them. In such a case we are to think of the partition as at the retina. In view of the extension of the concept of observation to include interpretation in term of principles, it is desirable to distinguish between cognitive and perceptual partitions. The object may be observed through causation of perceptible effects, so that the two partitions are different. The position of the cognitive partition depends upon the interest of the observer. If a physicist is looking at a pointer on a scale, its status depends on the purpose of the observation. If he is using the instrument to measure an electric current, the pointer is an extension of the observer; the object is the electric current. If the physicist is calibrating his instrument, the pointer is part of the object of observation; the light by which the pointer is seen is then an instrument which belongs to the observer. If he studies the properties of light by photographing spectral lines, the light is the object of observation, and a line is registered on the plate, which plays the role of observer. But if the physicist examines the spectral line, it becomes the object, and the light reflected by it in turn is an instrument.

In the analysis of observation the cognitive partition between object and observer may be displaced in opposite directions. The naïve observer probably assumes that in visual perception he is in direct contact with a distant object; indeed, the child reaches for the moon. In perception the partition is habitually at the object. But it is a hypothesis that our visual perception of a distant object is dependent on the radiation that produces its visual aspects. Physical investigation reveals that the radiation is affected by an intervening medium, and so the cognitive partition is placed at the organism to which the observer is now restricted. The problem of the physicist ends when he reaches the boundary of the organism, but the biologist displaces the partition into the body of the observer. The optometrist places the partition at the retina of the eye, and the physiologist of the nervous system displaces it still farther into the organism. While the biologist displaces the partition farther and farther into the organism, the physicist displaces it farther and farther into the physical object. In macrophysics he observes the properties of bodies that are expressible in terms of perceptible phenomena; in microphysics he penetrates to the molecule, the atom, and now the nucleus. The perceptible effects of microphysical entities, which are not directly perceptible, serve as instruments of observation which thereby become incorporated into the observer. After much experience with the condensation tracks produced by electrons and other elementary particles, one may come to view the perception of the tracks as an observation of the particles. It is almost as if the perceptual partition had been displaced so that it coincides with the cognitive one.

The position of the cognitive partition is of fundamental significance in quantum theory. In an observation of a microphysical quantity there occurs an interaction between object and instrument; the instrument reacts against the object and may produce an unpredictable, finite change in the value of a quantity that is canonically conjugate to the one being observed. In such observations it is not possible to control the action of the measuring instrument upon the object, for the instruments cannot be investigated while serving as means of observation. It is impossible to assign definite canonically conjugate quantities simultaneously, since the experimental arrangements through which the effects of microphysical entities are registered are mutually exclusive. The situation in microphysics is expressed by the concept of complementarity and may be illustrated by the following example. The position of a particle may be observed by allowing it to impinge on a screen, which in order to define position must be rigidly attached to the frame of reference. During the interaction between particle and screen there is an unpredictable exchange of momentum between them. The momentum given to the screen is absorbed by the frame of reference, and its value cannot be substituted in the principle of conservation of momentum to calculate the momentum given to the particle. The procedure for observing position excludes the possibility of using the screen to determine the momentum of the particle. If the screen is mobile in the frame of reference, it may be used to measure momentum, but then specification of position is lost. The observations of microphysics require interpretation in terms of classical concepts, but the fundamentally unpredictable, finite effects of the disturbances by the instruments of observation lead to a restriction in the applicability of classical concepts to microphysical objects. The cognitive partition between object and apparatus is the seat of an indeterminacy which limits theoretical physics to the statistical prediction of the results of classically interpreted experiments. The state of the object on one side of the partition is represented by a wave function that changes in accordance with a differential equation which exemplifies a principle of causality. On the other side of the partition there occurs a sequence of events which proceeds from the measuring apparatus to the observer in accordance with classical laws. The statistical interpretation of the wave function states that it is an instrument for predicting the results of observations registered with classically controlled apparatus and perceived after the manner of common experience. The quantum mechanical theory of microphysics has resulted in a limitation of the possibilities of observation.

III. Systematization

11. Classification

In empirical science particular cognitions are organized into systems of knowledge. The particular cognitions of daily life already involve order: the perception of a thing involves the hypothesis that the actual perception is correlated with possible perceptions; the concept of thing expresses a relatively invariable correlation of properties attributed to it. Science presupposes and continues the systematizing procedures of common experience.

A basic procedure for introducing order into knowledge is classification. Classification is founded on the similarities between things or events; it is based upon the fact that things are similar in specific respects and dissimilar in others. The ordering of things into classes is especially characteristic of description in sciences like botany and zoölogy, but the procedure originates in prescientific experience. The occurrence of general names in language indicates that classification is a primitive mental process. The word 'animal,' for example, shows that there has been formed a class of living things that have the power of self-movement. The employment of names to denote any one of a number of common things is evidence that particular cognitions of things have been systematized by classification.

The classifications of common experience are based upon superficial or striking properties of things, and this dependence on superficial resemblances also characterizes the early phases of science. Scientific classification, however, eventually comes to be based upon essential characters which may be discovered only by careful observation and experimentation. The ancients classified material things in terms of earth, air, fire, and water; this set of substances has been superseded by a system of elements, initially classified in terms of atomic weight but now in terms of atomic number. Physics is not ordinarily thought of as a classificatory science, yet it offers classifications such as those of spectra on the basis of quantum numbers characterizing the energy levels in the atom or molecule.

Classification is a characteristic procedure of the descriptive study of living things. The many plants and animals are classified according to the presence or absence of specific properties, functions, etc. A distinction is frequently made between artificial and natural classification. An artificial classification is based upon some superficial similarity in structure, color, habitat, etc. For example, animals may be classified as terrestrial or aquatic depending upon whether they live on land or in water. A natural classification is based upon the fundamental characters of things. The basic criterion is similarity of structure, the study of which is called morphology or anatomy, but similarity of function and behavior are also used. While classification occurs in daily life, science aims at systems of classification.

The basic classification in biology is the division of the organic world into the plant and animal kingdoms. A kingdom is generally progressively subdivided into phyla, subphyla, classes, orders, families, genera, and species. The scientific name of an organism is compounded of the names designating genus and species. Thus man is called *Homo sapiens.* He belongs to the species *sapiens,* the genus *Homo,* the family Hominidae, the order Primates, the class Mammalia, the subphylum Vertebrata, and the phylum Chordata of the animal kingdom. The natural systems of classifications of biology are designed to exhibit genetic relationships.

The principles of procedure for research on problems of classification have been set forth by Jepson, who has systematically described the flora of California. He stresses the importance of field studies of habits, life-history, soil exposure, and associated species. Field records must be made at the place and time of observation and should be validated by specimens for a herbarium. Observation of plants in their natural environment should be supplemented by experimentation with garden cultures. Jepson transplanted individuals of *Eschscholtzia californica* (California poppy) from the Great Valley to the seacoast. Characters attributed to assumed other species developed, and hence there was justified a reduction in the number of species. For the work of classification he sought the following data: (1) entire life-history of a species; (2) biogeographic status; (3) characters at the limits of the area in which it has its greatest development; (4) structure, character, and presence or absence of plant organs; (5) variation in the organs of a species, especially from one individual or from a series of individuals where these have common parentage; (6) results of multilation of an individual.

The concepts of species and genus are fundamental instruments of classification in biology, and Jepson shows how the definitions of these concepts depend upon the state of knowledge. In his work on the flora of California he lists seven species of the genus Eschscholtzia, while Fedde in *Das Pflanzenbuch* reports one hundred species in California. In Jepson the genus Ptelea is represented by one species, whereas Greene has six species for California. In his discussion of criteria for genera and species Jepson states that the species must consist of individuals bound together by intimate genetic connection as determined by the morphology, detailed structure, life-history, genetic evidence, geographic history, and ecologic status. The species should represent a natural unit, especially from the geographic standpoint, and every effort should be made to give it precise definition. Jepson states that a genus should include all species of close genetic connection which have a marked natural resemblance or are closely bound together by structural peculiarities which indicate a close line of descent or form a compact natural group. Genera so founded are sufficiently large to establish relationships on a recognizable scale and to bring out the intimate relationships which exist between floras of different regions or countries as a result of past migrations. Genera having marked characters should not be subject to a segregation which reduces the generic character to the level of a species character. It is, however, necessary that the limits of genera should with increase of knowledge of their structure be subject to revision and modification. That the characters for classification must be adapted to the specific problem, Jepson illustrates by the genus Arctostaphylos. By morphologic characters, or by biometric measurements, or by other methods determined in advance, there would scarcely be more than five or six species for California. He distinguishes twenty-five species on the basis of differences in reaction to chaparral fires; the responses are constant and fundamentally unlike and are further correlated with geographic and ecologic segregation.

A thing is characterized by a relatively invariable correlation of simultaneously existing properties. Similarity between members of a class signifies that such correlation is exemplified by each member. A classification therefore expresses general laws of correlation which, since they apply to simultaneously existing properties, express uniformities of coexistence. But, since functions are considered in classification, laws expressing correlations of properties involve those expressing correlations of events.

12. The Correlation of Events

The formulation of correlations of events is an important phase of systematization. Indeed, it has been argued that events are constitutive of reality. Examples of events are a flash of lightning, an eclipse of the sun, an earthquake, the birth of a living being. In daily life and qualitative science an event may extend through an appreciable duration, but for precision an event is idealized as the occurrence of properties at an instant. The records of events constitute the raw material for the systematizing activity of science.

A stage in the investigations of correlations of events is the determination of temporal sequences. The history of political events, historical geology, and paleontology are arrangements of events in temporal order. Science in the form of history systematizes observations of events by fitting them into schemes of development of the cosmos, life, and society. Empirical science also formulates laws which express regularities in the correlation of the general characters of events. Such laws provide a basis for prediction; in fact, their confirmation or disconfirmation depends on the occurrence or nonoccurrence of events predicted from them. On the view that events are the basic constituents of reality, laws of coexistence become special cases of laws of correlation of events.

Correlations of events in nature are generally complex, so that in science a phenomenon is analyzed into constituent elements. An example of resolution into concurrent factors is Galileo's analysis of the motion of a projectile. Neglecting the resistance of the air, the projectile describes a parabolic path. Galileo analyzed the process into a superposition of two motions which may be considered independently: a horizontal motion with constant velocity and a vertical motion subject to the acceleration of gravity. The analysis of a phenomenon into successive elements is achieved by differential calculus. Kepler formulated the laws of planetary motion in terms of concepts that characterize the motion as a whole. One of his laws states that the orbits of the planets are ellipses. Newton discovered the differential equation which describes the instantaneous character of the motion. He expressed the acceleration, which is a derivative with respect to time, as determined by a force which is a function of the distances and masses of surrounding bodies. The differential analysis gives an exact formulation of the popular concept of causality.

The concept of causality expresses a relation between phenomena, such that one phenomenon is viewed as the cause of some other phenomenon, the effect. The cause is the condition of the effect; a description of the causes of a phenomenon constitutes an explanation. One may exemplify causality by illustrations drawn from all realms of experience. For example, the action of a force on a body is the cause of its acceleration; the application of a stimulus to an organism is the cause of a response. The concept of causality is best understood by an analysis of the physical concept of causality. Indeed, the hypothesis has been entertained that all natural phenomena are analyzable into physical processes. The typical physical cause is the action of force.

In the life of the individual it is probable that the concept of force is derived from experiences of his own exertions and that of his fellows. The individual exerts a force, for example, with a hand, and observes that it produces effects. A father forces a child to fill the wood box. Bodies are set in motion or brought to rest; forces can act in opposite directions and annul one another. The primitive concept of force is derived from experiences of our own exertions and of our fellows; it expresses production, creation, generation, efficacy.

316

Since the concept of force was originally derived from the forces exerted by an individual, it is understandable that primitive attempts at explaining natural phenomena were in terms of the theory of animism. Preceding the origin of empirical science men invented animistic explanation of natural phenomena. Natural bodies were interpreted to be the abodes of principles of life; for example, the lodestone, which attracts iron, was interpreted to be the seat of a soul. It is to be recognized that animism was an expression of the demand for causal explanation. Scientific progress began when men directed their attention to the perceptible properties of things, observed correlations of properties and sequences of phenomena, and explained the behavior of things in terms of the causal efficacy of other natural things. Animism did not, however, disappear with the development of science. Thales, the first historical figure of Greek science stated, "All things are full of gods." Empedocles conceived of the forces of attraction and repulsion as instances of love and hate. In modern times Kepler thought of the planets as guided in their orbits by angels, and it may be contended that vitalism in biology is a relic of animism.

Comte has explained in his law of the three stages that every science starts at a theological stage, passes through a metaphysical one, and then achieves final form in a positivist stage. The several sciences are at different stages of development. The operational point of view in physics is recognition that physical science has most completely realized the final form; this may be exemplified by the content of the physical concept of causality. Physical causality may be illustrated by the Newtonian theory of the motion of a body in a gravitational field. In this theory material bodies are conceived to have the physical property, mass. Between two material bodies there is a force of attraction which varies directly as the product of the masses and inversely as the square of the distance between them. Fixing our attention upon one of the bodies, we may say that it is acted upon by a force which is exerted by the other body, or, more precisely, that the first body has an acceleration which depends upon the distances and masses of surrounding bodies. Thus one

317

seeks the causes of a phenomenon pertaining to a given body in the correlated states of other bodies. The cause of the acceleration of the body is described not in terms of a vital principle within the body but in terms of the observable properties of other bodies. In the seventeenth century the exertion of a force was viewed as a state of activity of one body that produced an acceleration in another body. Causality was thus interpreted to be the expression of power, efficiency, production, necessary connection. The concept of causality was then in a metaphysical stage which retained traces of animism.

The concept of efficient causality was criticized by Hume. He analyzed the causal process in the collision of two billiard balls. If a moving ball strikes a ball of equal mass which is at rest, the first ball is brought to rest, while it communicates its state of motion to the second ball. We say that the motion of the first ball is the cause of the motion of the second ball, which is the effect. In observing this process, Hume found only a sequence of phenomena; the state of motion of the one ball was succeeded by the state of motion of the second ball. On close observation one would observe that as the two balls come in contact there is a deformation of the surfaces of contact and then a recovery from the deformation, during which process the first ball is brought to rest and the second ball moves away with the original state of motion of the first ball. At no time while the balls are in contact can one see why the process must occur as it does and not in some other way. Prior to the observation of a collision of two balls one could not predict the outcome of the collision. According to Hume, the concept of efficient causality merely expresses a uniformity of sequence of phenomena.

The concept of causality as correlation was definitely formulated by John Stuart Mill in his canons of induction. Mill's canons are exemplified by the method of concomitant variations which states that whatever varies in any manner whenever another phenomenon varies in some particular manner is either a cause or an effect of that phenomenon, or is connected with it through some fact of causation. Mill's canons offer criteria by which one can determine whether or not there is a causal relation between specific phenomena. The mathematical form of causality purges it of the last vestiges of efficiency. Causal laws are stated as functional relations between numerical measures of variable quantities.

The mathematical expression of causal laws may be illustrated by the Newtonian theory of gravitation. If two bodies having masses m_1 and m_2 are at a distance r, each of these bodies will exert a gravitational force upon the other which is directly proportional to the product of the masses and inversely proportional to the square of the distance between them. Let us fix our attention upon m_1. The physical description of the phenomenon is that m_1 is accelerated by a force which is exerted by m_2. The mathematical expression of the law of motion is given by the differential equation

$$m_1 \frac{dv_1}{dt} = G \frac{m_2 m_1}{r^2}.$$

One should also add that, while m_2 is exerting a force upon m_1, the latter is exerting an equal and opposite force upon the former. The causal process in the system consisting of the two bodies is a mutual action.

A special case is that in which m_2 is the mass of the earth and m_1 is the mass of a freely falling body. For the region in the neighborhood of the surface of the earth we may assume that the factor Gm_2/r^2 is a constant g. Let s be the distance measured downward from a point above the surface of the earth. Since $dv_1/dt = d^2s/dt^2$, the differential equation becomes

$$m_1 \frac{d^2s}{dt^2} = m_1 g \qquad \frac{d^2s}{dt^2} = g.$$

One can integrate this equation and express the coordinate s and the speed as functions of the time and two arbitrary constants. Thus

$$s = s_0 + v_0 (t - t_0) + \tfrac{1}{2}g (t - t_0)^2.$$

The constants s_0 and v_0 are the values of the distance and the speed at an initial time $t = t_0$. Hence, if one knows the position

319

and speed at an initial time, one can calculate the position and speed at some past or future time.

Hume characterized cause and effect as contiguous in time. If in our example the force exerted by m_2 is the cause and the acceleration of m_1 is the effect, it appears that cause and effect are simultaneous, for the acceleration is simultaneous with the force. We could, however, say that the cause precedes the effect if, after a body were introduced into the vicinity of m_1, it would take a finite time for the gravitational force to begin to act on m_1. But, according to the Newtonian theory, gravitational attraction is propagated with an infinite speed. Hence we can find no meaning for the statement that the cause precedes the effect. Again, contiguity of cause and effect in space means that the body exerting the force is in contact with the one accelerated. On the Newtonian theory of action at a distance spatial contiguity is also lost. In the present example discontinuity in causal action gives rise to an ordinary differential equation for the motion. The contiguity of a causal process in space and time is exemplified by wave motion in an elastic medium. If a portion of the medium is set in vibration, the state of motion is communicated by contiguous action to neighboring parts and travels with a finite speed. The space-time contiguity of the process is represented by a partial differential equation for the displacement as a function of the space coordinates and the time. The causal factor is represented in the differential equation by the dependence of the velocity upon the density and elasticity of the medium.

The search for causes is guided by a principle of causality. In qualitative terms the principle is expressed by the proposition, 'the same cause produces the same effect.' For example, if for a system subject to a definite law of force the same initial conditions are realized at some other time and in some other place, the motion will be the same. Suppose that I drop a body from a certain height above the surface of the earth; a specific motion will occur. The principle of causality predicts that if at some other time and place a body is dropped from the same height, the motion will be similar to the first one.

320

The principle of causality thus appears to assert the existence of causal laws that are independent of time and place. This would imply that causal laws are significant because the order of nature is one in which certain patterns in phenomena recur. In view of the universal interrelatedness of things, however, it would appear that the state of the whole universe is the condition of every phenomenon. But since the state of the universe apparently never recurs, we could not observe the repetition of a specific process in some other place at another time. At first glance it would appear that the principle of causality is empty.

The answer to the foregoing objection is that it is possible progressively to isolate systems and processes. In a mechanical experiment on the surface of the earth it is possible in practice to ignore the influence of the heavenly bodies. In general, the universe is a set of loosely coupled systems. Physical forces usually vary inversely as the second power of the distance and therefore decrease rapidly with distance. For ordinary accuracy the physicist may view his laboratory as an isolated system. Against a background which may be considered constant, the same relative initial conditions give rise to similar processes. Causal processes can be isolated by controlling the state of the environment.

13. Successive Approximation

The control of the conditions under which a causal law is exemplified proceeds by successive approximation. In preliminary experiments one must presuppose that the conditions are constant and thereby obtain an approximate law. With the aid of approximate laws one can then define the conditions of an experiment more precisely, or correct for the disturbing influences, and thus determine a law to a higher order of approximation. Galileo's first experiments on the acceleration of a ball rolling down an inclined plane were performed with crude apparatus. After the laws of dynamics were discovered from the action of gravity, it was possible to define the conditions of the experiment more accurately and indeed to explain how Galileo's experiments were disturbed by friction.

Examples of the method of successive approximation are offered by contemporary physics. It is incorrect to think that the theory of relativity and the quantum theory have destroyed classical physics. Classical theory has to be assumed to a first approximation in order to define the experimental conditions under which relativity holds to a higher approximation. Thus in his first paper on the special theory Einstein begins the systematic discussion with the statement, "Let us have given a system of coordinates, in which the equations of Newtonian mechanics hold to the first approximation." The formulation of the postulates of the theory which corrects classical dynamics requires a system of coordinates which is defined by the condition that the classical theory holds in it to the first approximation. In order that the foregoing procedure may apply, the more precise theory must contain the first approximation as a limiting case. In the special theory of relativity the length and mass of a body are functions of its speed; for speeds that are small in comparison with the speed of light one obtains the classical assumption that length and mass are independent of speed. The classical dynamics is a limiting case of relativistic dynamics.

According to the general theory of relativity, the path of a ray of light is curved in a gravitational field; as is well known, this prediction has been verified by the measurement of the deflection by the sun of light from a star. The observations and calculations whereby this result is verified presuppose, however, that the law of the rectilinear propagation of light holds in a region near the surface of the earth. The experimental procedure is justified because the earth's gravitational field is relatively small, and in the limiting case of zero gravitational fields relativistic theory reduces to the limiting assumption that light travels in a homogeneous medium in Euclidean straight lines.

Classical physics is a necessary basis for quantum physics. Quantum phenomena occur under macrophysical conditions and are measured by apparatus which registers results that are interpreted in terms of classical concepts. The employment of classical physics in the control of microphysical phenomena is justified by the fact that the classical laws are limiting cases of the quantum laws. Since observations of microphysical phenomena are subject to statistical laws, the causal laws of classical physics render possible the definition of experimental conditions in which causality fails.

On account of the complexity of organisms, it is difficult to control the conditions of a process in a single living system. The biologist therefore uses a procedure, called comparative experimentation by Claude Bernard, in which another system serves as a control. Suppose, for example, that it is desired to determine the effect of modification or removal of a deep-seated organ of an animal. Such an experiment requires an operation which disturbs neighboring organs. In order to distinguish between the effect of the operative procedure and that of disturbing the specific organ, the biologist performs a similar operation on a similar animal, but without disturbing the organ under investigation. A controlled experiment requires comparison of the results upon at least two organisms, under conditions which are the same in each experiment except in one respect. Comparative experimentation may use two animals of the same species, or the same animal at different times or different parts of one animal at the same time.

Controlled experimentation in biology is facilitated by the use of cultures. The problem of plant nutrition is the determination of the substances necessary for the structural composition and metabolism of the higher plants. Experimental procedure consists in placing the roots of the plant in a water culture, which provides a controllable external medium from which the plant can absorb the nutrient substances. The nutritional requirements of all sorts of plants have been discovered by varying the kinds and amounts of salts in the medium. An important procedure for physiology is the cultivation of fragments of tissues and organs of animals outside of the organism. Dr. Carrel deposited small fragments of living tissues in fluid plasma or in an artificial medium. The maintenance of life in such culture mediums renders possible controlled experimentation on living processes.

14. Successive Definition

With the development of science there has been discussed the problem of the genesis of scientific laws. At first sight it appears to be evident that the laws of empirical science are generalizations from observation. But laws serve to define concepts, and observation employs laws as principles of interpretation. In the spirit of Kant, who taught that the category of causality is an a priori condition of the possibility of experience, Dingler holds that the principles of physics are postulates which ought to be chosen in accordance with a principle of simplicity. In the present work a solution of the problem is offered by the theory of successive definition. According to this theory, the status of a natural law may change in the development of science. A law which originates as a generalization from experience may be transformed into a convention that expresses an implicit definition of the concepts it involves. The theory of successive definition has been anticipated in the discussions of arithmetic, geometry, time, and weight. I shall now use classical dynamics for a more detailed explanation. Some concepts must be initially assumed as understood; I shall assume that, in addition to the concepts of geometry and time, we have a statical concept of force. Examples of forces are weight and the force exerted by a stretched spring. If a body is supported at rest by a stretched spring, the interpretation of the phenomenon in statics is that the weight acting downward is balanced by the equal and opposite upward force exerted by the spring. If the body is released, it falls under the action of its weight, which is assumed to be the same as when the body is at rest. Similarly, if a spring is stretched a given distance, it is assumed to exert the same force whether it is accelerating a body or is balanced by some other force.

Let us now apply forces to various bodies. It is found that the velocity increases in the direction of the force. In order to describe the action of force, we may assign to a body in motion the physical quantity momentum, *I,* which may be defined by the postulates that a body at rest has zero momentum and that the momentum communicated to a body by a constant force is proportional to the product of force and time. Experiment shows that for velocities small in comparison with the velocity of light the momentum is directly proportional to the velocity. We may introduce a factor of proportionality m and write $I = mv$. The usefulness of our definition of momentum depends on the fact that regardless of the kind of force employed to generate momentum in a given body the factor m is the same. Hence the physical quantity m, the mass, is viewed as an intrinsic property of the body, which for classical dynamics is independent of velocity, but for relativistic dynamics depends on velocity. The outcome thus far is that we have defined momentum in terms of an impulse equation and have transformed the empirical law of the proportionality between momentum and velocity into a definition of mass.

The foregoing dynamical example illustrates the fact that generalizations from experience become definitions of new concepts. I cite some further examples. The law expressing the dependence of the stress in an elastic body upon the strain becomes a definition of elastic constant. The law which states the functional relation between the length of a wire and its temperature becomes the definition of coefficient of linear expansion. Electrical resistance and the constant in the general gas law are other examples of constants that are defined in terms of empirical laws which have been transformed into definitions. A related example of the transformation of empirical laws into definitions is given by the principle of the conservation of energy. In dynamics it is possible to define energy so that in isolated ideal systems it is constant. On the basis of experiments which showed that a definite amount of heat can be produced by the performance of a definite amount of work, the mechanical principle was extended to a general principle for all natural processes. As Poincaré noted, this principle, which was initially an empirical hypothesis confirmed by experiments demonstrating the mechanical equivalence of heat, has acquired the status of a definition. If in a physical process the total change of known forms of energy is not zero, a new kind of energy is assumed in order to preserve the principle.

Further study of dynamics reveals an alternating procedure in successive definition. We initially adopted force from statics, but, having determined how to assign masses to bodies, we may calculate momentum from $I = mv$ and define force in the more general sense by Newton's equation of motion, which states that force is equal to the rate of change of momentum. The usefulness of this definition depends on the fact that simple laws of force may be found in important applications, for example, the inverse square law for gravitation and electrostatics, and Hooke's law which states that in elastic bodies stress is proportional to strain. Thus a limited concept may provide the basis for a law which is used to define a new concept. Then the law may be employed with the new concept to define a general concept which replaces the original limited one. In the foregoing example the equation of motion was used alternately to define momentum and force. The fundamental laws of dynamics have become conventions which implicitly define the concepts that they involve. With C. I. Lewis we view the principles of fundamental sciences like geometry and dynamics as definitions of concepts which serve to interpret the data of observation. It must be recognized, however, that the suitability and applicability of a conceptual scheme are the subject matter of hypotheses which must be confirmed or disconfirmed by observation.

15. Atomism

Thus far we have studied procedures for the systematization of cognitions of directly observable things and phenomena. I shall now consider systematization from a more detailed and constructive point of view. Perceptible phenomena can be analyzed into nonperceptible processes; empirical laws can be derived from more ultimate laws. In physics the transition is from a macrophysical level to a deeper microphysical one.

The more ultimate point of view may be called atomism in a general sense. Atomic theory vividly illustrates the method of hypothesis.

The fundamental ideas of an atomic theory were created by the early Greek philosophers. As Meyerson has so clearly shown, the mind seeks identities in the natural world. This disposition expressed itself in early Greek science in the endeavor to interpret natural things as modes of a permanent substance. Attempts to provide for change in a theory of substance led to the atomic theory of Leucippus and Democritus. According to atomism, substance consists of countless atoms in the void, and these constitute natural bodies. Natural phenomena consist of changes in the groupings of atoms. Thus the theoretical demand for persistent substance is reconciled with the acknowledgment of the reality of change. It is unfair to state that the ancient atomic theory was only speculative. As is exemplified in the exposition of Lucretius, the Greeks explained many phenomena qualitatively in terms of atomism.

Quantitative development of the atomic hypothesis began when it was used by Dalton to explain the laws of chemical combination in the opening decade of the nineteenth century. Chemical processes are exemplified by the rusting of iron upon exposure to the atmosphere and the decomposition of water into hydrogen and oxygen by electrolysis. Such processes are characterized as composition and decomposition of substances. The criteria of substances are initially qualitative properties like color, odor, hardness, but are ultimately physical properties such as density, melting-point, boiling-point, specific heat, electrical conductivity, spectrum, etc. Thus the procedures for observing physical properties are basic to chemistry. The chemist, furthermore, has characteristic techniques for separating substances in physical mixtures by using differences in boiling-point and solubility, by filtering, etc. He employs methods such for producing chemical changes as heating, mixing solutions, electrolysis. In chemical phenomena the physical properties of the final substances are usually quite different from those of initial ones. Chemistry originated in antiquity with procedures of cooking, the working of metals, the tanning of leather; and the study of chemical phenomena was furthered by the alchemists' attempt to transform baser metals into gold. But the quantitative development of chemistry only began in earnest during the closing decades of the eighteenth century, when Lavoisier demonstrated the conservation of mass in chemical reactions. The use of the chemical balance to weigh materials which are mixed or produced in a reaction renders possible the quantitative formulation of an atomic theory.

The atomic theory of chemistry is based upon three fundamental laws: the law of conservation of mass, the law of definite proportions, and the law of multiple proportions. The foregoing laws, which are derived from chemical experiments, are readily explicable by the atomic theory in which the masses of individual atoms are assumed constant and the same for a given element. The constancy of atomic masses provides a basis for the conservation of mass. In recent years it has been discovered that there exist isotopes, that is, atoms of the same element possessing different atomic weights. It may also be noted that in order to extend the law of conservation to nuclear reactions the relativistic equivalence between mass and energy must be invoked. The hypothesis that the molecules of a substance are always composed of the same kinds of atoms explains the law of definite proportions. The hypothesis that molecules may be formed of different numbers of the same kinds of atoms explains the law of multiple proportions.

Atomism in the theory of matter furnished a basis for an atomic theory of electricity. Faraday discovered the laws of conduction of electricity through electrolytes. An explanation of these laws is immediately given by the hypothesis that in an electrolyte molecules are dissociated into positively and negatively charged ions which carry integral multiples of a unit of electric charge.

Further progress in atomism was made by the kinetic-molecular theory of heat. This theory was based upon the discovery of the mechanical equivalence of heat, which provided the empirical foundation for the hypothesis that the heat content of a body consists of molecular mechanical energy. The kinetic theory of matter has been especially developed for gases. In this theory a homogeneous gas consists of countless molecules, similar in mass, and moving with high speeds. In a collision between molecules there is conservation of momentum and energy. In order to make calculations from the hypotheses, it is necessary to use statistical assumptions and methods. It is the statistically defined quantities, however, that are significant for observable phenomena; an important part of the theory consists of assumptions correlating the statistical quantities with experimentally measurable quantities such as pressure and temperature. For example, the pressure of a gas is assumed to be equal to the time average of the total transport of momentum to unit area per unit time. That is, the pressure indicated by a manometer is the resultant force per unit area produced by the reflection of the molecules by the boundary of the gauge. The temperature of a gas is assumed to be proportional to the time average of the kinetic energy per degree of freedom. On simplifying assumptions it is possible to deduce the general gas law and other laws for gases. Thus the observable, macrophysical properties of gases are explained in terms of the action of microphysical bodies.

Another advance in atomic theory was the molecular explanation of the Brownian movement. The success of the atomic theory in chemistry and in the theory of gases failed to convince notable doubters. The kinetic picture was viewed as a fiction which served only as an instrument for economical thought. Atomic weights were merely combining ratios and not significant of realities. The doubters were practically all silenced, however, by the molecular explanation of the Brownian movement. If colloidal particles suspended in a liquid are viewed through an ultramicroscope, the particles are observed to move in an irregular and random manner. The kinetic explanation is that the particles are sufficiently light so that they are appreciably affected on impact with a molecule. The irregular, zigzag motion of the particles is caused by irregular bombardment by the molecules of the liquid. In observations of the Brownian movement, one therefore observes the effects of a single molecule.

The present illustration shows that a principle of contiguous causality is a factor in the observation of physical objects. The properties of nonperceptible entities are inferred from the behavior of perceptible bodies in collisions which are assumed to satisfy principles of the conservation of momentum and energy. The molecule must be assumed in order to interpret perceptible phenomena in accordance with accepted physical principles. Thus the physical existence of molecules, atoms, electrons, radiation, etc., is like the existence of the physical properties of perceptible bodies. If a colloidal particle exists, then so does the molecule which interacts with it in conformity to physical principles. If a zinc sulphide screen exists, then so does the alpha particle which excites it to scintillate. The functional relations which are expressed by the laws of nature relate the physical properties of perceptible bodies to the physical properties of microphysical entities. The physical world is the object of a hypothetico-deductive system which is assumed in order to interpret the results of observation—initially to interpret a datum of perception as an aspect of a body to which one attributes mass, temperature, electric charge, etc., on the basis of its behavior; further to interpret phenomena such as Brownian movements, scintillations, and condensation tracks as the effects of microphysical entities; and then to express macrophysical processes as statistical resultants of microphysical processes.

The development of atomism is one of increasing detail in its representation of physical objects. Dalton failed to distinguish between atoms and molecules. In simplified kinetic theory the volumes of molecules are neglected and also the forces between them, except in impact. The atoms were initially assumed equal in mass, but isotopes were discovered. Electric phenomena in gases led to the discovery of the electron, and Rutherford's discovery of the nucleus provided a basis for the picture of the atom as a positive nucleus surrounded by shells of electrons. A first clue to the structure of the nucleus was given by radioactivity, which was interpreted as the disintegration of unstable nuclei and the correlated emission of alpha particles, beta particles, and gamma rays. In recent years instruments have been invented that will communicate to electrified particles energies which are high enough to shatter the nucleus. At present the nucleus is assumed to be constituted of protons and neutrons.

The preceding discussion shows that the concept of atom is relative to experimental procedure. The generic meaning of the term is something that cannot be divided, but the concept of indivisibility is relative to the instruments employed. The chemical atom of the nineteenth century was not divisible by ordinary chemical methods, but its outer structure was shattered by electric discharges, and now its inner structure is being smashed by the projectiles from powerful atomic guns.

In the history of physics theories of continuity have competed with atomism. The Cartesian vortices of the seventeenth century, the nineteenth-century ether models of the atom, and recent electromagnetic field theories of the electron testify to the scientific impulse to reduce apparent discontinuity to continuity. In a field theory of matter the fundamental physical quantities are those that characterize the electromagnetic field in space-time. Regions of high value of the field are interpreted to be electrified particles, the inertial mass of which consists of the energy of the surrounding field. Since the field is continuous, the separateness of the electrified particles is only an appearance. Despite attempts to build theories of matter by modifying Maxwell's equations and by generalizing the theory of relativity, theories of continuity are not playing a vital role in contemporary physics.

16. Statistics in Quantum Theory

The discussion of atomism in physics may be supplemented by an exposition of the basic significance of statistical laws in quantum theory. The wave function that represents the state of a microphysical system satisfies a differential equation which expresses determinism. But the results of observations on quantities characterizing a system are subject to statistical laws. Statistical laws, which in classical kinetic theory are founded on determinism, are fundamental in quantum theory.

The statistical laws of quantum theory are exemplified in observations on the state of polarization of light. If ordinary light enters a Nicol prism, the emergent beam consists of plane-polarized light. Since light exhibits corpuscular properties, the beam is conceived to consist of photons which are in a state that is defined by the plane of polarization. An observation on the state of polarization of light is performed by allowing the beam to enter a crystal of tourmaline. If all the light passes through, it has been observed to be plane-polarized in a plane perpendicular to the optic axis of the crystal. If no light passes through, its plane of polarization has been observed to be parallel to the axis. If the fraction of the original beam that passes through is expressed as $\sin^2 a$, the plane of polarization has been observed to be inclined at an angle a to the axis of the crystal. For a constant experimental arrangement the results of an experiment are reproducible. The effects registered in observation are produced by the mass effect of many photons in accordance with the statistical law that a fraction $\sin^2 a$ of the total number passes through and a fraction $\cos^2 a$ is absorbed. The result of an experiment with a single photon, however, is not predictable with certainty.

In order to describe the individual experiment, I shall, in conformity with Dirac, represent the state of polarization perpendicular to the optic axis by ψ_1 and the state parallel to it by ψ_2. The state inclined at an angle a, and represented by ψ_0, may then be expressed as formed by the superposition of states ψ_1 and ψ_2. If c_1 and c_2 designate the weights of the component states, we may write $\psi_0 = c_1\psi_1 + c_2\psi_2$. The action of the tourmaline in an observation on the photon in state ψ_0 is to force it to jump unpredictably into state ψ_1 or ψ_2, and the probabilities are respectively proportional to the squares of the weights. The probability of jumping into state ψ_1 and passing through is $\sin^2 a$, and the probability of jumping into state ψ_2 and being absorbed is $\cos^2 a$. If the photon is initially in state ψ_1, the result of an observation may be predicted with certainty.

The general formulation is as follows. Of any atomic system one may say that it can be prepared so that it is in a determinate state. The preparation is carried out with the aid of deterministic macrophysics. The quantum theory assumes that whenever a system is in a determinate state it can be regarded as formed by the superposition of two or more states. In consequence of this superposition the results of observation are in general not predictable with certainty. There is a finite probability that a result will be observed which is characteristic of one component state, and a finite probability that the result will be characteristic of another component state. If the system is initially in one of the component states, the result of an observation is predictable with certainty.

17. Atomism in Biology

The systematization and explanation introduced by atomism are exemplified in biology. The phenomena of heredity are explained by a theory of genes which is analogous to atomic theory.

The concept of heredity expresses the empirical generalization that organisms are similar to their parents. The scientific study of heredity presupposes an analysis which distinguishes different characters of an organism, so that a complex process may be analyzed into its constituents. In organisms created by sexual union traits arise that are combinations of those of their progenitors.

The fundamental law of heredity was formulated by Mendel as a result of his experiments on plant hybridization. He studied in varieties of garden peas the inheritance of selected characters such as length of stem, whether tall or short; form of ripe seeds, whether round or wrinkled; color of food material within the seeds; etc. Mendel crossed two forms having distinct characters and counted the number of descendants in successive generations possessing one or the other of these characteristics. He first determined that the selected characters were constant for certain varieties, a procedure analogous to the isolation of pure substances in chemistry. He then crossed varieties having

different characters and observed the offspring. When a tall
variety was crossed with a short one, the offspring in the first
filial generation were all tall. If these individuals were bred
among themselves, the result was a ratio of three tall to one
short. This ratio was a consequence of the fact that in the
second generation the proportions of pure tall, impure tall,
and pure short were 1:2:1. Correns crossed a white-flowered
variety of Mirabilis, the four o'clock, with a red-flowered one
and obtained blended, pink hybrids. The offspring of the pink
flowers were white, pink, and red in the proportions 1:2:1. The
Mendelian law of heredity is analogous to the law of definite
proportions in chemistry.

The explanation of Mendelian inheritance is based upon the
constitution of the germ cell. The occurrence of pure dominants
and pure recessives from hybrid parents is explained by the
hypothesis that the germ cells carry only specific unit characters, for example, the factors for red or white flowers. Since all
germ cells are pure with respect to a type of character, the
hybrid offspring of parents having contrasting characters will
produce in equal numbers germ cells bearing the dominant
character and those bearing the recessive character. The chance
combination of these two classes of male and female cells will
yield the typical Mendelian proportion: 1DD, 2D(R), 1RR.
The law of heredity therefore has an atomistic basis similar to
that for chemistry.

The explanatory stage of systematization in the science of
heredity is devoted to the factors in the germ cells which
determine traits or characters. Within the nucleus of the cell
occurs a substance called chromatin, which takes the form of
threads, or chromosomes, preparatory to cell division. The
chromosomal theory of heredity is that the determinants of
particular traits, called genes, are located in linear series in the
chromosomes. By the use of special fixing and staining methods and observation under a microscope it may be observed
that the chromosomes contain distinguishable structures called
chromomeres. John Belling set forth the parallelism between
the serial arrangement, structure, attraction between homol-

ogous entities, rate of division, and number of chromomeres, and the corresponding properties of the genes. Belling concluded that correct scientific procedure demands the adoption, as a working hypothesis, of the assumption that chromioles and chromomeres are genes, doubtless with more or less of an envelope.

Confirmation of the preceding hypothesis has been obtained by a study of the large chromosomes in the salivary gland of *Drosophila melanogaster.* Painter and his co-workers separated the elongated threads within the nuclear wall and observed on the chromosomes a great variety of bands, some broad and deeply staining, others narrow or made up of a series of dots. The patterns of bands and lines were characteristic of a given element, and it was possible to recognize the same element in the nuclei of different individuals. Irradiation with X-rays produced changes in the structure of a chromosome; there occurred translocations of elements, deletions or breaks, and these were observed under the microscope. The correlation of a short deletion with the absence of a trait fixed the location of the corresponding gene. By a genetic study of the characters transmitted, and a cytological study of the changes in the structure of the chromosomes, it was possible to correlate traits with position and thereby to locate the genes.

IV. Conclusion

18. Unity of Science

The present monograph on the procedures of empirical science may properly be concluded with an appraisal of the prospects for a unified science.

A basis for unity is the circumstance that the initial subject matter of the several sciences is furnished by common experience. The first objects of empirical science are things and phenomena given in perception, space-time structures whose properties are described in terms of perceptible qualities and relations. The motion of bodies, the behavior of organisms, and the relations between societies are initially described by concepts abstracted from perception. A body whose law of fall is investigated in physics may be characterized as extended, heavy, smooth, and gray. Gold is described as heavy and yellow. Living organisms are characterized by growth, reproduction, and death. Carnap has shown how the symbols for such perceptible things and properties may be used to construct a language for science.

Unity is introduced into science by the fundamental position of physics. In generalized physics there are fashioned precise concepts of space and time which serve as instruments for the description of the general properties of matter and energy in specialized physics. General and specialized physical concepts are instruments for the description of chemical, biological, behavioristic, and social phenomena. The chemist identifies substances by their physical properties, such as density, specific heat, boiling-point, characteristic spectrum. The biologist studies the chemical constitution and reactions of matter constituting a living organism, investigates the exchanges of energy between organism and environment, and interprets phenomena of the nervous system to be electrical. In order to study the responses of an organism to its environment, the behaviorist subjects it to experiments with physically controlled apparatus. It therefore appears that the methods of observation and experimentation of physics constitute a unified procedure for science. Science starts with the perceptions, analyses, and operations of daily life, and progressively applies the measuring rods, clocks, balances, thermometers, and ammeters of the physicist in pursuit of precise data. Claude Bernard especially emphasized the significance of physico-chemical techniques for biology. The procedures of specialized physics, however, must be applied with discrimination in investigations of organisms. New methods must continually be devised to solve new problems in physics. It is therefore to be expected that the special techniques of physics will have to be appropriately modified on application to living processes. It is an open question whether or not all natural laws are reducible to the laws of specialized physics. However, since the phenomena of science are spatio-temporal processes, one must recognize with the doctrine of physicialism that the procedures of generalized physics are the basis of all empirical science. In this unity of procedure resides the unity of science.

One may further ask whether or not it is possible to construct a single deductive theory for all science. Rationalists in the past have sought to unify all knowledge by a single principle, but the logical study of deductive systems has shown that a set of postulates is required for a fruitful theory. It may therefore be doubted that a limited set of principles will systematize both physical and biological laws. In agreement with Bohr, Heisenberg has stated[4] that new phenomena require new concepts and laws for their description and has stressed the relatively closed character of systems for different realms of phenomena.

In considering the possibility of a single system of science, it is instructive to review the progress toward systematic unity in physics. In the seventeenth century Descartes sought to reduce all the phenomena of the material world to matter in motion. A great impetus to a mechanical theory of nature was given when Newton systematized the knowledge of gravitational phenomena, expressed in Galileo's law of falling bodies and Kepler's laws of planetary motion, by the application of a law of gravitation to the laws of dynamics. Huyghens provided a basis for the phenomenon of light by a material ether, while Newton proposed a corpuscular theory. During the nineteenth century elastic solid theories of the ether were developed, and heat was reduced to the mechanical energy of the systems of molecules into which perceptible bodies were resolved. Maxwell created the electromagnetic theory of light with the aid of Faraday's theory of a medium and attempted to explain it in terms of the mechanical properties of an ether. Thus unity in physical theory was sought on the basis of a mechanical theory of nature. But the mechanical theory no longer provides a basis for systematic unity in physics. Electrodynamic theories have been proposed which make electric charges and their electromagnetic fields fundamental. Since the advent of the general theory of relativity, in which the force of gravitation is replaced by space-time curvature, theories have been developed which reduce physical quantities to characteristics of curved space-time. Quantum mechanics had to be developed in order to systematize observations on microphysical processes.

In the face of apparent disunity, developments in contemporary physics inspire the hope that quantum mechanics and the theory of relativity may be united in a single theory. And because of the basic function of generalized physics and the ever increasing development and adaptation of the techniques of specialized physics, the progress of physics toward unity augurs well for the unity of all empirical science.

NOTES

1. R. Carnap, *The Unity of Science* (London, 1934).

2. Cf. C. W. Morris, *Logical Positivism, Pragmatism, and Scientific Empiricism* (Paris, 1937), p. 35.

3. Quoted by Harold Chapman Brown, "Intelligence and Mathematics," in *Creative Intelligence*, ed. John Dewey (New York, 1917).

4. W. Heisenberg, *Wandlungen in den Grundlagen der Naturwissenschaft* (Leipzig, 1935).

Selected Bibliography

BELLING, JOHN. *The Ultimate Chromosomes of Lilium and Aloe with Regard to the Numbers of Genes.* "University of California Publications in Botany," Vol. XIV, No. 11. Berkeley, 1928.

BERNARD, CLAUDE. *Experimental Medicine.* Trans. HENRY COPLEY GREENE. New York, 1927.

BOHR, N. *Atomtheorie und Naturbeschreibung.* Berlin, 1931.

BROWN, HAROLD CHAPMAN. "Intelligence and Mathematics" in *Creative Intelligence.* Ed. JOHN DEWEY. New York, 1917.

BRUNSWIK, EGON. *Wahrnehmung und Gegenstandswelt.* Leipzig and Wien, 1934.

CAMPBELL, N. *What Is Science?* London, 1921.

CARNAP, R. *Physikalische Begriffsbildung.* Karlsruhe, 1926.

———. *The Unity of Science.* Trans. M. BLACK. London: Kegan Paul, 1934.

———. "Testability and Meaning," *Philosophy of Science*, October, 1936, and January, 1937.

DIRAC, P. A. M. *Principles of Quantum Mechanics.* Oxford, 1935.

HEISENBERG, W. *Wandlungen in den Grundlagen der Naturwissenschaft.* Leipzig, 1935.

JEPSON, W. L. *A Manual of the Flowering Plants of California.* Berkeley, 1925.

LENZEN, V. F. *The Nature of Physical Theory.* New York, 1931.

———. *Physical Causality.* "University of California Publications in Philosophy," Vol. XV. Berkeley, 1932.

———. *The Schema of Time.* "University of California Publications in Philosophy," Vol. XVIII. Berkeley, 1936.

———. "The Partition between Physical Object and Observer," *American Physics Teacher,* Vol. V (1937).

MACKENSEN, OTTO. "Locating Genes on Salivary Chromosomes," *Journal of Heredity,* Vol. XXVI (1935).

MORE, L. T. *Isaac Newton.* New York, 1934.

MORRIS, C. W. *Logical Positivism, Pragmatism, and Scientific Empiricism.* Paris, 1937.

NEURATH, OTTO. *Empirische Soziologie.* Wien, 1931.

NOÜY, LECOMTE DU. *Biological Time.* London, 1936.

PAINTER, THEOPHILUS S. "Salivary Chromosomes and the Attack on the Gene," *Journal of Heredity,* Vol. XXV (1934).

REICHENBACH, H. *Philosophie der Raum-Zeit Lehre.* Berlin and Leipzig, 1928.

RUSSELL, B. *Introduction to Mathematical Philosophy.* London, 1920.

WHITEHEAD, A. N. *The Principle of Relativity.* Cambridge, 1922.

WOLF, A. *Essentials of Scientific Method.* London, 1928.